Handbook of Surface Mount Technology

by
Stephen W. Hinch

Hewlett-Packard Company
Santa Rosa, California

Longman
Scientific &
Technical

Copublished in the United States with
John Wiley & Sons, Inc., New York

Longman Scientific & Technical,
Longman Group UK Limited,
Longman House, Burnt Mill, Harlow,
Essex CM20 2JE, England
and Associated Companies throughout the world.

Copublished in the United States with
John Wiley & Sons, Inc., 605 Third Avenue, New York,
NY 10158

First published 1988

British Library Cataloguing in Publication Data

Hinch, Stephen W.
  Handbook of surface mount technology.
  1. Electronic equipment. Components.
  Assembly. Applications of surface mount
  technology
  I. Title
  621.3815′1

ISBN 0–582–00517–5

Library of Congress catalog card number 88–081411

ISBN 0–470–21094X (USA only)

Printed and bound in Great Britain
at The Bath Press, Avon

To Nicki, Gregory, and Juliana,
the ones who really made it possible

A Note About Units

While much of the scientific world has long since converted to the SI system of units, the electronics industry continues to employ a hopeless tangle of metric and English systems. Many components, for instance, are defined in English units: component lead pitches of 0.050 and 0.025 inches have become worldwide standards. While it would be possible to simply refer to them as 1.27 and 0.63 mm lead pitches, this is not the industry convention and would undoubtedly lead to much confusion. The situation is not likely to improve in the near future, since the committee that recently developed the fine-pitch chip carrier specifically rejected the suggestion to use metric dimensions. They instead adopted the 0.025-in lead pitch.

In many other cases, metric dimensions govern; component lead pitches of 1.0, 0.8, 0.6, and 0.5 mm have also become worldwide standards. It would be equally inappropriate to refer to these components by some equivalent dimension in inches.

In an attempt to avoid confusion, units of length are expressed in both inches and millimeters throughout this book, with the industry-preferred unit being specified first. As an example, the 0.050-in component lead pitch is expressed as "0.050 in (1.27 mm)," which indicates that the dimension in inches is preferred. Conversely, the component lead pitch of 1.0 mm is expressed as "1.0 mm (0.040 in)," indicating that the metric dimension is preferred. Conversion to the non-preferred unit is rounded to the nearest sensible dimension and may not always be exact. On a dimension with no industry-preferred unit, metric dimensions are adopted.

Fortunately, most other dimensions in common use conform closely to the SI system. Temperature is nearly always expressed in degrees Celsius, for instance, although force is commonly reported in grams-force rather than newtons. For these units, no attempt is made to include the corresponding English dimension.

Preface

Surface mount technology has been called the most significant development in electronics assembly since the advent of the printed wiring board. Whether or not this is true, SMT, as it is called, is making dramatic changes in the way electronic assemblies are manufactured. Although related to traditional through-hole processes, SMT requires different components, assembly equipment, and design methods. Engineers familiar with through-hole assembly have found that they must learn entirely new technologies to stay abreast of the evolving demands.

The importance of the change can be gauged by the sheer number of seminars, conferences, technical papers, consulting firms, and organizations devoted expressly to surface mounting. It would seem that there is no end of opportunity for the engineer desiring to learn about SMT. Unfortunately, much of the existing information is incomplete or highly specialized. What has been lacking is a thorough, balanced treatment of the entire subject from a single source.

This book is written for the practicing engineer—the person who is called on to install a surface mount factory or support an existing facility. Although it heavily emphasizes practical solutions to practical problems, the theoretical basis for these solutions is also provided. By building on the material within the text, solutions to new or unusual problems can readily be formulated.

The text is divided into four parts. The first provides a management overview of SMT. It describes the benefits and limitations of the technology and introduces the issues that form the basis for the remainder of the book. Part II describes the characteristics of surface mount components, with a particular emphasis on information needed for proper selection. Design considerations are discussed in Part III. The emphasis is on factors that contribute to reliability and manufacturability of the finished assembly.

Finally, Part IV describes surface mount manufacturing technologies. It reviews alternative assembly flows and explores the factors to be considered in the selection of each process step.

The preparation of this book has been a formidable challenge that would have been impossible without the support of a great many people. I would like to especially thank all my colleagues involved in SMT at Hewlett-Packard. Much of what I have learned about the technology has been assimilated from them, and I would not have been able to complete the task without their support and encouragement. I particularly thank Don Rice for reading virtually the entire text and providing valuable critique. Major sections were also reviewed by Keith Stracchino and Tom Chang. I am deeply indebted to them for their many helpful suggestions. Mai Chow and Yousef Heidari provided valuable insight in several areas. Jody Hug prepared a number of the illustrations. Many other individuals were also instrumental and I thank them collectively.

A number of individuals from within the industry have also provided valuable contributions. I particularly thank Dieter Bergman and Tony Hilvers of IPC, Joseph Ranieri and Jack Vestal of Universal Instruments, Tom Beck of Henry Mann, Inc., Norman Hodson of Dynapert/Precima, Harold Hyman of Dynapert/HTC, Mark Kastner of Signetics, Jim Walker of National Semiconductor, and Jim Austin of Automation Technology.

Finally, I acknowledge the superb support I have received from the staff at Longman Scientific and Technical. I thank my editor, Richard Krajewski, for all his help and encouragement during the long months of preparation.

Contents

A note about units   iv

Preface   v

PART I: OVERVIEW   **1**

Chapter 1 Introduction   **3**

1.1 Selection of surface mount technology   5
  1.1.1 Benefits   5
  1.1.2 Limitations   14
1.2 Technology classifications   18
  1.2.1 Classification by process technology   19
  1.2.2 Classification by end assembly characteristics   23
  1.2.3 Functional modules   24
1.3 Standards and specifications   25
  1.3.1 Institute for Interconnecting and Packaging Electronic Circuits
    (IPC)   26
  1.3.2 Department of Defense   27
  1.3.3 Electronic Industries Association (EIA)   28
  1.3.4 International Electrotechnical Commission (IEC)   29
  1.3.5 Other national organizations   30

PART II: COMPONENTS   **31**

Chapter 2 Passive components   **33**

2.1 Fixed resistors   34

   2.1.1 Rectangular chip   34

   2.1.2 MELF (*Metal ELectrode Face*) resistor   37

   2.1.3 Preferred resistor construction   40

2.2 Potentiometers and variable resistors   41

   2.2.1 Sealed-element construction   42

   2.2.2 Open-element construction   43

   2.2.3 General potentiometer requirements   44

2.3 Resistor networks   45

2.4 Fixed capacitors   48

   2.4.1 Ceramic capacitors   48

   2.4.2 Tantalum electrolytic capacitors   55

   2.4.3 Other capacitor types   59

2.5 Inductors   59

   2.5.1 Wirewound inductors   59

   2.5.2 Multilayer inductors   61

Chapter 3 Semiconductor devices   **63**

3.1 Design considerations for surface mount semiconductors   63

   3.1.1 Solder joint design   64

   3.1.2 Thermal expansion mismatch   64

   3.1.3 Package thermal resistance   64

   3.1.4 Solder joint temperature   72

   3.1.5 Environmental resistance   74

3.2 Discrete semiconductor package styles   76

   3.2.1 SOT-23   76

   3.2.2 SOT-89   78

   3.2.3 SOT-143   79

   3.2.4 DPAK   79

   3.2.5 MELF   80

   3.2.6 Selection criteria for discrete semiconductors   81

3.3 General integrated circuit design considerations   83

   3.3.1 Pinout configuration   84

   3.3.2 Leadless vs. leaded design   84

   3.3.3 Lead configuration   84

   3.3.4 Lead coplanarity error   87

3.4 IC package types   88
    3.4.1 Small outline integrated circuit (SOIC)   88
    3.4.2 Plastic leaded chip carrier (PLCC)   90
    3.4.3 Quadpack   91
    3.4.4 Leadless ceramic chip carrier (LCCC)   94
    3.4.5 Leaded ceramic chip carrier (LDCC)   95
    3.4.6 Advanced package configurations   95
3.5 IC package selection criteria   102

Chapter 4 Connectors and electromechanical devices   **105**

4.1 Connectors   105
    4.1.1 Solder joint stresses   106
    4.1.2 Connector design factors   107
    4.1.3 Connector types   110
4.2 IC sockets   111
4.3 Test clips   114
4.4 Switches and relays   116

Chapter 5 Solder materials and solderability   **119**

5.1 Tin-lead phase diagram   119
5.2 Solder alloys   120
    5.2.1 Selection process   121
5.3 Solderability   122
5.4 Soldering fluxes   124
    5.4.1 Solvent-soluble fluxes   125
    5.4.2 Water-soluble fluxes   127
    5.4.3 Flux efficacy   127
5.5 Causes of solderability problems   128
    5.5.1 Oxidation   129
    5.5.2 Contamination   129
    5.5.3 Porous solder coating   129
    5.5.4 Improper joint metallurgy   129
    5.5.5 Solder coating grain structure   131
    5.5.6 Thin top coating   131
    5.5.7 Wicking   131
5.6 Solderability specifications   132
5.7 Solderability tests   133
    5.7.1 Fluxes for solderability testing   133

5.7.2 Dip test   134
5.7.3 Wetting balance   136
5.7.4 Resistance to dissolution of metallization   141
5.7.5 Other test methods   142
5.8 Aging   144
5.8.1 Steam aging   145
5.8.2 Dry heat aging   146
5.9 Specifying component termination materials   147

PART III: DESIGN   **151**

Chapter 6 Assembly design and reliability   **153**

6.1 The surface mount solder joint   153
6.1.1 Solder joint failure modes   153
6.1.2 Leadless joints   155
6.1.3 Leaded joints   156
6.1.4 Solder joint stresses   156
6.2 Packaging and interconnection structures   158
6.3 Organic-based materials   159
6.3.1 Fabrication processes   159
6.3.2 Paper-based materials   166
6.3.3 Epoxy-fiberglass materials   166
6.3.4 Polyimide-fiberglass materials   166
6.3.5 Aramid-fiber materials   167
6.3.6 Other organic-based materials   167
6.4 Constraining core materials   168
6.5 Ceramic substrates   170
6.6 Compliant layer materials   170
6.7 Impact of assembly process on reliability   171
6.7.1 Solder alloy selection   172
6.7.2 Solder volume   172
6.7.3 Component placement   173
6.7.4 Soldering process   173
6.7.5 Flux removal   174

Chapter 7 Design and layout guidelines   **177**

7.1 Printed wiring board   177

7.1.1 Board size and construction   177

7.1.2 Tooling holes   181

7.1.3 Fiducial marks   181

7.1.4 Conductor routing   182

7.1.5 Via holes   182

7.2 Overall board layout   184

7.2.1 Component orientation   185

7.2.2 Component density   185

7.2.3 Test points   186

7.3 Component land patterns   187

7.3.1 Adhesive location for wave soldered components   187

7.3.2 Standard land pattern formulae   188

7.3.3 Passive component land patterns   188

7.3.4 Discrete semiconductor land patterns   192

7.3.5 SOIC package land patterns   195

7.3.6 PLCC package land patterns   196

7.3.7 LCCC package land patterns   196

7.3.8 Gull-wing quadpacks   196

7.4 Other design considerations   197

PART IV: MANUFACTURING TECHNOLOGY   199

Chapter 8 SMT factories and process flows   201

8.1 Process flow alternatives   202

8.1.1 Adhesive attach/wave soldering overview   202

8.1.2 Reflow soldering overview   203

8.1.3 Comparison of process flows   206

8.2 Mixed assembly technology   208

8.2.1 Conventional through-hole approach   208

8.2.2 All SMT approach   209

8.3 Double-sided SMT   211

8.3.1 Combined reflow/wave soldering   211

8.3.2 Double-sided reflow   213

8.4 Factory floor layout   215

8.4.1 Fully automated factory design   215

8.4.2 Semiautomated factory design   221

8.5 Factory cost analysis   222

8.6 Factory design recommendations   225

Chapter 9 Solder pastes and application techniques   **227**

9.1 Rheology   227
   9.1.1 Viscosity   227
   9.1.2 Surface tension   229
9.2 Viscosity measurement   230
   9.2.1 Rotating-spindle viscometer   230
   9.2.2 Cone-plate viscometer   232
9.3 Solder pastes   233
   9.3.1 Solder powder   233
   9.3.2 Flux   237
   9.3.3 Rheological modifiers   238
   9.3.4 Solvents   238
9.4 Solder paste specifications and tests   238
   9.4.1 Percent metal   239
   9.4.2 Viscosity   240
   9.4.3 Slump   240
   9.4.4 Solder balls   241
   9.4.5 Flux activity   242
   9.4.6 Working life   243
   9.4.7 Shelf life   243
9.5 Screen printing   244
   9.5.1 Screen printing theory   245
   9.5.2 Screen printing equipment   246
9.6 Application of paste by syringe   254
   9.6.1 Air-driven syringe   254
   9.6.2 Peristaltic pump   254
   9.6.3 Positive-displacement pump   256
9.7 Alternative solder application processes   256
   9.7.1 Deposition on printed wiring board   257
   9.7.2 Pretinned components   258
   9.7.3 Fluxing   258
APPENDIX Brookfield viscometer test procedure   258

Chapter 10 Component placement   **261**

10.1 General machine construction   261
10.2 Equipment characteristics   263
   10.2.1 Accuracy   263
   10.2.2 Speed   271

10.2.3 Flexibility   274
10.3 Equipment classification   278
   10.3.1 Sequential placement   278
   10.3.2 Simultaneous placement   286
   10.3.3 In-line placement   286
10.4 Equipment design considerations   286
   10.4.1 Overall mechanical structure   288
   10.4.2 X-Y transport mechanism design   289
   10.4.3 Coordinate registration   292
   10.4.4 Component feeders   297
   10.4.5 Computer control   297
   10.4.6 Component verification   299
10.5 Component feeding systems   301
   10.5.1 Tape and reel feeding   302
   10.5.2 Magazine feeding   304
   10.5.3 Bulk feeding   310
   10.5.4 Matrix tray feeding   311

Chapter 11 Reflow soldering   **313**

11.1 Reflow theory   314
   11.1.1 Temperature profile   314
11.2 Reflow-related parts movement   317
   11.2.1 Self-alignment   317
   11.2.2 Skewing   317
   11.2.3 Tombstoning   318
11.3 Reflow alternatives   322
11.4 Reflow by thermal conduction   323
   11.4.1 Conveyorized production systems   323
   11.4.2 Modified soldering irons   324
11.5 Vapor phase reflow   325
   11.5.1 Vapor phase theory   325
   11.5.2 Vapor phase fluids   328
   11.5.3 Vapor phase equipment design   329
11.6 Infrared reflow   334
   11.6.1 IR sources   337
   11.6.2 Temperature profiling   340
   11.6.3 Reflow atmosphere   341
11.7 Laser reflow   341

11.7.1 Laser sources   343
11.8 Reflow by thermal convection   344
11.9 Comparison of reflow techniques   345

Chapter 12 Wave soldering   **347**

12.1 Wave soldering overview   347
12.2 Flux application   349
  12.2.1 Foam fluxing   349
  12.2.2 Wave fluxing   350
  12.2.3 Spray fluxing   350
12.3 Board preheating   351
12.4 Wave soldering   352
  12.4.1 Single-wave systems   352
  12.4.2 Solder shadowing   357
  12.4.3 Dual-wave systems   357
  12.4.4 Drag soldering   360
  12.4.5 Soldering temperature profile   361
12.5 Wave soldering with oil intermix   363
12.6 Adhesives   363
  12.6.1 Adhesive choices   364
  12.6.2 Epoxies   365
  12.6.3 Acrylics   365
  12.6.4 Dispensing methods   366
  12.6.5 Component compatibility with adhesive   370

Chapter 13 Post-solder cleaning   **373**

13.1 Types of contamination   374
  13.1.1 Rosin flux residues   375
  13.1.2 Organic acid flux residues   375
  13.1.3 White residues   375
13.2 Cleaning process selection   377
  13.2.1 Cleaning under surface mount devices   377
13.3 Solvent cleaning   379
  13.3.1 Solvent power   380
  13.3.2 Fluorinated solvents   382
  13.3.3 Chlorinated solvents   390
  13.3.4 Health and safety aspects   390
  13.3.5 Environmental impact   391

13.3.6 Water extraction in solvent systems   391

13.4 Solvent cleaning processes   392

13.4.1 Batch vapor degreasers   392

13.4.2 In-line cleaning   394

13.4.3 Ultrasonic agitation   397

13.4.4 Selection of a suitable solvent cleaning process   397

13.5 Aqueous cleaning   398

13.5.1 Water hardness   398

13.5.2 Aqueous solutions   399

13.5.3 Aqueous cleaning systems   400

13.5.4 Environmental considerations   402

13.5.5 Safety considerations   402

13.6 Measurement of cleanliness levels   403

13.6.1 Visual inspection   403

13.6.2 Solvent extract resistivity   403

13.6.3 Insulation resistance   404

13.7 Cleaning philosophy: When is it necessary?   405

Chapter 14 Inspection and test   **409**

14.1 Inspection philosophy: To inspect or not to inspect   410

14.1.1 Control charts   410

14.2 In-process inspection points   413

14.3 Inspection techniques   417

14.3.1 Visual inspection   418

14.3.2 Machine vision   420

14.3.3 Three-dimensional vision   421

14.3.4 X-ray inspection   423

14.3.5 Infrared inspection   426

14.4 Electrical test   426

14.4.1 Functional testing   427

14.4.2 In-circuit testing   428

14.4.3 Test strategy development   431

14.4.4 Guidelines for in-circuit testing   435

Chapter 15 Repair of surface mount assemblies   **439**

15.1 Design for repairability   440

15.2 Repair processes   444

15.2.1 Preparation   444

15.2.2 Preheating   446
15.2.3 Component removal and replacement   446
15.2.4 Cleaning   454
15.3 Design modifications   454
15.4 Field repair strategy   457
15.4.1 On-site component-level repair   458
15.4.2 Board exchange program   458
15.4.3 Throw-away assemblies   459
15.4.4 Selecting a field repair strategy   459

APPENDIX A Acceptance criteria for visual inspection of surface mount
assemblies   461
APPENDIX B Glossary   467

Index   473

Part I
Overview

1

Introduction

Printed wiring technology, although developed during the Second World War, first gained widespread acceptance in the 1960s. At that time electronic circuitry was assembled from discrete components that required relatively few connections to the board. Early integrated circuits rarely employed more than 16 leads, and through-hole assembly technology (in which component leads were inserted and soldered into holes through the board) could easily accommodate the demands of the day. With the advent of the microprocessor and the growth of computer technology, circuit complexity has increased to the point that through-hole component mounting techniques are no longer adequate. Some types of digital integrated circuits, for example, must make well over 100 connections to the board. Through-hole packages with leads on 0.100-in (2.54-mm) centers become extremely inefficient for such large lead counts.

Surface mount technology (SMT) was developed in part to overcome the limitations of existing techniques. Unlike the through-hole components of Fig. 1.1a, surface mount components are soldered directly to the board surface (Fig. 1.1b). Although the difference may at first seem insignificant, this change offers a number of advantages, including smaller size, lower weight, better electrical performance, and reduced cost.

In principle, surface mount technology is not new. Various approaches have been used to mount components to the surface of boards almost since the inception of the printed wiring concept. The integrated circuit flatpack (Fig. 1.2), for example, was the first package designed expressly to house ICs and is a true surface mount product. Earlier types were through hole designs adapted from discrete semiconductor packages.

Surface mounting has been the predominant assembly method in the ceramic hybrid industry for many years because of the small physical size and improved performance it affords. It has also been popular in high-

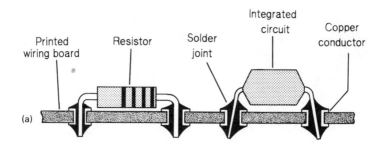

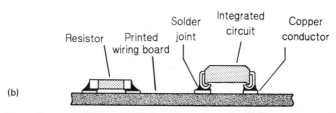

FIG. 1.1 Comparison of through hole and surface mount technologies: a. through hole, b. Surface mount.

FIG. 1.2 IC flatpack and carrier trays. These packages have leads on 0.100-in pitch and are typical of those commonly used during the mid-1960s. (Photo by the author.)

frequency circuits, where the lower parasitic reactances provide a clear advantage over through-hole designs.

These earlier approaches, however, have been limited to special applications. Process technology has lacked standardization and has been oriented toward manual assembly. As a result, costs have never been competitive with through-hole printed wiring technology.

While SMT has evolved from this background, it is not simply a new application of old technology. The term "surface mount technology," as it has come to be known in the industry, is concerned with cost-effective methods for mounting components to the surface of printed wiring boards (PWBs) or ceramic substrates in an automated fashion. It is characterized by the fact that solder is employed to form both electrical and mechanical connections from component to board, thus distinguishing it from chip-and-wire or conductive epoxy methods of assembly.

1.1 SELECTION OF SURFACE MOUNT TECHNOLOGY

Surface mount technology is often a cost-effective solution to complex packaging needs. However, this is not always true, so designers contemplating its use should understand all potential tradeoffs. Careful review of these benefits and limitations can help the designer determine whether SMT is the proper choice for any particular design.

1.1.1 Benefits

By incorporating SMT into product designs, several potential benefits can be obtained. These include:

Size/weight

Surface mount assemblies can be made considerably smaller and lighter than equivalent through-hole circuits. Size reductions of 25–90% are commonly reported.[1, 2, 3] An excellent example of the improvement that can come by converting to SMT is shown in Fig. 1.3.

Factors that contribute to this improvement are as follows:

1. Component Size

The size of a component is frequently limited by packaging requirements rather than by the functional device itself. For through-hole components, leads must be rugged enough to survive the insertion process without damage. Typical lead diameters range from 0.020 to 0.035 in (0.5 to 0.9 mm) and are rarely smaller than 0.015 in (0.4 mm). Drilling and imaging tolerances on the printed wiring board limit how closely these leads may be spaced; a standard through-hole lead pitch is 0.100 in (2.54 mm). This, in turn, limits how small component packages may be made.

FIG. 1.3   Police radar detector. This is an example of a commercially successful use of surface mount technology. The surface mount design is functionally superior to the previous through hole version, yet has an outline only slightly larger than a package of cigarettes. (Used by permission. Cincinnati Microwave, Inc.)

In contrast, many SMT device types have no leads at all. Instead, the metalized ends of the components themselves serve as the connections to the board. Even when leads are employed, they can be closely spaced. A standard surface mount IC lead spacing is 0.050 in (1.27 mm), and some devices have leads on centers as tight as 0.020 in (0.5 mm). As a result, component packages can be made two to five times smaller than their through-hole equivalents (see Fig. 1.4). Table 1.1 compares the printed wiring board area required for several equivalent through-hole and surface mount components.

2. Interconnectivity

The term "interconnectivity" refers to the number of solder joints that can be realized per unit area on the printed wiring board. It is thus related to component size and is most important for complex digital designs. Such circuits are likely to employ high pin-count ICs and are the biggest beneficiaries of SMT package improvements.

The industry-standard dual-in-line (DIP) package (Fig. 1.5) is extremely inefficient for devices with more than 28 leads. The highest lead-count DIP

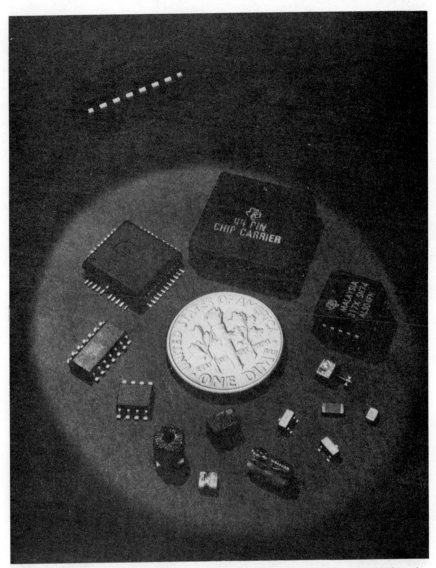

FIG. 1.4 Representative surface mount components. Clockwise from top right: 44-pin and 20-pin PLCCs, tantalum capacitor, ceramic capacitors, SOT-23 transistors, various inductors, 8-pin and 14-pin SOICs, 44-pin gull wing quadpack. Compare in size to the 16-pin DIP package in the background. (Photo by the author.)

commercially available is the 64-lead package, and it occupies over 3 square inches of board space. Both through-hole and surface mount alternatives have been developed to address high pin-count requirements. These include:

a. Pin-Grid-Array (PGA). This is a through-hole design with leads on the entire underside of the package (Fig. 1.6). The advantage of the pin-grid-array is that it markedly improves interconnectivity while maintaining compatibility with existing assembly processes. However, it has several cost and performance disadvantages.

Routing of the interconnections between semiconductor die and package leads is a complex task that requires the use of multilayer ceramic construc-

	Component Outline Area (mm²)	
Component Type	Surface Mount	Through-Hole
1/4 watt resistor	5.1	23.5
100 pF ceramic capacitor (COG dielectric)	2.4	7.5
0.1 μF ceramic capacitor (X7R dielectric)	9.3	16.2
Small signal transistor	6.7	16.4
1 watt power transistor	62	217
16-pin integrated circuit	62	146
68-pin integrated circuit	640	1875*

*64-pin DIP.

TABLE 1.1   Approximate PWB area required for various components

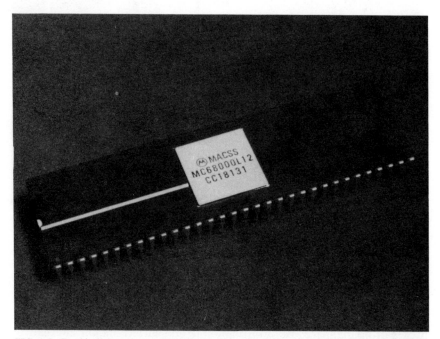

FIG. 1.5   Dual in-line package. This 64-lead package consumes an area of about 20 square cm and represents the practical maximum lead count for the dip configuration. (Used by permission. Motorola, Inc.)

FIG. 1.6   Pin grid array package. (Used by permission. National Semiconductor, Inc.)

tion. Routing complexity not only increases cost, it also degrades high frequency performance. Ceramic PGAs are easily an order of magnitude more expensive than post-molded plastic designs. Newer organic-substrate products for non-hermetic applications reduce this cost differential somewhat, but not entirely.

PGAs are also costly to assemble onto boards. Automatic insertion is not usually practical because the large number of leads requires tight placement tolerances. Unless production volumes are extremely high, it is not economical to invest in specialized assembly equipment for this process. As a result, many pin-grid-arrays are manually inserted—increasing both cost and defect rate.

Repair is an additional concern. To successfully remove a defective device, all leads must be simultaneously heated to the reflow temperature without damaging any of the plated through holes. Holes must then be carefully cleared of excess solder to permit insertion of the replacement device. Although not a unique problem to PGAs, the sheer number of holes for each device significantly increases the likelihood of damage.

b. Surface Mount Packages. Surface mount IC packages provide a considerable improvement in interconnectivity at prices comparable to through-hole packages. With the standard 0.050 in (1.27 mm) pitch, packages to at least 84 leads are practical. Above this number, lead density can be increased by decreasing lead pitch. The practical limit for existing surface mount proces-

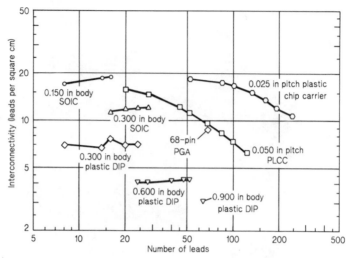

FIG. 1.7 Interconnectivities of various IC package types. The data includes an allowance for clearances between packages.

ses is in the range of 0.5 to 0.6 mm (0.020 to 0.025 in) lead pitch. Devices with spacings as tight as 0.3 mm (0.011 in) have been investigated, but such fine pitch packages require highly modified assembly methods.[4]

The effective interconnectivity of various through-hole and surface mount packages is plotted in Fig. 1.7. The data incorporates allowances for clearance around the packages to accommodate manufacturing and repair requirements and thus represents realistically achievable lead densities in actual production designs.

3. Via Hole Diameters

The only holes required on an SMT printed wiring board are vias—holes used to electrically connect the various layers of circuit traces but which do not accept component leads. These hole diameters can be very small to minimize the impact on available board area. Theoretically, via diameters are limited only by the current-carrying requirements of the circuit. Typical diameters range from 0.3 to 0.5 mm (0.013 to 0.020 in), and holes as small as 0.15 mm (0.006 in) diameter can be manufactured.[5]

4. Double-Sided Component Mounting

It is rarely practical to mount through-hole components on both sides of a board because component leads penetrate the board and cause mechanical interference on the underside. In addition, such designs are not compatible with the wave soldering process and must be laboriously hand soldered. With SMT, each side of the board is independent. By use of appropriate double-sided manufacturing techniques (Chapter 8), twice as much board area can be made available for component mounting.

Performance

Performance-related benefits can be summarized as follows:

1. Frequency Response

The performance of high-frequency circuits is limited primarily by component-related parasitic reactances. The stray inductance and capacitance associated with through-hole component leads restrict circuit operation to frequencies below about 500 MHz. With surface mount packages, parasitic reactances can be significantly reduced. In part this is due to the shorter component leads, but equally important are the shorter overall interconnect distances between components. Using leadless devices, operation to at least 3 GHz is possible. Specialized stripline packages perform at even higher frequencies. In many applications, circuit performance is limited more by the characteristics of the printed wiring board than by the surface mount component packages.

2. Package Propagation Delay

The time required for an electrical signal to propagate from the input to the output of an integrated circuit is the *package propagation delay*. It is a measure of the speed of a digital circuit and is therefore a restriction on circuit performance. Although total circuit propagation delay is also a function of the layout of the printed wiring board, package propagation delay is a primary influence.

   Fig. 1.8 compares parasitic reactances (a primary cause of propagation delay) for several IC package types. As can be seen, surface mount packages have smaller, more uniform reactances which have less impact on overall propagation delay. Packages with leads on all four sides demonstrate better performance than those with two parallel rows of leads. This is because the difference in length from the shortest to longest lead on the package is less severe.

3. Shock and Vibration Resistance

Surface mount components are smaller and lighter than their through-hole equivalents. As a result, the overall printed wiring assembly can be made more resistant to shock and vibration. While the improvement on a single printed wiring board is significant, the benefit to the overall product can be of even greater importance. By employing SMT, the total number of boards can be reduced, thus simplifying the associated mounting and support structures.

4. Electromagnetic Interference

Through SMT, sensitive circuits can often be combined onto a single board, simplifying shield design. Also, while through-hole component leads serve as tiny antennas that radiate and receive undesirable signals, surface mount leads do not penetrate the board and thus reduce this problem.[2]

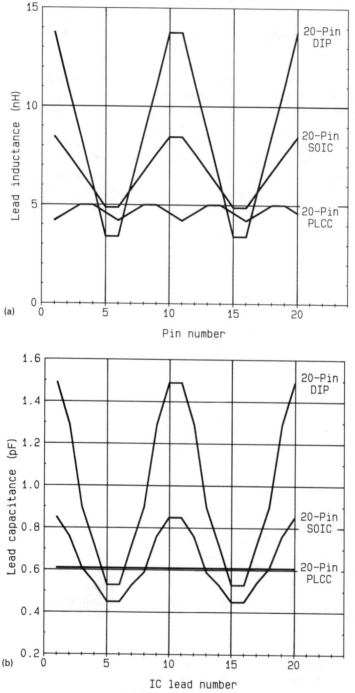

FIG. 1.8 Approximate parasitic reactances for various styles of 20-pin IC packages: a. Lead inductances, b. Lead capacitances. (Data provided by Texas Instruments.)

Cost

Although cost improvement is inherent in each of the above elements, several additional factors can heavily influence overall costs. These include:

1. Cost of Raw Laminate

Printed wiring board laminate costs scale directly with board size. Since SMT designs can be two to ten times smaller than through-hole equivalents, laminate costs will be proportionally less.

2. Drilling Costs

Generally, surface mount boards have fewer drilled holes than through-hole boards. Since holes are needed only as vias to connect between layers rather than to accommodate component leads, drilling costs should, in principle, be reduced. However, the actual savings depends heavily on board design. Holes for through-hole components are often also used as vias; when these are absent, vias must be expressly added.

Hole diameter is also a factor. If all holes are 0.5 mm (0.025 in) or larger in diameter, boards can be drilled by stacking several together and drilling them simultaneously. As diameters decrease below about 0.45 mm (0.018 in), boards must normally be drilled singly. Since all drilling is performed in one setup, even a single hole this small forces a reduced stack height, seriously impairing the throughput of the drilling process. Smaller drill bits also cost more, wear out sooner, and suffer higher breakage rates.

3. Printed Wiring Board Assembly Costs

Assembly costs for an automated SMT line are not appreciably different than for an automated through-hole line. Cost differences depend more on actual factory design than on any inherent benefit of SMT. Factory design and cost structures are discussed in Chapter 8.

4. System-Level Costs

The most significant cost reduction occurs at the overall system level. In many cases, circuitry that would otherwise require multiple boards can be combined onto a single board. This reduces both the material costs and the assembly labor associated with top-level product design. Actual savings are highly dependent on the design of the individual product and cannot easily be generalized.

Quality

While surface mount technology may not be inherently superior to through-hole mounting, the more demanding nature of the process has forced manufacturers into automation; manual production is impractical for all but the smallest product volumes. The higher level of automation required for most facilities yields a side benefit of improved quality and more consistent output.

At the same time, SMT has benefited from enlightened attitudes throughout the industry. Both component suppliers and assembly houses have often used SMT production lines as pilot vehicles for quality improvement programs. As a result, the quality of surface mount products frequently equals or exceeds that of through-hole equivalents.

1.1.2 Limitations

It is important that the design engineer understand the limitations of SMT. Some limitations are inherent, while others arise from the immature state of SMT development. Improper application of the technology can result in expensive designs yielding less than optimum performance.

Mechanical Strength

The solder joints of surface mount components become both the electrical and mechanical contacts to the board. The amount of solder available is generally much less than at a through-hole joint, so its mechanical strength is less. Since leads do not penetrate the board, they cannot reinforce the joint. Proper joint formation is therefore critical to the reliability of the assembly.

Theoretical calculations indicate that while a through-hole joint may be an order of magnitude stronger than required, the margin for surface mounting may be as little as 20%.[6] In practical terms, over 90% of the joints on a through-hole board may fail visual inspection without compromising mechanical reliability. Surface mounting, however, requires joints much closer to theoretical perfection. For many component types, at least 80% of the fillet must be properly formed to insure reliable operation.

Leadless components suffer from an additional concern. The coefficient of thermal expansion for a ceramic component body is less than half that of the organic printed wiring board. This difference in expansion over temperature must be entirely absorbed within the solder joints. Over the full product operating temperature range, large stresses can build in the joints, causing eventual failure. Specialized techniques as described in Chapter 6 must be employed to eliminate this problem.

Properly designed and formed surface mount joints are reliable over a wide operating temperature range—they are routinely employed in military and high-reliability equipment. However, they are much less tolerant of processing errors. A much higher level of process control must be maintained over the surface mount assembly process than has historically been necessary for through-hole insertion and soldering.

Thermal Management

If product reliability is not to be compromised, care must be exercised to control the effects of heat generated by the operating assembly. Potential reliability problems are caused by two factors:

1. Component Density

If the same semiconductor die as used in a DIP package is repackaged in surface mount form, it will still dissipate the same amount of power. A number of these devices, mounted on a board at the increased densities permitted by SMT, will cause a dramatic increase in the thermal dissipation per unit area. The devices will run hotter, causing a serious degradation of component reliability. (A rough rule of thumb is that every 10°C rise in temperature cuts semiconductor device reliability in half.) To avoid this problem, more sophisticated cooling techniques, lower-power device technologies, or both, must be employed.

2. Package Thermal Resistance

Heat is conducted away from a surface mount semiconductor die primarily via the package leads. These leads generally have a smaller cross-sectional area than through-hole devices, so the package thermal resistance is higher. To minimize the reliability impact, device power dissipation must be restricted or additional cooling techniques (such as heat sinks or forced-air cooling) must be employed. Thermal resistance characteristics of selected semiconductor packages are discussed more fully in Chapter 3.

Except at the very highest operating frequencies, thermal management is not a significant problem when low-power CMOS digital logic families are employed. With higher-power analog and digital components, a careful analysis must be made of the potential thermal impact before deciding to adopt surface mount technology.

Market Entry Costs

Because of the extent of automation required to establish a competitive surface mount assembly facility, it should not be undertaken lightly. Table 1.2 illustrates the investment that might be required to implement what would be considered an entry-level facility. The extent of the outlay might equal or exceed that for a through-hole assembly line. Facilities with an existing base of through-hole equipment may find it difficult to justify the large incremental investment for the relatively low product volume projected to utilize this capability. Unfortunately, without easy access to the technology, designers may avoid the use of SMT altogether. In these situations it may be more practical to channel SMT demand through a contract assembly house until such time as product volume warrants the development of an internal facility.

Equipment	Cost Range
Screen Printer	US $10k–$100k
Pick-and-Place Machine	$100k–$500k
Reflow Soldering System	$50k–$200k
Cleaning System	$50k–$125k
Miscellaneous Equipment	$25k–$100k
Total Expense	US $235k–$1025k

TABLE 1.2.   Approximate SMT factory capital investment entry level factory

Standards

Because of its relative immaturity, standards in all areas of the technology are in a continuing state of evolution. Two areas that have been extensively addressed are components[7, 8] and design of printed wiring boards. Other areas have not yet received as much attention. For example, there are many variations in assembly process flows. This dilutes the ability of process engineers to draw from previous development work and forces component and equipment manufacturers to accommodate a multiplicity of processes. Until such issues are resolved, a high overall degree of standardization will not be possible.

Standardization is an area of much current activity, so readers are encouraged to consult the various standards-setting organizations for the latest information. A review of these organizations and applicable standards is presented in Section 1.3.

Test

Attaching components to the surface of the board presents several problems at final test. Assemblies must be carefully designed if they are to be electrically testable. Most difficulties arise when an in-circuit ("bed-of-nails") test technique is used. These issues, discussed more fully in Chapter 14, include:

1. Node Visibility

By design, in-circuit testers probe the board at a number of locations (called *nodes*) to stimulate the circuitry and measure the response. Fixture probes must be able to access all nodes necessary to characterize the board. Nodes that can be probed are said to be *visible* to the tester. In the past, fixtures only probed the underside of the board. This was acceptable because all component leads penetrated the board and were visible from the underside. Surface mount components are not always visible from the underside and so special provisions must be made to achieve visibility. Typical solutions are either to add via holes so that all nodes are visible on the underside or to employ a somewhat more complicated double-sided fixture that probes both sides of the board.

2. Lead Spacing

Fixtures for in-circuit testers generally cannot probe nodes spaced closer than 0.050 in (1.27 mm) apart, although some new probe designs reduce this spacing to 0.040 in (1 mm). Such probes are fragile and must be replaced often in production environments. Probes designed for 0.100 in (2.54 mm) spacings are more rugged and are preferred for use whenever possible.

Many types of surface mount components have lead spacings less than 0.050 in (1.27 mm); they canot be probed directly even with 0.050-in probes. To accommodate these devices, component land patterns often employ a "fan-out" design such as that shown in Fig. 1.9 to increase the spacing between nodes. This inevitably reduces the maximum component density that can be achieved.

Functional testing, because it depends only on access to the board inter-connect structure, is not restricted by surface mount topologies. This advan-tage is one reason why functional testing is sometimes advocated for SMT assemblies. However, historical problems still present formidable obstacles:

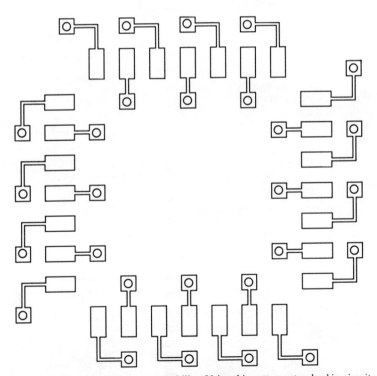

FIG. 1.9 Fan-out pattern to improve testability. Using this pattern, standard in-circuit probes spaced on 0.100-in centers can be used to test devices with 0.050-in lead pitch.

faults cannot easily be traced to individual components and the time required to write a functional test program is much longer than for an in-circuit program. Until these difficulties can be overcome, in-circuit testing will probably continue to be a popular method of troubleshooting defective board assemblies.

1.2 TECHNOLOGY CLASSIFICATIONS

Several schemes for classifying SMT assemblies have been proposed, based either on the process technology used to manufacture the board or on the configuration of the final product. The more widely used schemes are described below.

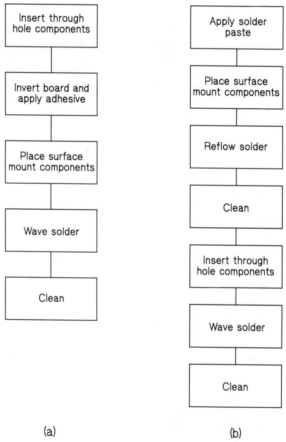

(a)   (b)

FIG. 1.10   Simplified SMT process flow diagrams.
a. Adhesive attach/wave soldering, b. Reflow soldering.

1.2.1 Classification by Process Technology

Two classes of surface mount process technology have been described in the literature.[9] These are *adhesive attach/wave soldering* and *reflow soldering* (formerly called solder paste/reflow). General characteristics of each process are described in the following pages, and simplified process flow diagrams are shown in Fig. 1.10. Detailed descriptions of the processes, costs, and factory designs are the subject of Chapter 8.

Adhesive Attach/Wave Soldering

This method was developed to take maximum advantage of existing assembly equipment. Through-hole components are inserted from the top of the board, while surface mount components are glued on the underside. Both are wave soldered simultaneously, with the SMCs actually travelling through the solder wave. A representative board is illustrated in Fig. 1.11.

The first step in this process is to insert, but not solder, all through-hole components. Leads must be clinched or other steps taken to prevent components from falling out during subsequent processing. The board is then inverted and adhesive dispensed at all locations where surface mount components are to be placed. (Because the adhesive would interfere with the proper formation of solder joints, care must be taken to prevent it from running onto the component lands.) The board is then populated with SMCs and the adhesive is cured. The SMCs are now securely held, permitting the board to be wave soldered. Both surface mount and through-hole joints are formed simultaneously. The final step is to remove flux residues in a suitable cleaning process.

Reflow Soldering

This approach can be used to attach a wide variety of surface mount components. It is more flexible than wave soldering, being suitable for components that would be damaged by immersion in molten solder. SMCs can be mounted on the top of the board alongside through-hole devices, on the underside, or both.

In the single-sided process, all SMCs are mounted and soldered prior to inserting any through-hole devices. The first step is to dispense solder, usually in the form of a solder paste, onto the board at the sites of the SMC joints. Components are then placed onto the board, being temporarily held in place by the solder paste. The solder is reflowed, most often by either a vapor phase or infrared reflow oven. Flux is then removed in a cleaning process and through-hole components are finally added via traditional insertion and wave-soldering technology. Typical reflow-soldered assemblies are pictured in Figs. 1.12 and 1.13.

FIG. 1.11   Wave soldered surface mount components. This controller board for a 3½ in flexible disk drive illustrates the complexity often achieved in current designs. The chip resistors and capacitors have been wave soldered, while the IC quadpacks were reflow soldered in a subsequent step. Flux residues evident around the ICs indicate that they were attached after the final cleaning operation. The coil windings in the upper portion of the figure are mounted directly on the printed wiring board to form part of the disk drive motor. (Photo by the author; board provided by Brooks Technical Group.)

FIG. 1.12 Military application of SMT using reflow soldered components. Leadless chip carriers as used in this design are gradually being phased out of military applications in favor of more reliable leaded chip carriers. (Used by permission. J. Hagge, "Critical Component Requirements for Vapor Phase Soldering Leadless Components on Circuit Board Assemblies for Military Electronics," *IEEE CHMT-6, No. 4.* Copyright 1983 IEEE.)

Combining Process Flows

More complex assemblies are manufactured by combining these two basic approaches in various ways. For instance, since reflow soldering places surface mount components on the top side of the board and adhesive attach/wave soldering places them on the underside, the two processes may be combined to obtain double-sided capability. Fig. 1.14 shows an assembly made in this manner.

Another technique, useful when large numbers of ICs are to be mounted, employs double-sided reflow. Components are placed and reflowed on the top side, then the board is inverted and the process repeated. Normally,

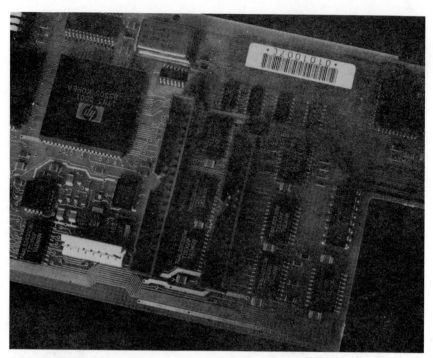

FIG. 1.13 Commercial application of reflow soldered components. This board makes extensive use of chip components and plastic packaged ICs. Reflow soldering is more practical than wave soldering for this type of design. (Photo by the author.)

FIG. 1.14 Double sided SMT in a hard disk-drive controller board. Top side is mixed through hole and reflow soldered surface mount components. Bottom side has wave soldered passive devices. (Hewlett-Packard Co.)

FIG. 1.15 Double-sided reflow soldered memory board. Each side has 184 DRAMs for a total of 10 megabytes of memory. The through hole connectors are hand soldered after all surface mount soldering has been completed. More recent designs using 1 megabit DRAMs in SOJ packages can contain over 40 megabytes in a similar space. (Used by permission. Edge Computer Corporation.)

through-hole components are inserted after all surface mount processing is complete. A typical assembly is illustrated in Fig. 1.15.

1.2.2 Classification by End Assembly Characteristics

Two schemes have been proposed for classifying assemblies by end assembly characteristics. One popular method was initially presented by HTC Corporation and has been widely adopted within the industry. The other, somewhat more comprehensive classification, has been developed by the Institute for Interconnecting and Packaging Electronic Circuits (IPC).

HTC Classification Scheme[10]

This scheme divides surface mount assemblies into three classes, defined as follows:

Type I: Total Surface Mounting
Assemblies in this category consist entirely of surface mount components and may be mounted on one or both sides of the board. Substrate materials may either be ceramic or organic printed wiring boards.

Type II: Mixed Technology

These assemblies combine all types of surface mount components with through-hole components on the same board. Surface mount components may be mounted on one or both sides of the board. Substrate material is usually restricted to organic printed wiring boards.

Type III: Underside Attachment

These assemblies are actually a subset of Type II. Surface mount components are restricted to small passive devices and discrete semiconductors that can be adhesively attached and wave soldered to the bottom of conventional through-hole assemblies.

IPC Classification Scheme[8]

This approach has been patterned after the successful classification scheme that IPC developed for through-hole mounting. It uses a matrix format to fully define the characteristics of the assembly. One element in the scheme describes component mounting complexity:

Class A: Techniques involving through-hole component mounting only
Class B: Techniques involving surface mount component mounting only
Class C: Techniques combining through-hole and surface mounting on the same board.

The other aspect defines the level of component attachment:

Type 1: Components mounted on one side of the board only
Type 2: Components mounted on both sides of the board

Using this scheme, a total surface mount assembly with components on one side of the board is designated Class B1, while an assembly that mixes through-hole components with surface mount components on both sides of the board is designated Class C2.

1.2.3 Functional modules

A special application of surface mount technology is the *functional module*, illustrated in Fig. 1.16. In this approach, an entire functional circuit is concentrated onto a single surface mount module. Either a ceramic or organic printed wiring board can serve as the substrate material. The module interfaces to a printed wiring motherboard via edge clips inserted in conventional through-hole fashion.

Functional modules are an easy way to enter surface mount technology. Module design and assembly can be contracted to a specialty assembly house with expertise in SMT. It is then unnecessary for the final assembler to establish SMT assembly capability because fully assembled and tested modules can be purchased as a unit from the subcontractor.

FIG. 1.16   Surface mount functional module. This approach is suitable for adding small blocks of SMT to a predominantly through hole board. (Photo by the author.)

Although functional modules are attractive in many situations, they are not a total solution. Lowest cost and highest performance is achieved by eliminating the extra level of interconnections and mounting SMCs directly on the final board.

1.3 STANDARDS AND SPECIFICATIONS

The success of any technology depends on a uniform understanding of expectations. Specifications are used to define the acceptability of the materials or services being procured and are an essential part of the agreement between purchaser and supplier.

Although specifications can be, and often are, developed on an individual basis between the contracting parties, the process is considerably simplified through the use of widely accepted and easily accessible industry standards. In the absence of such standards, the cost of generating acceptable specifications may be prohibitive. Many organizations are active on a national or international basis to develop and promote standards in all aspects of the technology. Such standards can be conveniently divided into three categories: those describing design requirements, those concerned with materials specifications, and those that address manufacturing process technology. Although an exhaustive treatment of all such standards is not possible, the major organizations and a sampling of their relevant work are described in the following paragraphs.

1.3.1 Institute for Interconnecting and Packaging Electronic Circuits (IPC)

This organization was founded in 1957 to develop standards and technical documentation for the printed wiring industry. Its original name was *Institute of Printed Circuits*. In 1977, the name was changed to reflect the evolution in electronic packaging, but the acronym IPC was retained.

IPC is a nonprofit trade organization comprised of representatives from member companies. Membership is open, for a fee, to any organization involved in electronic packaging. IPC has prepared a large number of specifications relating to fabrication and procurement of printed wiring boards, interconnection structures, and populated assemblies. Many of these documents have been specifically revised to include reference to surface mount technology. The following documents are particularly relevant to SMT.

IPC-CM-770 Component Mounting Guidelines for Printed Boards
Contains reference material for systems designers and component assemblers covering: component types; manual insertion; connectors/sockets; modules; terminals; jumpers; aids for manual insertion; automatic insertion/attachment; conformal coating; and solder joint reliability.

IPC-R-700 Modification and Repair of Printed Boards and Assemblies
Contains industry accepted procedures for modifying and repairing printed board assemblies. Sections include: terms and definitions, one- and two-sided boards; multilayer; component replacement; modification and repair procedures; and repair testing.

IPC-A-610 Acceptability of Printed Board Assemblies
Contains visual acceptability guidelines for printed board assemblies. Shows preferred, acceptable, and rejectable illustrations for general categories including: handling techniques; mechanical hardware; component installation; soldering; cleanliness; marking; coatings; and laminate surface conditions.

IPC-SM-780 Advanced Packaging and Interconnection of Electronic Components With Emphasis on Surface Mounting Technology
Includes information for all aspects of surface mounting. Covers techniques for component intermixing, issues for mounting electronic and electromechanical components, and a discussion of chip-on-board technology.

IPC-SM-782 Surface Mount Land Patterns (Configurations and Design Rules)
Contains descriptions of surface mount components and processes; packaging and interconnection structures; component land pattern designs; layout design rules; testability; and quality assurance requirements.

1.3.2 Department of Defense

Many requirements for electronic materials, processes, and assemblies have been defined by the Department of Defense and related government agencies. Because of their widespread applicability, military specifications are often employed in commercial situations outside of government control. Requirements for such items as solders and fluxes, for example, are so completely defined by government specifications that it is seldom necessary to impose additional requirements.

Although it is common to lump all government documents into the general category "military specifications," there are certain distinct classifications. *Military Specifications* are developed by the Department of Defense; they control the procurement of products or services. *Federal Specifications* are similar documents prepared by certain other government agencies for widespread use. *Military Standards* are reference documents that define test methods and general requirements. Other government agencies have from time to time developed additional specifications but these are rarely used outside the issuing organizations. Some of the more important documents governing aspects of surface mount technology are described in the following paragraphs.

Federal Specification:

QQ-S-571
Specifies requirements for solder, tin alloy, lead-tin alloy, and lead alloy.

Military Specifications:

MIL-F-14256
Defines requirements for liquid solder fluxes.

MIL-P-55110
Defines requirements for printed boards consisting of a conductor pattern on the surface of one or two sides of an insulating interface and associated interfacial connections and standoff terminals.

Military Standards:

MIL-STD-202
Defines test methods for electronic and electrical component parts.

MIL-STD-275
Establishes design principles governing the fabrication of rigid single- or double-sided printed boards and the mounting of parts (including integrated circuits) and assemblies thereon for use in electronic equipment.

MIL-STD-883
Specifies test methods and procedures for microelectronic parts and assemblies.

DOD-STD-2000
This family of documents defines soldering requirements for electrical and electronic equipment.

1.3.3 Electronic Industries Association (EIA)

The EIA has developed standards in many areas of electronic technology since 1924. Of particular interest are their component standardization activities. The Parts Engineering Panel develops standards for passive components and electromechanical devices. The Joint Electron Device Engineering Council (JEDEC) develops standards for semiconductor devices.

Parts Engineering Panel

The various committees that comprise the Parts Engineering Panel have established standards for many types of passive components: resistors, capacitors, inductors, relays, switches, and connectors. Those of particular importance in surface mount technology are as follows.

IS-30 Resistors, Surface Mount
Defines standards for chip resistors.

IS-36 Ceramic Capacitors
Defines standards for surface mount ceramic capacitors.

IS-28 Fixed Tantalum Chip Capacitors—Standard Capacitance Range
Defines surface mount tantalum capacitors in industry-standard body sizes.

IS-29 Fixed Tantalum Chip Capacitors—Extended Capacitance Range
Defines surface mount tantalum capacitors in special high-capacitance body sizes.

EIA-481 Taping of Leadless Components for Automatic Insertion
Sets standards for tape-and-reel packaging of surface mount components.

JEDEC

This council promotes the development and standardization of test methods, nomenclature, and product characterization of solid state devices. It also defines mechanical outlines for semiconductor packages. Two levels of definition are supported. The initial level, *registration*, denotes a package that meets certain minimum requirements but may not be widely used. *Standardization* is reserved for those package types that meet more stringent requirements, enjoy widespread support, and are produced by a number of manufacturers.

Relevant JEDEC documents include:

EIA/JEDEC Publication No. 95
Contains outline drawings and mechanical specifications for all registered and standard solid state component packages.

EIA/JEDEC Standard No. 11 Chip Carrier Pinouts for Logic Devices
Specifies electrical pinouts for logic devices.

EIA/JEDEC Standard No. 21-A Configurations For Solid State Memories
Defines pinouts for memory devices.

1.3.4 International Electrotechnical Commission (IEC)

This body is affiliated with the International Organization for Standardization (ISO). Founded in 1906, the IEC is presently composed of 42 national committees that work together to prepare "international" standards. A number of IEC standards relating to surface mount technology have been developed. They are widely used, especially by European organizations. IEC standards have been less of an influence in the United States, where EIA/JEDEC standards predominate. However, in recent years, a concerted effort has been made by both IEC and the EIA to work closely together to achieve unified worldwide standards.

Relevant IEC standards include:

IEC 68-2 Basic Environmental Testing Procedures
Describes current environmental and reliability tests recommended for through-hole and surface mount components.

IEC 115-1 Fixed Resistors
Has been amended to add terms and methods of tests applicable to chip resistors.

IEC-384-3 Sectional Specification, Fixed Tantalum Chip Capacitor with Solid Electrolyte
Describes standards for SMT tantalum capacitors.

IEC 384-10 Sectional Specification, Fixed Multilayer Ceramic Chip Capacitors
Defines standards for ceramic chip capacitors.

1.3.5 Other national organizations

Many other countries have strong national standards organizations. Some of the more active include B.S.I. in the United Kingdom, DIN in West Germany, UTE in France, and EIAJ in Japan. A complete discussion of the activities of all these organizations is beyond the scope of this book. Readers are urged to consult these organizations directly for up-to-date information on their activities.

REFERENCES

1. Jones, P. R. "Leadless Carriers, Components Increase Board Density by 6:1," *Electronics*, Aug. 25, 1981, pp. 137–140.
2. Marcoux, Phil. "Surface Mount Assemblies Shrink Circuitry," *Electronic Packaging and Production*, Jan. 1984, pp. 82–86.
3. Lyman, Jerry. "Surface Mounting Alters the PC-Board Scene," *Electronics*, Feb. 9, 1984, pp. 113–124.
4. Takiar, Hem P. "TAB Technology—A Review," Presented at *Electro/86*, Boston, MA, May 13–15, 1986.
5. Bergman, D., Gray, F. and Hinch, S. *Surface Mounting of Electronic Components*, IPC Workshop conducted May 1986, Irvine, CA.
6. Manko, Howard. "Soldering and Fine-Line Boards—Part 2," *Electri·onics*, Oct. 1984, pp. 15–19.
7. Hinch, Steve. "SMT Component Standards Needed Now," *Circuits Manufacturing*, Mar. 1986, pp. 45–56.
8. IPC-SM-782, *Surface Mount Land Patterns* (*Configurations and Design Rules*), Institute for Interconnecting and Packaging Electronic Circuits, Mar. 1987.
9. Hinch, Stephen W. and Wong, Yeng P. "Setting Up Production of Surface Mount Assemblies," *Electronic Packaging and Production*, Jan. 1984, pp. 66–71.
10. Hall, James. *Soldering Techniques For Surface Mount Circuits*, HTC Corporation.

Part II
Components

2

Passive components

Passive components have played a major role in the transition to surface mount technology. Resistors, capacitors, and inductors have been mounted to the surface of hybrid circuits for a number of years, and the transition to SMT has been relatively straightforward. As a result, an extensive range of products is now available, and numerous standards have been developed.

This is not to say that the transition has come entirely without difficulty. Many problems arise when components designed for use in low-volume, manually assembled hybrids are employed in automated SMT lines. The package shapes, dimensional tolerances, and solderability of these components are often inadequately specified. In many cases, the solution has been to introduce new product families designed expressly for SMT.

The great majority of passive SMCs are low-power devices of one watt or less dissipation. Although higher-power packages have been developed, they have not yet found wide acceptance in the industry. They are usually physically large packages that must be mechanically secured to the board. As a result, more steps must be added to the process, often defeating the original reasons for adopting SMT.

Selection of appropriate component families must be based on several factors:

- adequate electrical characteristics
- adequate reliability in the intended environment
- suitable physical size and shape
- compatibility with the assembly process
- ready availability at reasonable cost, preferably from multiple sources

This chapter discusses characteristics of surface mount passive devices. Semiconductor devices are described in Chapter 3, other components in Chapter 4, and soldering requirements in Chapter 5.

2.1 FIXED RESISTORS

Both rectangular and cylindrical surface mount fixed resistors are readily available. The choice of which to use depends on such factors as performance, cost, and process compatibility.

2.1.1 Rectangular chip

Physical characteristics

Most rectangular chip resistors are based on thick film process technology. As shown in Fig. 2.1, the active element consists of a thick film resistor paste, which has been screened and fired over a ceramic base. The base material is normally 96% alumina (a composite of 96% aluminium oxide, Al_2O_3, and 4% other oxides). The resistive element is a ruthenium oxide or similar paste. To protect the resistor, a glass layer is fired over it.

Electrical contact is made from the ends of the device. A thick film conductive material, usually platinum-silver or platinum-palladium-silver, is fired to form the electrodes. To prevent dissolution of this precious metal electrode during soldering, a thin barrier layer is applied over it. The barrier consists of a metal, such as nickel or copper, that has low solubility in tin-lead solder. Finally, a tin or tin-lead coating is applied over the barrier metal to provide a highly solderable surface.

Using thick film processes, resistors can be produced with tolerances from about 1% to 20% of design value. The 20% tolerance product can sometimes be manufactured directly from the as-fired film, but tighter tolerances must be trimmed into tolerance. This is done by purposely printing the film from 20% to 40% under value. The resistance is then increased by cutting across a portion of the element while simultaneously monitoring resistance. When the desired value is reached, the process is automatically stopped.

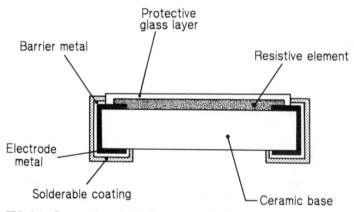

FIG. 2.1   Construction of thick film rectangular chip resistor.

FIG. 2.2   Laser trimmed resistor element.

Trimming is performed either with a high-power laser or air-abrasive system. Since trimming reduces the effective width of the resistive element, power handling capability is also reduced. The appearance of the film after trimming is shown in Fig. 2.2.

For tolerances below 1%, thick film construction is no longer adequate, and more expensive thin film processes must be used. In most cases, the resistive element consists of a sputtered layer of tantalum nitride. As with thick film chips, the resistance of the deposited film is purposely low in value and is brought into tolerance by trimming. Rather than using a mechanical approach, the resistance is adjusted by heating the film in an oxygen environment for a set period of time. This converts the surface of the film to an insulating layer of tantalum pentoxide. As the tantalum pentoxide layer grows, the thickness of tantalum nitride is reduced, thereby increasing resistance. Tolerances to at least 0.1% can be achieved.

Mechanical characteristics

The resistor family shown in Fig. 2.3 is widely available and is defined in an EIA standard.[1] The three sizes in this family cover power ratings of 0.0625 W, 0.125 W, and 0.250 W.

The common nomenclature defining resistor sizes employs a four-digit code. The first two digits describe the resistor length (in hundredths of an inch), and the last two refer to its width:

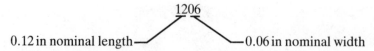

The nomenclature is only approximate; in the case of the 1206 resistor, the true nominal dimensions are 3.2 mm (0.126 in) by 1.6 mm (0.062 in). A similar size code is used for many other chip components, including ceramic capacitors, tantalum capacitors, and inductors. Although resistor size codes are most often based on English dimensions, metric size codes are also used. The metric code describes dimensions in tenths of a millimeter. The 1206 resistor described above, for instance, has a metric size code of 3216.

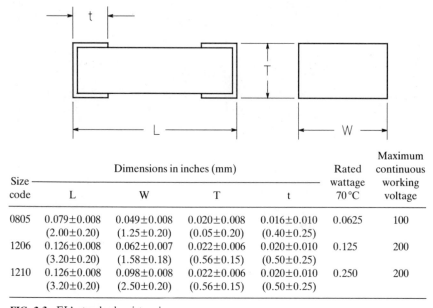

Size code	Dimensions in inches (mm)				Rated wattage 70 °C	Maximum continuous working voltage
	L	W	T	t		
0805	0.079±0.008 (2.00±0.20)	0.049±0.008 (1.25±0.20)	0.020±0.008 (0.05±0.20)	0.016±0.010 (0.40±0.25)	0.0625	100
1206	0.126±0.008 (3.20±0.20)	0.062±0.007 (1.58±0.18)	0.022±0.006 (0.56±0.15)	0.020±0.010 (0.50±0.25)	0.125	200
1210	0.126±0.008 (3.20±0.20)	0.098±0.008 (2.50±0.20)	0.022±0.006 (0.56±0.15)	0.020±0.010 (0.50±0.25)	0.250	200

FIG. 2.3   EIA standard resistor sizes.

Electrical characteristics

The most popular member of the standard family is the 1206 resistor. It is rated for 0.125 W power dissipation or 200 V DC maximum continuous voltage. The 0805 resistor (metric 2012 size code) is rated at 0.063 W or 100 V DC and is designed for use in low power applications where small size is important. Higher power requirements are met by the 1210 size code (metric 3225), which is rated at 0.250 W or 200 V DC. Recommended power derating characteristics for this family are presented in Fig. 2.4.

These products are commonly available in resistance values from 10 ohms to 1 megohm and in several resistance tolerance ranges. Most popular is the 5% tolerance for general-purpose applications and the 1% tolerance for

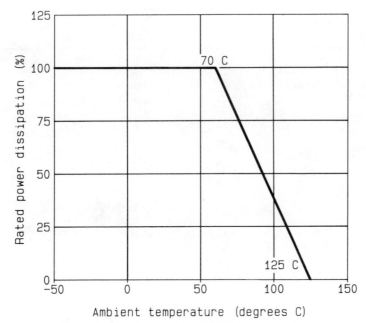

FIG. 2.4   Power derating characteristics for thick film chip resistors.

precision requirements. Other common tolerances include 2%, 10%, and 20% products. Precision resistors can be obtained in tolerances of 0.5%, 0.25%, and 0.1%.

Standard resistance values for the range 10 ohms to 100 ohms are shown in Table 2.1. Values listed in this table are applicable for products with tolerances from 0.5% to 20%. All other decades follow the same sequence.

Other rectangular chips

Rectangular chip resistors have been manufactured in many physical sizes other than those described above, primarily for military use in ceramic hybrid assemblies. Although standards have been developed for some of these sizes, they should not be confused with the surface mount product family described above. Often, these other products have not been adequately specified for automatic handling in high volume applications.

2.1.2 MELF (Metal ELectrode Face) resistor

The MELF resistor shown in Fig. 2.5 is adapted from conventional through-hole resistor technology. Rather than attaching leads for insertion mounting, the electrodes are metalized and solder-coated for surface attachment. In all other respects MELFs take advantage of existing manufacturing

Resistance Tolerance			Resistance Tolerance		
0.5,1.0	2.0,5.0	10,20	0.5,1.0	2.0,5.0	10,20
10.0	10	10	31.6	—	—
10.2	—	—	32.4	—	—
10.5	—	—	33.2	33	33
10.7	—	—	34.0	—	—
11.0	11	—	34.8	—	—
11.3	—	—	35.7	36	—
11.5	—	—	36.5	—	—
11.8	—	—	37.4	—	—
12.1	12	12	38.3	—	—
12.4	—	—	39.2	39	39
12.7	—	—	40.2	—	—
13.0	13	—	41.2	—	—
13.3	—	—	42.2	—	—
13.7	—	—	43.2	43	—
14.0	—	—	44.2	—	—
14.3	—	—	45.3	—	—
14.7	—	—	46.4	—	—
15.0	15	15	47.5	47	47
15.4	—	—	48.7	—	—
15.8	—	—	49.9	—	—
16.2	16	—	51.1	51	—
16.5	—	—	52.3	—	—
16.9	—	—	53.6	—	—
17.4	—	—	54.9	—	—
17.8	—	—	56.2	56	56
18.2	18	18	57.6	—	—
18.7	—	—	59.0	—	—
19.1	—	—	60.4	—	—
19.6	—	—	61.9	62	—
20.0	20	—	63.4	—	—
20.5	—	—	64.9	—	—
21.0	—	—	66.5	—	—
21.5	—	—	68.1	68	68
22.1	22	22	69.8	—	—
22.6	—	—	71.5	—	—
23.2	—	—	73.2	—	—
23.7	—	—	75.0	75	—
24.3	24	—	76.8	—	—
24.9	—	—	78.7	—	—
25.5	—	—	80.6	—	—
26.1	—	—	82.5	82	82
26.7	27	27	84.5	—	—
27.4	—	—	86.6	—	—
28.0	—	—	88.7	—	—
28.7	—	—	90.9	91	—
29.4	—	—	93.1	—	—
30.1	30	—	95.3	—	—
30.9	—	—	97.6	—	—

TABLE 2.1   Standard resistance values for the 10 to 100 decade resistance tolerances from 0.5 to 20%

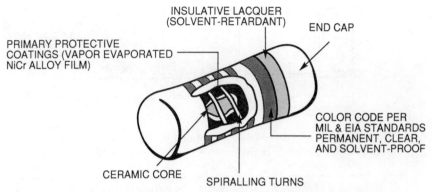

FIG. 2.5 Construction of MELF resistor. (Used by permission. Panasonic Industrial Company, Division of Matsushita Electric Corporation of America.)

techniques. As a result, they enjoy a slight cost advantage over rectangular chips.

Physical characteristics

The most commonly used MELFs are of either carbon film or metal film construction. Carbon film resistors are low-cost products intended for general-purpose use. The somewhat more expensive metal film products offer tighter tolerances, improved temperature stability, and better noise performance.

Both products employ a similar physical construction. A cylindrical cera-mic core serves as the base. The resistive element, either a carbon film or nickel-chromium alloy, is vapor-deposited on the surface of the ceramic. Metal end caps are then welded to the base to form the electrodes. (In some products, a cermet glaze is employed in place of the caps.[2]) Resistance is trimmed to value through a standard spiral cutting technique using an abrasive wheel or laser. An insulating, solvent-resistant resin coating is applied over the element, and color coding bands are applied to indicate resistance value.

Electrical characteristics

Carbon film resistors are typically available in values from about 1 ohm to 2 megohms. Tolerances to about 5% are easily produced. Metal film resis-tors range in value from at least 10 ohms to 1 megohm with 1% or better tolerance. Several power ratings are presently available from 0.125 W to 1 W dissipation. Most common are the 0.125 W/200 V and 0.250 W/300 V fami-lies, as illustrated in Fig. 2.6.

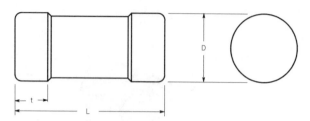

Type no. DIN 44061	Dimensions in inches (mm)			Rated wattage (70 °C)	Maximum continuous working voltage
	L	D	t		
0204	0.137±0.003 (3.48±0.07)	0.054±0.003 (1.38±0.07)	0.020 min (0.5 min)	0.125	200
0207	0.230±0.008 (5.90±0.20)	0.087±0.004 (2.20±0.10)	0.024 min (0.6 min)	0.250	300

FIG. 2.6   MELF resistor outline drawing.

Mechanical characteristics

The MELF format was developed in Japan, and most standards originated there. The degree of standardization is not as great as with rectangular chips, and slight variations in actual dimensions may occur from one manufacturer to another. Different manufacturers have sometimes adopted different package sizes for parts with similar electrical characteristics, so it is wise to verify part interchangeability before procuring parts from a new supplier.

MELF resistors were originally designed for the adhesive attach/wave solder assembly process. Although reflow soldering processes do not re-quire adhesive attachment, best process yields are still obtained when adhe-sive is used. Otherwise, the cylindrical package shape may allow the device to roll off the board during soldering. In the United States, where reflow soldering is popular, MELFs have not gained a large market share. In the Far East, surface mount components are often wave soldered, and both MELF and rectangular chip resistors are used extensively.

2.1.3 Preferred Resistor Construction

There is general agreement that both MELF and rectangular chip resistors should employ the following construction:

Wrap-around terminations

Most automated equipment cannot easily determine orientation of the resistor element. Therefore, terminations on rectangular chip resistors shold wrap around to cover the top, end, and bottom of the chip, as shown in Fig. 2.1. This configuration facilitates soldering regardless of whether the element is mounted away from the board ("face up") or toward the board ("face down"). For highest process yields, terminations should extend a minimum of 0.25 mm (0.010 in) on the top and bottom faces. This insures reliable joints and reduces the risk of tombstoning during soldering.

Solder-coated terminations

Best solderability is obtained when resistor terminations are coated with tin-lead alloy. A metal barrier between this outer coating and the precious metal base layer is essential to prevent rapid dissolution of the base metal during the soldering process.

Resistors used in conventional ceramic hybrids are sometimes attached with electrically conductive epoxy rather than solder. In this case, terminations should not be solder-coated. Instead, the epoxy must bond directly to the precious metal electrodes. This is necessary because epoxy resins are not efficient barriers to moisture penetration. In humid environments, solder-coated terminations can oxidize even when entirely covered by the resin. This results in increased contact resistance and electrical noise.

Dimensional control

Resistors designed for automated assembly must be manufactured to tighter tolerances than those used for manual assembly. The tolerance on length and width should be no greater than ±0.2 mm (0.008 in), and that on height should be no greater than ±0.1 mm (0.006 in).

2.2 POTENTIOMETERS AND VARIABLE RESISTORS

Strictly speaking, a variable resistor is a two-terminal device that allows adjustment of a resistance value, while a potentiometer is a three-terminal device that can be adjusted to tap a portion of a fixed resistance. In practice, the two terms are often used interchangeably. In this book, the term "potentiometer" is used to refer to both devices.

Potentiometers are produced in two configurations: sealed-element and open-element construction. Sealed units (Fig. 2.7) are completely enclosed and employ gaskets to prevent penetration of moisture or other contaminants. Although the seal is not truly hermetic, it protects the element from exposure to fluxes and cleaning solvents. Open units (Fig. 2.8) take an opposite approach; they are designed to maximize access of cleaning solvents to remove flux contamination.

It is generally agreed that the highest level of reliability is achieved by protecting the element against contaminants. Therefore, sealed units are often specified for industrial and high-reliability use. Open units are less expensive to manufacture and are preferred in consumer products and other noncritical applications.

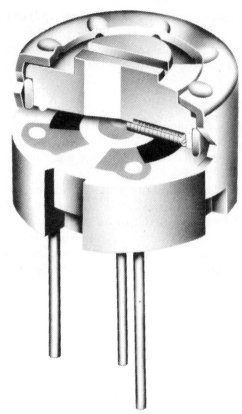

FIG. 2.7 Sealed potentiometer internal construction. (Used by permission. Murata Erie North America, Inc.)

FIG. 2.8 Open-element potentiometer construction. (Used by permission. Copyright 1985 Bourns, Inc.)

2.2.1 Sealed-element construction

Few standards exist for sealed surface mount potentiometers. The earliest designs were conventional through-hole products that had their leads formed for surface attachment. More recently, several product families designed expressly for surface mounting have been introduced. Pinout configurations and lead spacings have not yet been standardized among all manufacturers.

Sealed units are available in a number of configurations: single-turn or multiple-turn adjustment screws, top- or side-mounted adjustments, and various degrees of environmental resistance. Several designs are pictured in Fig. 2.9.

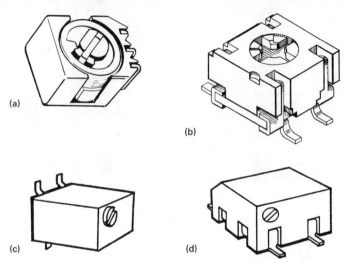

FIG. 2.9 Sealed potentiometer package styles: a. Single-turn, horizontal adjust, b. Single-turn, vertical adjust, machine adjustable, c. Multi-turn, vertical adjust, d. Multi-turn, horizontal adjust. (Used by permission. Copyright 1985 Bourns, Inc.)

Simply sealing a potentiometer with a gasket does not guarantee improved performance. Surface mount reflow and wave soldering processes are more severe than comparable through-hole processes, primarily because of the large temperature gradients encountered. When a sealed potentiometer is immersed in cleaning solvent immediately after soldering, its internal air temperature can drop extremely rapidly, causing a partial vacuum to form inside the package. If the seal is not designed to tolerate this condition, contaminants can be sucked inside, defeating the entire reason for sealing the product. Once inside, these contaminants are not easily removed, so eventual failure is a virtual certainty. This problem can be reduced by careful seal design, but it is always wise to minimize thermal gradients within the process.

2.2.2 Open-element construction

These products account for the highest consumption of SMT potentiometers, being extensively used in consumer electronic applications. Open units are usually single-turn, top-adjust designs. Although no industry-wide

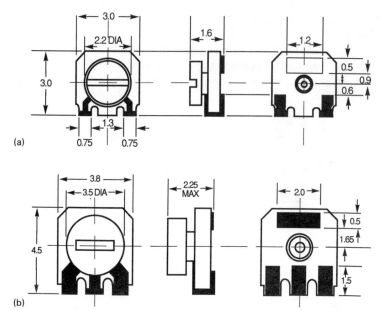

FIG. 2.10   Open-construction potentiometers: a. 3-mm body, b. 4-mm body.

specifications have been formally developed, the 3-mm and 4-mm sizes shown in Fig. 2.10 are widely available. Performance specifications vary by manufacturer, but a typical power rating is 0.05 W for the 3-mm style and 0.1 W for the 4-mm style. Packaging options include bulk, stick, and tape-and-reel.

2.2.3 General potentiometer requirements

Potentiometers must be carefully designed to maintain compatibility with SMT assembly equipment. On some products, the wiper adjustment interferes with the vacuum pick-up nozzle of the placement machine, preventing reliable acquisition of the component. Such potentiometers must either be placed manually or with specialized robotic eiquipment.

Pick-up problems can be eliminated by ensuring that the vacuum tool contacts a flat surface on the part. This is not generally a problem for products with side-mounted adjustments; the tool contacts the molded plastic body of the part. With a top-mounted adjustment, this is not possible, and the tool must contact the wiper. For best compatibility with automatic equipment, the slots for the adjustment tool should not extend all the way to the edge of the wiper surface (see Fig. 2.8). This permits the tool to form an unbroken seal entirely around the top of the wiper face.

Some package styles, especially those that are simple adaptations of through-hole designs, are incompatible with tape-and-reel packaging. The form factors of these styles are rarely optimized for surface mount tape-and-reel specifications. Lead configurations can also cause the parts to bind in the tape pocket, preventing withdrawal of the parts. If tape-and-reel packaging of parts is essential, consult component suppliers to determine which styles are compatible.

2.3 RESISTOR NETWORKS

Resistor networks consist of several individual resistors connected in a predefined configuration and housed in a single package (Fig. 2.11). They are not, however, discrete resistors that have been assembled into a common package. Instead, they consist of thick film or thin film resistive elements deposited on a ceramic base and encapsulated in a plastic or ceramic body.

Electrical Characteristics

The three circuit configurations illustrated in Fig. 2.12 are most common. The isolated resistors of Fig. 2.12a, all of the same nominal value, are useful whenever a large number of identical resistors is required in a circuit. In this

FIG. 2.11 Resistor networks. (Used by permission. Copyright 1985 Bourns, Inc.)

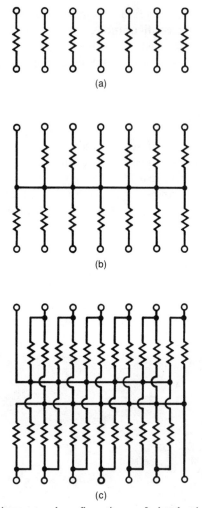

FIG. 2.12   Common resistor network configurations: a. Isolated resistors, b. Single resistors with common pin, c. Dual-line terminator.

case, the primary benefit is a simple reduction in size over a similar number of discrete resistors.

Fig. 2.12b illustrates a network of several resistors, all nominally equal in value, with one lead connected to a common pin. This configuration is useful for pull-up or pull-down applications in digital circuits, where each resistor is connected to a common voltage source. This network reduces the amount of circuitry necessary on the printed wiring board in addition to providing a size reduction over discrete resistors.

The network of Fig. 2.12c is a dual-line terminator used in digital circuitry. A series of resistor pairs is connected across two common lines. The junctions of these resistors are brought out to individual pins in the network.

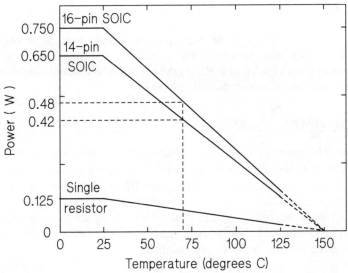

FIG. 2.13   Typical power derating curve for resistor networks in SOIC packages.

They thus serve as a voltage divider between power and ground lines and are used for dual-line termination and pulse squaring in TTL circuitry.

Other configurations such as ladder networks and isolated voltage dividers are available for specialized applications. Custom circuits in nearly any configuration can also be produced if expected volumes are sufficient to justify the development costs.

Typical resistor values range from 100 ohms to 100 kilohms, with extended values available for some package styles. Low-cost thick film products offer resistance tolerances between 1% and 20% and individual resistor power ratings of 0.062 W to 0.250 W. The more expensive thin film networks provide tolerances of 0.1% to 1% and resistance ratio matching of 0.05% to 0.5%. Individual resistor power ratings are somewhat lower than for thick film designs, being in the range of 0.05 W to 0.1 W.

The overall package power rating for a resistor network is invariably lower than the sum of the power ratings of the individual resistors. Therefore, it is not possible to simultaneously operate all resistors in a package at maximum power. However, since most resistor networks are used in low-power digital circuits, this is not usually a problem. Typical power derating characteristics are illustrated in Fig. 2.13.

Mechanical Characteristics

Resistor networks are typically housed in standard IC packages. The SOIC (small outline integrated circuit) and PLCC (plastic leaded chip carrier) configurations described in Chapter 3 are popular for commercial use, while the leadless chip carrier is preferred for the military/high-reliability market.

Unfortunately, there is little agreement as to preferred package outlines. While some suppliers offer PLCC packages, others prefer SOIC. Even among those who employ the SOIC, there is little consensus regarding preferred body width. Standards for resistor networks are currently being considered by both EIA and IEC. As these standards reach the industry, the range of product offerings should eventually stabilize.

2.4 FIXED CAPACITORS

The two predominant classes of surface mount fixed capacitors are the ceramic and the tantalum dielectric families. Ceramic capacitors are generally used in the range of 1 pF to 1 µF capacitance and at working voltages of about 25 to 200 V DC. Tantalum capacitors cover from about 0.1 µF to 100 µF at working voltages from 6 to 50 V DC. Other capacitor families, such as plastic film and aluminum electrolytic, are available, but for various reasons have not yet been widely accepted.

2.4.1 Ceramic capacitors

Ceramic capacitors were one of the first surface mount components to be widely used. As a result, a high degree of standardization has been achieved worldwide. General characteristics of these devices are as follows:

Physical construction

The internal construction of a multilayer ceramic capacitor is shown in Fig. 2.14. It consists of alternating layers of dielectric and electrode materials, printed consecutively and co-fired at a temperature of 1000–1400 °C. The dielectric is usually a barium titanate composite, and the electrodes are

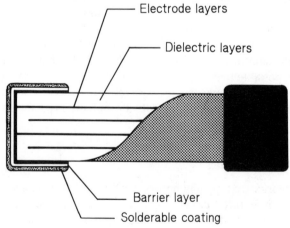

FIG. 2.14   Internal construction of ceramic capacitor.

platinum-silver or platinum-palladium-silver thick films. Alternate electrodes are connected to opposite end terminations to form a set of parallel-
plate capacitors.

The number and thickness of the dielectric layers determine the final
capacitance. As few as two or as many as 50 layers may be necessary. For a
given number of layers, increased capacitance is obtained by reducing
dielectric thickness. Two factors determine the practical minimum thickness. First is the required dielectric breakdown voltage, which is inversely
proportional to thickness. Second is the increased potential for failure due to
internal pinhole defects. For rated voltages to 50 V DC or higher, best
reliability is achieved with dielectric thicknesses of at least 0.025 mm
(0.001 in). For consumer and low-voltage applications, dielectric thicknesses are sometimes reduced to 0.013–0.015 mm (0.0005–0.0006 in).

As with chip resistors, the end terminations are protected with a nickel or
copper barrier layer to prevent dissolution of the precious metal electrode
during soldering. The top coating on the terminations is a solderable tin or
tin-lead alloy.

Mechanical characteristics

Fig. 2.15 shows the mechanical dimensions of the five standard capacitor
sizes defined by the Electronic Industries Association document EIA-198.

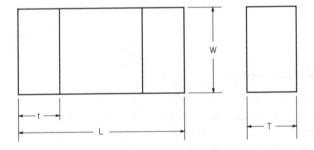

Dimensions in mm (in)

Size code	L	W	Tmax	tmax
0805	2.0±0.2	1.25±0.2	1.3	0.7
	(0.079±0.008)	(0.049±0.008)	(0.051)	(0.028)
1206	3.2±0.2	1.6±0.2	1.5	0.7
	(0.126±0.008)	(0.063±0.008)	(0.059)	(0.028)
1210	3.2±0.2	2.5±0.2	1.7	0.7
	(0.126±0.008)	(0.098±0.008)	(0.067)	(0.028)
1812	4.5±0.3	3.2±0.2	1.7	0.75
	(0.177±0.012)	(0.126±0.008)	(0.067)	(0.030)
1825	4.5±0.3	6.4±0.4	1.7	0.75
	(0.177±0.012)	(0.252±0.016)	(0.067)	(0.030)

FIG. 2.15   EIA standard capacitor dimensions.

They range in size from 2.0×1.3 mm (0.080×0.050 in) to 4.5×6.4 mm (0.180×0.250 in). Thickness is normally specified only as a maximum value, and is set either the same as the chip width or 1.7 mm (0.067 in), whichever is smaller. Actual thickness is then governed by the required number of dielectric layers, so wide variations can exist between low-value and high-value capacitors in a given package size.

Unfortunately, automated assembly equipment cannot easily accommodate these large variations. To avoid this problem, some users specify a single standard thickness near the maximum for all capacitors of a given size code. Smaller capacitors must be built up by increasing the thickness of the outside dielectric layers.

The nomenclature used to describe capacitor sizes is similar to that used for resistors (Section 2.1.1). English size codes are normally used by US manufacturers, but many European and Asian producers prefer metric codes.

The 1206 capacitor is the most widely used size. Similar to the 1206 resistor, it accepts an identical land pattern and can be obtained in a broad range of capacitance values. Curiously, the largest EIA standard size, the 1825 size code, has not gained widespread acceptance. Instead, most manufacturers offer a 2220 or 2218 size for their highest capacitance values. As with chip resistors, dimensional tolerances of all sizes are on the order of ± 0.20 mm (.008 in) to assure compatibility with component placement equipment.

Electrical characteristics

Electrical performance characteristics of ceramic capacitors depend on the nature of the dielectric material employed. Materials are usually classified according to the definition in EIA-198. In general, the higher the dielectric constant of a material, the worse the temperature stability and dielectric loss. Class 1 dielectrics, designated COG (formerly NPO) and CG, are based on various rare-earth titanates. They are highly stable and exhibit low dielectric losses. Class 2 dielectrics (Table 2.2) are based on barium titanate materials and exhibit higher temperature sensitivity and higher losses.

The three most common dielectric classes are COG, X7R, and Z5U. The COG dielectric offers the highest degree of temperature stability. It has a relatively low dielectric constant, so COG capacitors are larger and more expensive than other styles. The X7R dielectric has a higher dielectric constant and is preferred for many general purpose applications. The Z5U dielectric has the highest dielectric constant and is used in applications requiring high capacitance in a small physical volume. Important properties of these dielectrics are summarized in Table 2.3. The approximate physical sizes of COG, X7R, and Z5U capacitors are shown in Fig. 2.16.

Property	Code
Low Temperature Range	X = − 55 °C Y = − 30 °C Z = + 10 °C
High Temperature Range	5 = + 85 °C 7 = + 125 °C
Maximum Capacitance Change	V = + 22%, − 82% U = + 22%, − 56% T = + 22%, − 33% S = ± 22% R = ± 15% P = ± 10% F = ± 7.5% E = ± 4.7% D = ± 3.3%

TABLE 2.2   Ceramic dielectric classification EIA-198 class 2 dielectrics

	Dielectric Type		
Property	COG (NPO)	X7R	Z5U
Temperature range (Degrees C)	− 55 to + 125	− 55 to + 125	+ 10 to + 85
Capacitance change over specified temp.	± 30 ppm/°C	± 15%	+ 22% − 56%
Capacitance change with rated bias	± 30 ppm/°C	+ 15% − 40%	Not Specified
Aging rate per decade of time	0.00001%	2.5%	5.0%
Dielectric constant (K)	60–80	2200–3000	5000

TABLE 2.3   Properties of Ceramic Dielectric Materials

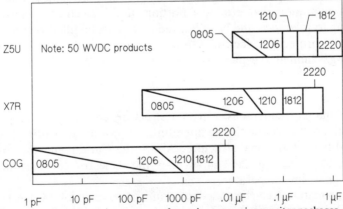

FIG. 2.16   Approximate capacitance ranges for various ceramic capacitor packages.

Several electrical characteristics bear further discussion. These are:

- capacitance
- Curie point
- voltage dependency
- aging
- process compatibility

Capacitance

Capacitance is determined from the formula

$$C = \frac{K\,A\,(n-1)}{113\,t}$$

where

C = capacitance in picofarads
K = dielectric constant
A = area of electrode overlap in square millimeters
n = number of electrodes
t = thickness of dielectric in millimeters

Capacitance is increased by increasing the dielectric constant, the area of electrode overlap, or the number of electrodes. It is also increased by decreasing the thickness of the dielectric layers.

The dielectric constant is defined as the ratio between capacitance when the desired material is the dielectric and the capacitance when replaced with an air dielectic. A material with a dielectric constant of 100, for example, will produce a capacitor 100 times larger in value than the same physical size capacitor using an air dielectric.

Unlike resistors, it is not usually practical to trim multilayer capacitors to value. Instead, each capacitor must be electrically tested and sorted into an appropriate tolerance range. In certain instances, a trimming operation can be performed. Capacitors that are too high in value are subjected to a bead blasting operation that erodes a portion of the electrode plates. After adjusting to tolerance, the bead-blasted area must be filled with a ceramic material to protect the electrodes from environmental damage. This form of trimming is limited to capacitors that employ the COG dielectric material.

Curie point

Barium titanate undergoes a crystal structure change at a temperature of about 120°C. Below this temperature, known as the Curie point, the material has a tetragonal structure. Above the Curie point, the structure changes to cubic. Fig. 2.17 shows how the dielectric constant increases rapidly near this temperature.

Certain materials can be added to barium titanate to shift the Curie point. The addition of lead titanate, for example, raises the Curie point tempera-

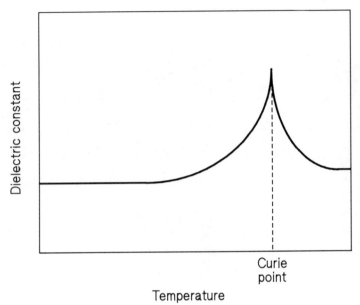

FIG. 2.17   Dielectric constant of barium titanate as a function of temperature.

ture, while strontium titanate reduces it. Very high capacitance values are sometimes achieved by lowering the Curie point to near room temperature to take maximum advantage of the increase in dielectric constant near this temperature. Unfortunately, such designs exhibit large capacitance shifts over relatively narrow temperature ranges—as much as 50% reduction in value when going from 25–50 °C.

Voltage dependency
Barium titanate is a ferroelectric material. As a result, its dielectric constant varies with applied DC voltage. With X7R dielectric, capacitance can decrease as much as 30% as the applied voltage increases to near the rated maximum. For Z5U dielectric, this reduction can exceed 75% of the zero-bias value.

When an AC voltage is applied, the effect is reversed. Rather than declining in value, capacitance increases with applied voltage. Large applied voltages can increase capacitance by 30 to 45% or more.

This change in capacitance with applied voltage is one reason many manufacturers suggest generous voltage derating factors when using X7R or Z5U dielectrics. The temperature-stable COG dielectric does not exhibit this characteristic.

Aging
Barium titanate exhibits another property typical of all ferroelectric materials, a reduction in dielectric constant with time. During the capacitor

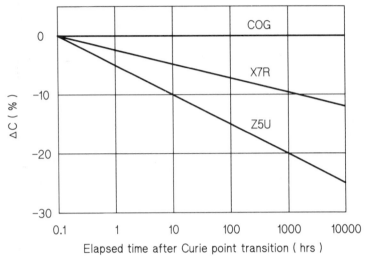

FIG. 2.18   Dielectric aging rates of ceramic materials.

manufacturing process, the material is fired at a temperature far above the Curie point. When the crystal structure changes as the capacitor cools below the Curie point, internal stresses develop in the material. These stresses relieve slowly over time, causing a drop in dielectric constant. The aging phenomenon is a logarithmic function expressed as percentage change in capacitance per decade of time. The various aging rates for different dielectric classes are shown in Fig. 2.18.

Ordinarily, aging is not a serious problem because capacitors are not used until hundreds of hours after initial firing. By that time, the dielectric constant has essentially stabilized. However, each time the capacitor is elevated to a temperature above its Curie point (as during the assembly soldering operation), aging effects are totally recovered. Upon cooling, the cycle begins again. Capacitance changes of 5–10% can occur during assembly, causing an otherwise good capacitor to initially appear out of specifications.

There is no known way to permanently accelerate the aging process. Application of rated voltage, however, can induce temporary effects. In critical applications, the temperature-stable COG dielectric material should be used because of its extremely low aging rate.

Process compatibility
Not all dielectric types are ideally suited for surface mounting. The COG dielectric is compatible with most soldering processes, but its relatively high cost limits it to applications where capacitance stability with temperature is a primary consideration. The most prevalent dielectric is the X7R class, which affords a good balance between cost and electrical performance. The Z5U

dielectric, although offering a higher capacitance per unit volume, is not widely used. This material has relatively low tensile strength and is easily fractured when exposed to the thermal shock of SMT soldering processes. Metal from the capacitor electrodes can migrate along fracture lines, eventually causing a catastrophic internal short circuit. Z5U has found some success in bypass applications where tight control over capacitance is not necessary, but even here, possible reliability problems are of concern.

Because of the potential of thermally induced fractures, some capacitor manufacturers recommend that the soldering temperature gradient be limited to a maximum of 2 °C per second.[3] Since it is not normally possible to exercise such tight control over the entire thermal cycle, a widely accepted practical approach is to impose a preheat requirement prior to soldering. A preheat temperature of 100–125 °C for 30–45 seconds can significantly reduce the risk of fracture. The transition rate from preheat to soldering temperature can then approach 20 °C per second with no reported degradation in reliability.

2.4.2 Tantalum electrolytic capacitors

The demand for higher capacitance values is usually met with tantalum electrolytic capacitors. The solid-electrolyte construction of the tantalum capacitor has proven better able to meet the demands of surface mounting than the wet-electrolyte aluminum capacitor.

Because of their small physical sizes, tantalum capacitors are primarily suited for small-signal and low-voltage applications. The available range of capacitance values and voltage ratings is considerably less than for through-hole devices.

Physical construction

The first SMT tantalum capacitors were adapted from products used in the hybrid industry. They were not suitable for automated handling, and no size standardization existed among manufacturers. More recently, the post-molded plastic body construction shown in Fig. 2.19 has gained general acceptance. Because of its repeatable body dimensions and flat top surface, this package is ideally suited for automatic assembly. Its non-hermetic construction makes it an attractive low-cost solution for commercial and general industrial applications, but less suitable for high-reliability use.

Important features of this design are: a) solid electrolyte capacitor element; b) post-molded resin package body; and c) external leads soldered or welded to the capacitor element. The leads fold under the capacitor body to provide a measure of compliance without significantly increasing the overall package dimensions.

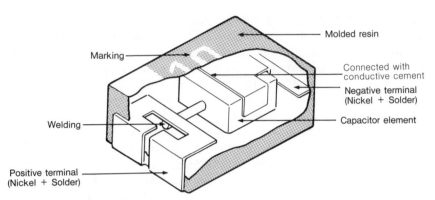

FIG. 2.19 Construction of post-molded tantalum capacitor. (Used by permission. Panasonic Industrial Company, Division of Matsushita Electric Corporation of America.)

Mechanical characteristics

Two tantalum capacitor families have been adopted by the EIA.[4,5] The four package sizes shown in Fig. 2.20a are designated *Standard Capacitance Range*. These sizes offer a good balance between cost and physical size. The family shown in Fig. 2.20b is designated *Extended Capacitance Range*; it offers increased capacitance per unit volume and a higher maximum capacitance value. Because of its somewhat higher cost, this family is normally specified only when its smaller size characteristics are especially important. It must be noted that while the EIA standards for these two families do not actually require post-molded plastic bodies, most manufacturers have opted to use this construction for their products.

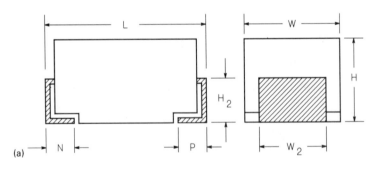

Dimensions in mm

Case Size	L	W	Hmax	N, P	W_2	H_2 min
3216	3.2±0.2	1.6±0.2	1.8	0.8±0.3	1.2±0.1	0.7
3528	3.5±0.2	2.8±0.2	2.1	0.8±0.3	2.2±0.1	0.7
6032	6.0±0.3	3.2±0.3	2.8	1.3±0.3	2.2±0.1	1.0
7243	7.2±0.4	4.3±0.3	3.1	1.3±0.3	2.4±0.1	1.0

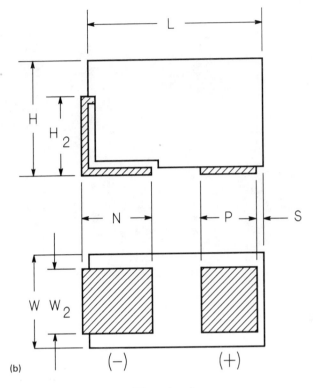

Dimensions in mm

Case size	L	W	Hmax	N	P	S	W₂	H₂ min
3518	3.5±0.2	1.8±0.2	2.1	0.2–1.7	0.2–1.3	0.1–1.0	1.5–2.0	0.7
3527	3.5±0.2	2.7±0.3	2.1	0.2–1.7	0.2–1.3	0.1–1.0	2.2–3.0	0.7
7227	7.2±0.3	2.7±0.3	3.1	0.5–2.5	0.2–1.8	0.1–1.3	2.2–3.0	1.0
7257	7.2±0.3	5.7±0.5	3.7	0.5–2.5	0.2–1.8	0.1–1.3	4.9–6.2	1.2

FIG. 2.20 Outline drawings for EIA tantalum capacitor families. a. Standard Capacitance Family, b. Extended Capacitance Family.

Electrical characteristics

The relationship between size and capacitance value for various voltage ratings is shown in Table 2.4 for the Standard Capacitance family and Table 2.5 for the Extended Capacitance family. As with most capacitors, best reliability is obtained when the applied voltage is considerably less than the maximum rating. This is especially true for the EIA Standard Capacitance Range products, as this family was originally developed for consumer applications. At rated voltage and 70 °C operation, a failure rate of 1% per 1000 hours of operation is not unusual. This compares to 0.1% per 1000 hours for a typical hermetically sealed through-hole capacitor operating under similar conditions. To achieve equivalent failure rates with the SMT

Capacitance	Working Voltage					
	4	6	10	25	35	50
0.1					3216	3216
0.15					3216	3528
0.22					3216	3528
0.33					3216	3528
0.47				3216	3528	6032
0.68					3528	6032
1.0					3528	6032
1.5			3216	3528	6032	7243
2.2		3216			6032	7243
3.3	3216			6032	7243	
4.7			3528		7243	
6.8		3528		7243		
10.0	3528		6032	7243		
22.0	6032					
33.0	6032		7243			
47.0		7243				
68.0	7243					

TABLE 2.4   EIA Standard Capacitance Range package sizes

Capacitance Value	Working Voltage					
	4	6	10	25	35	50
0.1						3518
0.15						3518
0.22						3518
0.33						3518
0.47					3518	3527
0.68					3518	3527
1.0					3518	7227
1.5				3518	3527	7227
2.2				3527	7227	7227
3.3						7227
4.7			3518			
6.8		3518	3527		7227	7257
10	3518	3527			7227	
15	3527	3527		7227		
22					7257	
47			7227	7257		
68		7227	7257			
150		7257				
330	7257					

TABLE 2.5   EIA Extended Capacitance Range package sizes

Standard Capacitance family, some manufacturers recommend that the applied voltage not exceed 50–60% of the rated working voltage. Design improvements currently in development may eventually eliminate the need for this large derating factor.

Tantalum capacitors are sensitive to the polarity of the applied voltage, and the positive terminal is clearly marked. In general, this voltage must never go negative. These devices are also sensitive to large ripple voltages, which can be of concern in power supply primary filter circuits. However, because of their solid electrolyte construction, they are the only electrolytic capacitors that are fully compatible with surface mount assembly processes.

2.4.3 Other capacitor types

Plastic film and aluminum electrolytic capacitors have been developed for surface attachment, but various difficulties have limited their use to relatively benign consumer-electronics environments. Both types can be damaged by the high temperatures encountered during the soldering process. In addition, aluminum electrolytics are susceptible to corrosion when exposed to the halogenated solvents typically used in the post-solder defluxing process. Through-hole capacitors can be sealed to prevent this problem, but such a solution has not yet proven feasible for surface mount designs.

Variable capacitors are available for high-frequency applications such as telecommunications and video products. A typical product line covers the range from about 1.5 pF to 50 pF in several steps. Adjustment capability ranges from about 2:1 for small capacitance values to 7:1 for higher values. Product offerings vary by manufacturer, but many of the same mechanical considerations discussed for potentiometers also apply to these devices.

2.5 INDUCTORS

Surface mount inductors are available in either wirewound or multilayer construction. Several levels of performance can be obtained, but the variety of product offerings does not yet approach that of through-hole technology.

2.5.1 Wirewound inductors

Wirewound inductors consist of a number of turns of fine wire wrapped around a core material. Low inductance values employ a ceramic core, while larger values need the higher permeability of a ferrite core. As shown in Fig. 2.21, the windings may be oriented either vertically or horizontally. Vertical windings permit the smallest case size but horizontal windings offer slightly better electrical performance.

Windings may be protected in one of two ways. The least expensive alternative is to conformally coat the device with an epoxy resin. However,

Ceramic or
ferrite core

Inductor windings

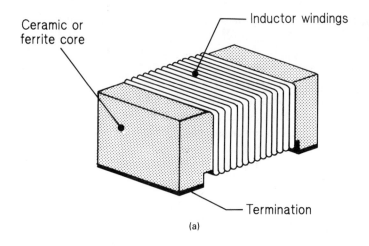

Termination

(a)

Ceramic or
ferrite core

Inductor
windings

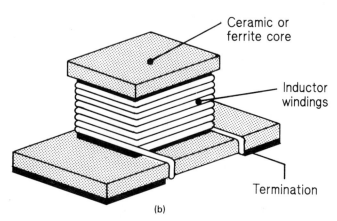

Termination

(b)

FIG. 2.21   Construction of wirewound inductors: a. Vertical windings, b. Horizontal windings.

conformally coated products have two drawbacks. Most serious is the poorly controlled surface geometry of the product. This can lead to difficulty in picking up the part with the vacuum tool on the placement machine. Additionally, some coating materials can dissolve in the fluorinated or chlorinated hydrocarbon solvents typically used in the defluxing process.

A more popular approach is to use a post-molded plastic body, as shown in Fig. 2.22. Although somewhat larger and more expensive than equivalent conformally coated products, these packages are much easier to handle during assembly. The external leads also offer a measure of compliance between device and board surface. As a result, fracturing of solder joints during temperature cycling is less likely to occur.

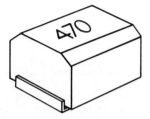

FIG. 2.22   Post-molded plastic wirewound inductor.

Although the EIA is considering the issue, there are as yet no officially recognized standard sizes for surface mount inductors. The two sizes shown in Fig. 2.23, however, are available from several manufacturers.[6] Inductance values range from about 0.1 μH to 1000 μH with standard tolerances of either 5% or 10%.

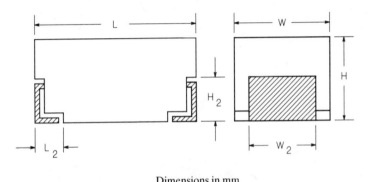

Dimensions in mm

Size Code	L	W	H	H_2 min	W_2	L_2 min
3225	3.2±0.2	2.5±0.2	2.2±0.2	0.5	1.9±0.1	0.4
4532	4.5±0.3	3.2±0.2	3.2±0.2	0.5	2.6±0.1	0.4

FIG. 2.23   Outline drawings for popular post-molded plastic wirewound inductors.

2.5.2 Multilayer inductors

Multilayer inductors are similar in construction to multilayer capacitors. They typically consist of alternating layers of ceramic or ferrite paste and conductor paste in a monolithic configuration. Inductance values extend from about 0.01 μH to 200 μH in body sizes identical to the 1206 and 1210 ceramic capacitors.

Multilayer inductors tend to have somewhat higher self-resonant frequencies, higher series resistances, and lower Q-factors than similar wirewound inductors. Commonly available tolerances are 5% and 10%. No industry standards have been explicitly developed for these parts, but manufacturers have tended to adopt ceramic capacitor outline dimensions in developing their product lines.

REFERENCES

1. *IS-30, Resistors, Surface Mount*, Electronic Industries Association, Aug. 1986.
2. Winkelmann, Bernd. "The New Chip Resistors," *Appliance*, June 1981.
3. Sarvis, John. *Chip Capacitors Relating to Surface Mounting Technology*, AVX Corporation, (undated).
4. *IS-28, Fixed Tantalum Chip Capacitor, Style 1 Protected—Standard Capacitance Range*, Electronic Industries Association, July 1986.
5. *IS-29, Fixed Tantalum Chip Capacitor, Style 1 Protected—Extended Capacitance Range*, Electronic Industries Association, July 1986.
6. Hinch, Steve. "SMT Component Standards Needed Now," *Circuits Manufacturing*, March 1986, pp. 45–56.

3

Semiconductor devices

Surface mount semiconductor devices (transistors, diodes, integrated circuits, and related products) employ the same silicon die as used in their through-hole counterparts. Any change in overall device reliability is strictly due to the difference in package format.

Several factors are of particular importance. Package environmental resistance, thermal design, and solder joint reliability are all critical to the reliability of surface mount assemblies. This chapter discusses both general design concepts and the specific characteristics of various semiconductor packages.

3.1 DESIGN CONSIDERATIONS FOR SURFACE MOUNT SEMICONDUCTORS

A semiconductor package performs several important functions. These include:

- protection of the silicon die from environmental contamination
- protection of the device against mechanical damage
- interface between silicon die and printed wiring board
- thermal path to conduct heat away from the device

The task of the device designer is to achieve the highest possible reliability at the lowest possible cost. This has led to the development of two major package families. *Hermetically sealed* packages provide the higher level of reliability, but at higher cost. *Plastic-encapsulated* packages provide a lesser level of protection, but at a much lower cost. The factors that contribute to device reliability are described in the following paragraphs.

3.1.1. Solder joint design

In through-hole technology, the device lead mechanically reinforces the solder joint so the strength of even a poorly made joint far exceeds that needed for mechanical reliability. Surface mount joints do not enjoy this luxury; no reinforcement is provided and mechanical strength is derived entirely from the solder. Solder joint design and its impact on assembly reliability are of such fundamental importance that they are discussed extensively in part III of this book.

3.1.2 Thermal expansion mismatch

Closely related to solder joint design is the subject of thermal expansion mismatch. The coefficient of thermal expansion (CTE) of a surface mount component generally differs from that of the substrate material to which it is mounted. As the temperature of the assembly varies, stresses due to this differential expansion must be partially absorbed in the joints. When the difference in CTE is extreme, the joints will exceed their elastic limits, eventually causing them to fail by fracturing. The problem is most severe with large mismatches, as when a large ceramic component is mounted directly to an organic printed wiring board. In this situation, failure can occur after only a few thermal cycles.

One solution to thermal mismatch is to make the joints more compliant by adding external leads. The strain can then be distributed over the entire length of the lead rather than over the short distance of the solder joint. Thermal expansion mismatch and lead compliance are discussed in detail in Chapter 6.

3.1.3 Package thermal resistance

For reliable operation, the temperature of a semiconductor junction must be maintained below a specified maximum value. The actual temperature limit depends on the semiconductor material employed, the intended product operating environment, and target reliability failure rate. Silicon semiconductors designed for the commercial and industrial marketplace frequently employ a 150 °C maximum junction temperature. Consumer-oriented products sometimes allow junction temperatures of 175 °C, while high-reliability designs may restrict them to 125 °C. Regardless of the actual temperature limit, heat generated in the junction must be efficiently removed from the device.

To a large extent the thermal performance of a surface mount semiconductor is established by the specific characteristics of the package. The amount by which the device junction temperature, T_j, exceeds ambient temperature, T_a, is proportional to the power dissipation, P_d:

$$T_j - T_a = \theta_{ja} P_d \tag{3.1}$$

The constant of proportionality, θ_{ja}, is termed the junction-to-ambient thermal resistance of the package.

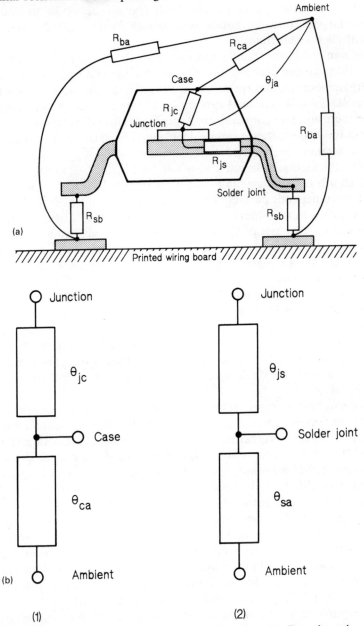

FIG. 3.1 Semiconductor thermal resistance: a. Heat transfer paths. R_{jc} = thermal conduction through case, R_{ca} = conduction from case to ambient, R_{js} = conduction through lead frame, R_{sb} = conduction into printed wiring board, R_{ba} = convection from printed wiring board to ambient. b. Simplified representations of thermal resistance. 1. Junction-case-ambient, 2. Junction-solder joint-ambient.

Total junction-to-ambient thermal resistance is determined by heat transfer through the two parallel paths shown in Fig. 3.1a. The first path consists of heat transfer through the package body and via convection to ambient. The second path consists of conduction through the device leads and then to ambient via the substrate.

Most semiconductor manufacturers simplify the thermal analysis by dividing θ_{ja} into two components: junction-to-case thermal resistance, θ_{jc}, and case-to-ambient thermal resistance, θ_{ca} (Fig. 3.1b). Junction-to-case thermal resistance is determined experimentally by measuring both junction temperature and case temperature at specified power dissipations. Case-to-ambient thermal resistance can be determined from the case temperature, ambient temperature, and power dissipation.

Unlike the thermal resistances illustrated in Fig. 3.1a, θ_{jc} and θ_{ca} shown in Fig. 3.1b are not fundamental properties of the device. The actual case temperature depends partially on the environment in which the device is situated, so the exact values for θ_{jc} and θ_{ca} are a function of device mounting characteristics. The use of θ_{jc} and θ_{ca} factors is a simplification which has gained widespread popularity in the industry. Care must be exercised when using these values to insure that they accurately represent the intended mounting conditions.

Junction-to-case thermal resistance is relatively insensitive to the manner in which the device is mounted, so a single θ_{jc} value can be used in most situations. Case-to-ambient thermal resistance, on the other hand, is highly sensitive to such factors as substrate material, land pattern shape, board size, and proximity of other devices. Approximate values are usually reported separately for devices mounted to printed wiring boards and to ceramic substrates.

Some manufacturers report thermal resistances referenced to solder joint temperature rather than case temperature. Junction-to-solder joint and solder joint-to-ambient thermal resistances, θ_{js} and θ_{sa}, are not the same as θ_{jc} and θ_{ca}. It is therefore important to understand the method used to determined published values. (Note that although the values of the component parts are different, the total thermal resistance, θ_{ja} is the same regardless of which method is used for calculation.)

The primary mode by which heat exits most surface mount semiconductor packages is via thermal conduction through the lead frame. Convection from case to ambient is less important. Since the leads of these packages are generally much smaller than equivalent through-hole devices, their thermal resistances are higher. Efficient thermal design at both the component level and the assembly level thus becomes much more important.

To improve thermal resistance, most surface mount semiconductors use copper-alloy lead frames. Copper offers the highest thermal conductivity of all commonly available lead frame materials. A surface mount IC package with copper leads compares favorably in thermal resistance to a DIP package with standard Alloy-42 steel leads (Fig. 3.2). In addition, copper's

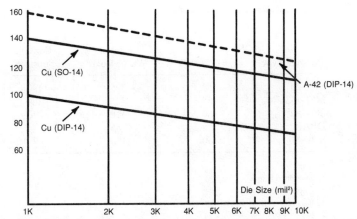

FIG. 3.2 Comparison of thermal resistance for copper and Alloy-42 lead frames for 14-lead DIP and SOIC packages. (Used by permission. J. Walker, "Reliability of Surface Mount Components and Assemblies," presented at Electro 1986, Boston, MA.)

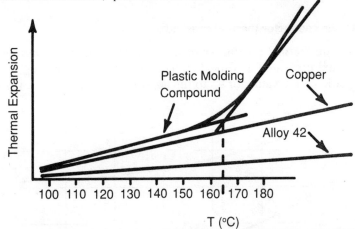

FIG. 3.3 Thermal expansion of copper, Alloy 42, and plastic molding compound for IC packages. (Used by permission. J. Walker, "Reliability of Surface Mount Components and Assemblies," presented at Electro 1986, Boston, MA.)

coefficient of thermal expansion is similar to that of molding compounds used in post-molded plastic devices (Fig. 3.3), so the probability of separation between the plastic and the lead frame is reduced.

Unfortunately, copper is not an ideal solution. Its CTE does not closely match that of silicon, so devices must be mounted to the frame by way of a polyimide or similar resilient adhesive rather than being eutectically attached. This can cause a slight increase in package thermal resistance. Copper lead frames are also less rigid than steel frames and are more easily bent during rough handling.

Forced air cooling is another effective technique for reducing total thermal resistance. Airflow acts primarily to reduce the temperature of the printed wiring board and secondarily to reduce the device case temperature.

		θ_{ja} (°C/W)	
Package Type	θ_{jc} (°C/W)	Printed Wiring Board	Ceramic Substrate
SOT-23[1]	150	325	180
SOT-143[1]	150	325	180
SOT-89[1]	60	110	40
DPAK[2]	6.25	65	—
SOD-80	50[3]	150[4]	70[4]

Notes:
1. Steel lead frame.
2. Copper lead frame.
3. θ_{js}.
4. θ_{sa}.

TABLE 3.1 Approximate thermal resistances of discrete semiconductor packages (measured in still air)

Discrete semiconductor thermal resistance

Approximate thermal resistances of several surface mount semiconductor packages are presented in Table 3.1. Total thermal resistance θ_{ja} is calculated by adding the value for θ_{jc} to the appropriate value for θ_{ca}. Knowing

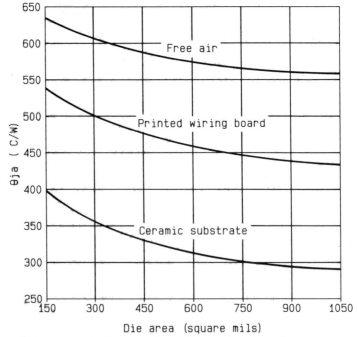

FIG. 3.4 Effect of die size on thermal resistance of SOT-23 package. (Reprinted with permission of *Solid State Technology*.)

the maximum permissible die and ambient temperatures, maximum device power dissipation can be calculated from eqn. [3.1].

Junction-to-ambient thermal resistance is always lower for a device mounted to a ceramic substrate than for the same device mounted to an epoxy-glass printed wiring board. Die size has a slight impact on θ_{ja}, with

Signetics

Thermal Considerations For Surface Mounted Devices

TYPICAL SMD THERMAL (θ_{JA})

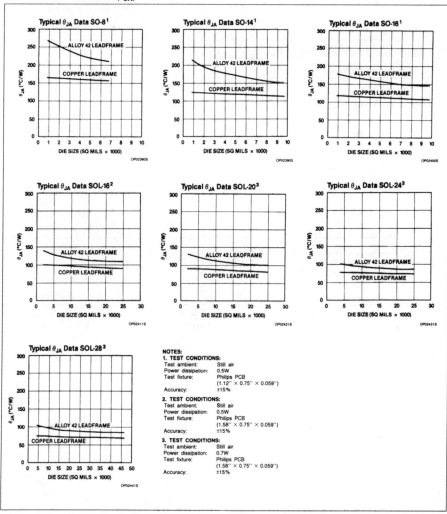

FIG. 3.5 Typical junction-to-ambient thermal resistances of SOIC packages. (Used by permission. Copyright 1986 Signetics Corporation.)

larger die resulting in lower thermal resistance. Figure 3.4 shows this relationship for the SOT-23 package.

Integrated circuit thermal resistance

The thermal resistances of SOIC and PLCC packages depend heavily on lead frame material, lead frame geometry, die size, and plastic molding material. The most comprehensive published study was conducted by N. V. Philips and Signetics.[1] The θ_{jc} and θ_{ja} values from this study for both package types are reproduced in Figs. 3.5–3.8. Values reported here show good correlation to less comprehensive unpublished data from other companies.

Signetics

Thermal Considerations For Surface Mounted Devices

TYPICAL SMD THERMAL (θ_{JA})

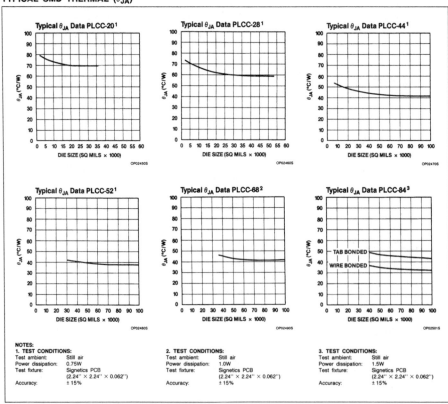

FIG. 3.6 Typical junction-to-ambient thermal resistances of PLCC packages. (Used by permission. Copyright 1986 Signetics Corporation.)

Signetics

Thermal Considerations For
Surface Mounted Devices

TYPICAL SMD THERMAL (θ_{JC})

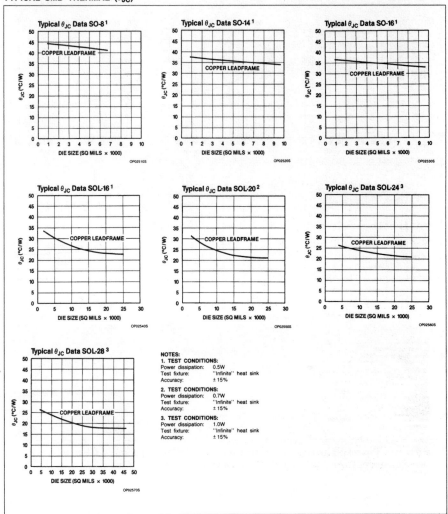

NOTES:

1. TEST CONDITIONS:
Power dissipation: 0.5W
Test fixture: "Infinite" heat sink
Accuracy: ± 15%

2. TEST CONDITIONS:
Power dissipation: 0.7W
Test fixture: "Infinite" heat sink
Accuracy: ± 15%

3. TEST CONDITIONS:
Power dissipation: 1.0W
Test fixture: "Infinite" heat sink
Accuracy: ± 15%

FIG. 3.7   Typical junction-to-case thermal resistances of SOIC packages. (Used by permission. Copyright 1986 Signetics Corporation.)

Signetics

Thermal Considerations For
Surface Mounted Devices

TYPICAL SMD THERMAL (θ_{JC})

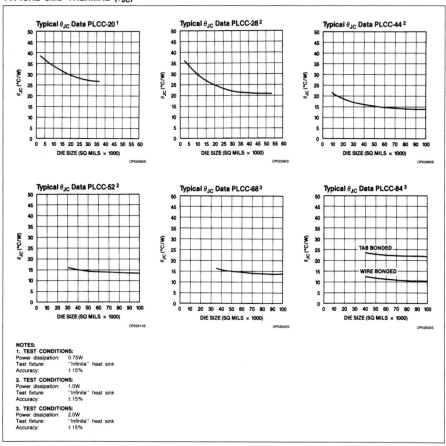

FIG. 3.8 Typical junction-to-case thermal resistances of PLCC packages. (Used by permission. Copyright 1986 Signetics Corporation.)

3.1.4 Solder joint temperature

Historically, the limit of device power dissipation has been established by the maximum permissible junction temperature. Surface mount devices may experience an additional limitation. The tensile strength and modulus of elasticity of tin-lead solder drop rapidly as temperature increases near the melting point, reducing the amount of stress the joint can absorb before failing. To reduce the risk of failure it may be necessary to restrict the

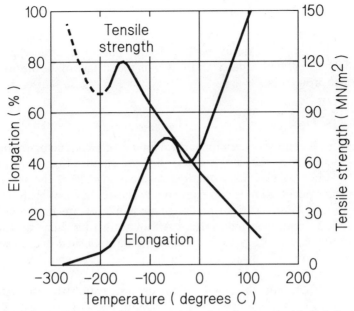

FIG. 3.9   Influence of temperature on elongation and tensile strength of Sn60 tin-lead solder. (Adapted from Ref. 10.)

maximum allowable solder joint temperature. The actual limit chosen depends on the level of risk that can be tolerated. The data in Fig. 3.9 suggests temperatures in the range of 100–125 °C, and these numbers have been recommended by some component manufacturers in their design guidelines.

This limitation can be significant for high-power packages with low thermal resistances. Consider the case of a 1 W power transistor package with junction-to-case thermal resistance of 30 °C per W. When operating at full rated power, the junction temperature is 30 °C above the case temperature. If a 110 °C solder joint temperature were specified, the device could not be operated above a junction temperature of 140 °C.

At present, there is no consensus as to the importance of limiting solder joint temperature in this manner. The mechanical properties of solder are a complex function of temperature, and only limited data is available. Solder is an elastic-plastic material that exhibits rapid creep and unknown crack propagation. The impact of its behavior on reliability is not well understood. The mere fact that tensile strength decreases is not enough to imply a reduction in reliability in the absence of a specific load. The practical effect of this condition has not been adequately discussed in the literature.

3.1.5 Environmental resistance

Most semiconductors employ two levels of protection against damage from the environment. The external package (either plastic or ceramic) provides the initial barrier, while a passivation layer on the surface of the die furnishes additional protection.

External package

The major reliability concern for surface mount semiconductors centers on plastic-encapsulated devices. Because they are smaller than the standard DIP, the volume of plastic surrounding the die is much less. The path length for moisture penetration is correspondingly shorter. Questions have been raised about whether surface mount semiconductors are therefore more susceptible to corrosion than DIPs.[2] Although this has been a historical problem for plastic DIP packages, there is little published data to suggest such a correlation for surface mount devices; there is some evidence to the contrary.[3,4]

Figure 3.10 presents the results of one extensive study that indicated no detectable difference in reliability between SOIC and DIP packages. Unfortunately, most published experiments do not isolate the contribution of the external package from that of the die passivation layer.

A more important concern is the purity of the plastic molding compound. Ionic contaminants in the resin, when exposed to moisture, react to form acids that quickly corrode unprotected portions of the die metallization. The problem can be avoided by selecting high-purity molding compounds with properties such as described in Table 3.2.

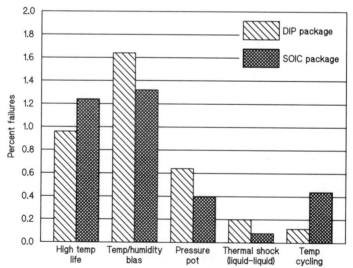

FIG. 3.10 Reliability comparison of linear ICs in DIP and SOIC packages. (Used by permission. Copyright 1986 Signetics Corporation.)

Property	Value
Sodium (Na^+) ion	< 5 ppm
Chloride (Cl^-) ion	<10 ppm
pH	4.1
Extracted conductivity	40 μυ/cm
Hydrolizable chloride	45 ppm

TABLE 3.2 Semiconductor Molding Compound Chemical Properties. (From Ref. 9. Used by permission.)

The coefficient of thermal expansion of the molding compound is another concern. It should be closely matched to that of the lead frame material so that thermally induced stresses on the die and lead frame are minimized. This reduces the potential for separation of the plastic from the lead frame. Cracks in this region are prime entry points for moisture and other contamination.

Die passivation

Until the early 1980s, most semiconductors used a silicon oxide-based passivation layer. Silicon oxide is a relatively brittle material that is prone to fracture. Moisture can enter the die through the fractures and corrode the underlying metallization. For this reason, silicon oxide serves more as protection against mechanical abrasion during manufacture rather than as a moisture barrier during operation.

Two recent developments have led to improved passivation technology. The first is the increasing popularity of passivation layers based on silicon nitride rather than on silicon oxide. Silicon nitride is a much superior barrier because it forms a dense, resilient coating that does not fracture easily. A second trend is toward dual-layer passivation systems (Fig. 3.11). Reliability is improved because of the low probability that defects on one layer will overlap those on the second. Various systems have proven to be effective, including dual-layer silicon nitride, silicon nitride over silicon oxide, and polyimide over silicon nitride.

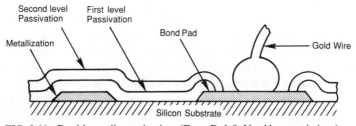

FIG. 3.11 Dual-layer die passivation. (From Ref. 9. Used by permission.)

It is now widely accepted that plastic-packaged devices should employ dual-layer passivation. At least one layer should be silicon nitride. Single-layer silicon oxide is acceptable for hermetically sealed devices, but since die for both plastic and hermetic products normally comes from a single fabrication line, this is not usually practical.

3.2 DISCRETE SEMICONDUCTOR PACKAGE STYLES

Most discrete semiconductors are housed in plastic-encapsulated packages. Outlines have been established for devices with power dissipation of up to several watts. Higher-power packages capable of handling up to 50 W have been investigated but are not yet commercially available.

The most common packages for discrete semiconductors are the *SOT* (small outline transistor) configurations: SOT-23, SOT-89, and SOT-143. These packages are post-molded plastic outlines that cover small- and medium-power applications to about 500-mW dissipation. Higher-power packages are less well defined. The DPAK has been developed for applications up to about 1.5 W, but it has not yet received widespread support. The conventional TO-220 package is sometimes used by forming its leads into a gull-wing configuration.

Two types of hermetically sealed packages are available. The cylindrical MELF package is often used for diodes, while transistors are usually packaged in ceramic chip carriers.

3.2.1 SOT-23

This package, illustrated in Fig. 3.12, is used for small-signal transistors and diodes with power dissipations less than about 200 mW. The small overall profile of the SOT-23 restricts its maximum die size to about 0.75×0.75 mm (0.030×0.030 in). It has been registered in the United States by JEDEC as the TO-236 outline and in Japan by EIAJ as the SC-59 outline (Fig. 3.13). Unfortunately, the two versions have significant differences, and even though they both claim the SOT-23 designation, they should not be used interchangeably.

Most US and European manufacturers produce packages that conform to the JEDEC outline. The only variable dimension is the standoff height from the board to the package body (dimension K in Fig. 3.13). The JEDEC outline presently allows two variations. The TO-236AA *high-profile* outline is used for reflow soldering applications. The large clearance between package and board permits cleaning solvents to penetrate and remove flux residues from under the device. The TO-236AB *low-profile* outline is used when the component must be adhesively mounted to the board. The minimal standoff height ensures that the adhesive will fill the gap between component and board.

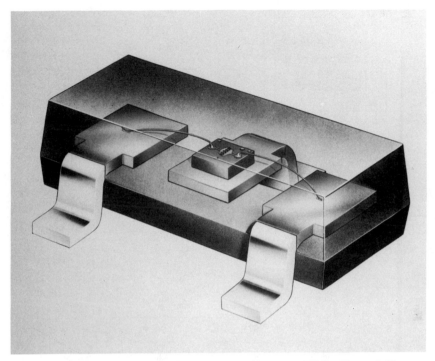

FIG. 3.12 Internal construction of SOT-23 package. (Courtesy of Philips Export B.V., Electronic Components and Materials Division.)

Assembly lines that use both reflow and wave solder operations may find it difficult to support both standoff heights in production. Two separate stock numbers are required for devices used in both processes, and the chance for confusion is great. For that reason, a third standoff height, the so-called *intermediate-profile* outline, has been proposed.[5] This version, with a 0.08–0.13 mm (0.003–0.005 in) clearance, is claimed to be compatible with both processes. It has not yet received a JEDEC registration number.

An alternative approach is to use the high-profile outline for both processes. Wave soldered devices can be secured either with a high-viscosity adhesive or by including an isolated copper pad in the artwork under the device. The pad reduces the clearance between device and board, permitting adhesive to more easily bridge the gap.

The SOT-23 package has also been adapted for special-purpose needs. A version with a clear plastic body, for instance, is used for light-emitting diodes, and a hermetic ceramic package has been developed for high-reliability use.

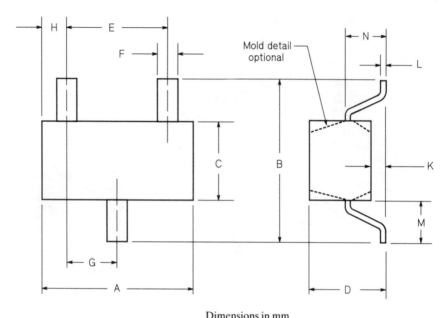

Dimensions in mm

Dimension	TO-236 min	TO-236 max	SC-59 min	SC-59 max
A	2.80	3.04	2.70	3.10
B	2.10	2.50	2.60	3.00
C	1.20	1.40	1.50	1.80
D	0.80	1.20	1.00	1.30
E	1.78	2.05	1.70	2.10
F	0.37	0.46	0.35	0.50
G	0.95	1.05	0.85	1.05
H	0.45	0.60	not specified	
K	– – see text – –		0.00	0.15
L	0.085	0.13	0.09	0.25
M	0.45	0.60	0.30	0.50
N	not specified		0.70	0.90

FIG. 3.13 Outline drawings for Japanese and US versions of SOT-23 package.

3.2.2 SOT-89

This package, illustrated in Fig. 3.14, is used for larger die sizes or higher power dissipations than can be accommodated with the SOT-23. It accepts semiconductor die up to about 1.5×1.5 mm (0.060×0.060 in) and, when mounted on an epoxy-glass printed wiring board, can dissipate up to about 0.5 W of power.

In the US, this package is registered by JEDEC as the TO-243. Unlike the SOT-23, the SOT-89 package outline is essentially identical around the world.

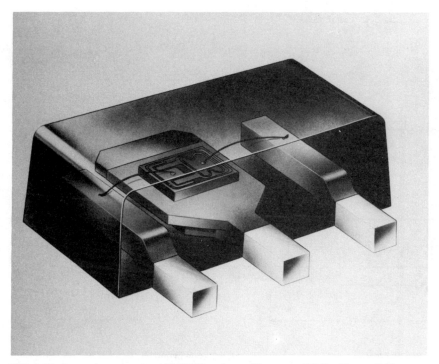

FIG. 3.14   Internal construction of SOT-89 package. (Courtesy of Philips Export B.V., Electronic Components and Materials Division.)

3.2.3 SOT-143

Small-signal devices with four leads are housed in the SOT-143, which is essentially an SOT-23 with an additional lead (Fig. 3.15). The package has received JEDEC registration as the TO-253. Body outline dimensions follow those of the TO-236 with the exception of standoff height. An *intermediate-profile* clearance of 0.05 to 0.13 mm (0.002 to 0.005 in) has been adopted. The SOT-143 is also produced in a version that matches the Japanese SC-59 body outline.

3.2.4 DPAK

A relatively new package outline for power devices is the DPAK, illustrated in Fig. 3.16. It has a maximum die size capability of 2.8 × 2.8 mm (0.112 × 0.112 in) and can dissipate up to about 1.5 W. The DPAK is not yet widely available, and dimensions vary among suppliers. One version has been registered with JEDEC as the TO-252 package outline.

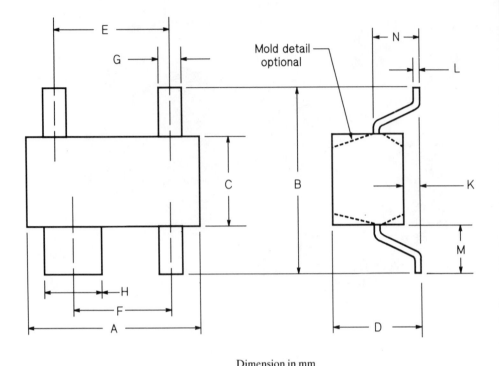

Dimension	Dimension in mm	
	min	max
A	2.80	3.04
B	2.10	2.50
C	1.20	1.40
D	0.80	1.20
E	-- 1.92 BSC --	
F	-- 1.72 BSC --	
G	0.37	0.46
H	0.76	0.87
K	0.051	0.127
L	0.085	0.13

FIG. 3.15   Outline drawing for TO-253 version of SOT-143 package.

3.2.5 MELF

Diodes are sometimes packaged in leadless versions of the axial lead DO-34, DO-35, or DO-41 glass packages. Two sizes have been registered by JEDEC under the DO-213 outline (Fig. 3.17). Similar in concept to MELF resistors, they are manufactured on the same equipment and have characteristics similar to their through-hole counterparts. Some manufacturers actually

FIG. 3.16   DPAK semiconductor package. (Used by permission. Copyright of Motorola, Inc.)

attach the leads to aid in fabrication and shear them off at the completion of the process. This approach, however, is not recommended for devices packaged in tape-and-reel or tube formats. Residual burrs can bind in the packaging material, making the devices difficult to extract with automated equipment.

MELF diodes are hermetically sealed and so are preferred for high-reliability applications. The MELF fabrication process is also inherently simpler than post-molded plastic technology, making them less expensive than the SOT-23 alternative. However, MELFs are more difficult to assemble onto boards. The cylindrical body shapes require a special placement tool for device pickup. Once placed, they tend to roll off the land pattern if not adhesively secured to the board. The latter problem has proven to be a serious obstacle in reflow soldering applications.

3.2.6 Selection criteria for discrete semiconductors

Plastic-encapsulated devices are recommended for most commercial and industrial applications in which ambient operating temperatures do not

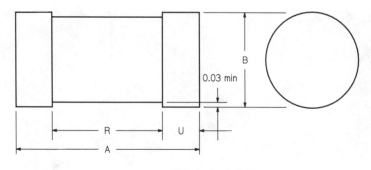

| Dimension in mm | | | |
Case style	A	B	R	U
DO-213AA	3.50±0.20	1.65±0.05	2.54 REF	0.48±0.07
DO-213AB	5.00±0.20	2.53±0.13	4.11 REF	0.48±0.07

FIG. 3.17 Outline drawings for MELF diode packages.

exceed 70 °C. For more extreme environments, devices should be protected within a hermetically sealed package.

When plastic packages are acceptable, selection criteria is relatively straightforward. Only two significant issues must be resolved: selection of a specific SOT-23 outline and decision between SOT and MELF packages for diodes.

There are few technical distinctions between the SC-59 and TO-236 package. The SC-59 can accommodate a slightly larger maximum die size, but this is rarely a significant concern. The choice is best made on the basis of availability. In the United States, the JEDEC-registered TO-236 package is most common. In the Far East, the situation is reversed, with the SC-59 outline being predominant. The situation in Europe is less settled, with both outlines readily available. A final decision can be made only by surveying anticipated suppliers to determine their preferred outline.

Another consideration is the choice of standoff height. The SC-59 outline is a low-profile package designed for adhesive attachment. Although it can be used in reflow processes, a better choice is the TO-236AA high-profile package. The 0.1-mm (0.004-in) minimum standoff of the TO-236AA permits more thorough penetration of cleaning solvents for removal of flux residues.

MELF packages are preferred for diodes when absolute lowest part cost is essential for devices adhesively attached to the board. For most reflow soldering processes, the cost of an additional adhesive step outweighs this slight cost differential. SOT packages may be a better choice in this situation.

When hermeticity is necessary, the alternatives are limited. MELF packages are recommended for diodes, but there are few choices for transistors.

Although a hermetic version of the SOT-23 has been developed, it is not widely available. The ceramic chip carrier packages described in Section 3.4.4 are most often used, but because of their large physical sizes they are best justified when multiple transistors can be incorporated in a single package.

3.3 GENERAL INTEGRATED CIRCUIT DESIGN CONSIDERATIONS

No surface mount integrated circuit package has yet achieved a status similar to that of the ubiquitous dual-in-line package. Several styles compete for market share, sometimes in overlapping applications (Fig. 3.18). Plastic packages include the SOIC, PLCC, and gull-wing quadpack. Ceramic chip carriers in both leaded and leadless configurations address the need for hermeticity. The flatpack, first developed in the early 1960s, continues to be used in a small number of applications.

Issues of general importance in the design of surface mount IC packages include the following:

- pinout configuration
- leadless vs. leaded design

FIG. 3.18   Representative IC package styles. Top row (l-r): 20-lead, 84-lead, and 68-lead PLCCs; middle row: Japanese-style quadpack, JEDEC registered 0.025-in lead pitch quadpack, C-quad; bottom row: various SOIC packages (Photo by the author.)

- lead configuration
- lead coplanarity error

3.3.1 Pinout configuration

Surface mount packages are produced in two general pinout configurations. For small devices from about 8 to 28 pins, a dual-in-line approach is used. Pins are arranged in two parallel rows similar to the through-hole DIP. For higher pin counts, a quad configuration is preferred. This style employs pins on all four sides of a square or rectangular package.

3.3.2 Leadless vs. leaded design

The very first surface mount flatpacks had long leads that extended straight out from the package body. Because the leads were fragile and easily deformed, flatpacks could not be automatically placed onto the printed wiring board. The lessons learned from the flatpack led to the development of leadless ceramic chip carriers. These packages do not employ external leads. Instead, they contact the board through metallized electrodes deposited directly on the ceramic package. Leadless chip carriers are fully compatible with automatic equipment. The absence of leads also simplifies the device manufacturing process and reduces the cost of the package. In addition, electrical performance is improved because parasitic lead reactances are lower in the leadless configuration.

Leadless packages have their own set of problems. As described in Section 3.1.2, the coefficients of thermal expansion between a ceramic chip carrier and organic board are not well matched. As temperature varies across the operational range, large stresses can develop within the solder joints. For packages of about 28 pins and above, joint failure can occur after relatively few thermal cycles. Various methods can be employed to overcome this difficulty (refer to Chapter 6), but at a considerable increase in cost compared to standard techniques.

Most plastic packages now use a leaded configuration to provide a measure of compliance between package and board. The popularity of leaded *ceramic* packages is also on the increase. Unlike the old flatpacks, leads are designed for compatibility with automated assembly equipment.

3.3.3 Lead configuration

Three lead configurations are commonly used for surface mount IC packages: gull-wing, J-lead, and I-lead. All are compatible with automated assembly equipment, but each has various advantages and disadvantages.

Gull-wing

As its name implies, the gull-wing lead flares down and outward away from the device body, forming a lap joint interconnection (Fig. 3.19a). It has been

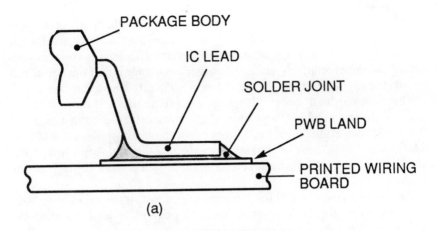

(a)

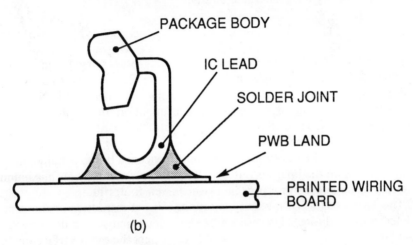

(b)

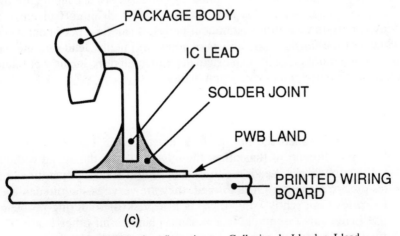

(c)

FIG. 3.19 SMT lead configurations: a. Gull-wing, b. J-lead, c. I-lead.

used for many years and has an established history of reliable performance.

A primary feature of this lead is the ease with which the finished joint can be visually inspected. The leads are readily accessible, making visual inspection of the joints relatively simple. Another advantage is that the device can be electrically tested through the use of a relatively simple probe fixture.

The exposed lead design also presents problems. It is susceptible to damage during handling, and even slight stresses can deform thin leads beyond specification limits. Leads bent out of the seating plane by as little as 0.12 mm (0.005 in) may not solder properly at assembly. Appropriate precautions must therefore be taken to prevent mechanical damage of the leads.

Another disadvantage is the large package footprint in relation to body size. Although the body itself is small, the extended leads increase the overall outline by a considerable amount.

J-lead

The J-lead was developed to overcome the disadvantages of gull-wing leads. In this configuration, shown in Fig. 3.19b, the lead is rolled under the package for protection against ordinary mechanical damage. While the ideal configuration is a half-circle radius of the termination, this geometry is not always easy to achieve. Some designs have a flattened appearance that resembles an L rather than a J shape.

Since the lead does not protrude from the package body, the amount of wasted space on the board is reduced. This also permits a larger maximum die size to be housed in a package with a given footprint.

The J-lead has its own set of limitations. Visual inspection of the completed joint is difficult because the solder fillet is partially hidden by the package body. It is usually only possible to inspect the outer surface of the joint. The overall package height must also be larger to accommodate the rolled-under lead. While this is advantageous for cleaning (solvent can readily penetrate under the component body), it can be a detriment when thickness of the finished assembly is of concern. Finally, lead forming has proven to be more difficult than originally anticipated, reducing yields and increasing costs for the device manufacturer.

I-lead

The I-lead, also called the *butt joint*, is illustrated in Fig. 3.19c. It is a relatively recent concept that offers the advantages of the J-lead without most of the drawbacks. Leads are formed in simple shearing operation that assures precise planarity. Once formed, they are very resistant to damage. Even if a lead is slightly bent, there is little risk of soldering problems because it remains essentially in the same plane as all other leads. The deformation would have to be so severe as to position the lead entirely off the corresponding land before a serious problem would occur. The mechanical strength of a properly formed I-lead has been shown to equal or exceed that of the gull-wing and J-lead configurations.

The primary disadvantage of the I-lead is that leads must be tinned with solder after shearing. Otherwise, the exposed base metal at the bottom of the lead will not exhibit acceptable solderability, and solder voids can occur under the lead. Large stress concentrations can build up in the solder surrounding the void, increasing the risk of fractures and subsequent mechanical failure of the joint. Solder tinning must be performed by dipping the leads in a solder bath or by use of a wave soldering machine.

3.3.4 Lead coplanarity error

Highest soldering yields are achieved when all device leads terminate on a single plane. This assures intimate contact between each lead and its corresponding land on the substrate. Under these conditions, solder simply forms a metallurgical bond between lead and substrate; it need not also bridge gaps between them.

In practice, it is not possible to perfectly form all leads in the same plane. Some leads may extend slightly below the norm, others slightly above. The amount of deviation between lowest and highest lead is the *coplanarity error*, often simply called *coplanarity* (Fig. 3.20). Because of coplanarity error, some leads will not make intimate contact with the board. Defects occur when the solder is not able to bridge between these leads and their corresponding pads.

Coplanarity error is quantified by placing the package on a flat surface and measuring the worst-case lead height off this surface. The amount of error that can be tolerated is partially determined by the soldering process employed. The wave soldering process, for example, supplies a large volume of solder to the joint. In this case, the acceptable coplanarity error may be greater than for a reflow process with limited solder volume. As a general rule, a lead coplanarity specification of 0.1 mm (0.004 in) is acceptable for reflow soldered components. Lower defect rates may be possible by reducing this specification to 0.05 mm (0.002 in), but few component manufacturers can economically meet such a requirement.

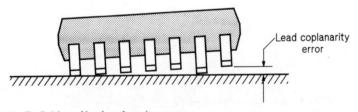

FIG. 3.20 Definition of lead coplanarity error.

3.4 IC PACKAGE TYPES

A multitude of package styles is available for surface mount integrated circuits. These range from relatively inexpensive post-molded plastic packages to hermetic ceramic packages. Characteristics of several of the more prevalent package styles are described in the following paragraphs.

3.4.1 Small outline integrated circuit (SOIC)

The SOIC was developed by Philips in 1971 for use in electronic wrist watches. As illustrated in Fig. 3.21, it employs the dual-in-line lead configuration with gull-wing leads spaced on 0.050-in (1.27-mm) centers. It is now widely used throughout the world, but exact mechanical dimensions vary among manufacturers. Two package outlines (Fig. 3.22) have been standardized in the United States by JEDEC under the MS-012 and MS-013 drawings. The *narrow-body* outline has a body width of 0.150 in (3.81 mm) and covers lead counts of 8, 14, and 16 leads. The *wide-body* outline, sometimes called the SOL (small-outline-large), has a body width of 0.300 in (7.62 mm) and covers lead counts of 16, 18, 20, 24, and 28 leads. Some manufacturers produce a 14-lead version of the wide-body outline, but this package is not formally recognized by JEDEC.

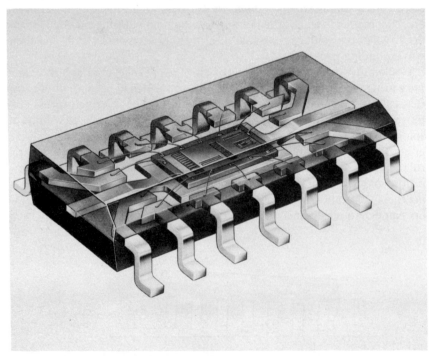

FIG. 3.21 Internal construction of SOIC package. (Courtesy of Philips Export B.V., Electronic Components and Materials Division.)

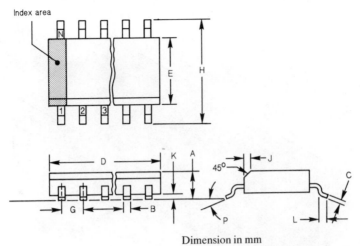

Dimension in mm

Dimension	0.150-in body			0.300-in body	
	min	max		min	max
A	1.35	1.75		2.35	2.65
B	0.35	0.49		0.35	0.49
C	0.19	0.25		0.23	0.32
E	3.80	4.00		7.40	7.60
G	-- 1.27 BSC --			-- 1.27 BSC --	
H	5.80	6.20		10.00	10.65
J	0.25	0.50		0.25	0.75
K	0.10	0.25		0.10	0.30
L	0.40	1.27		0.40	1.27
P	0°	8°		0°	8°
D SO-8	4.80	5.00	SO-16	10.10	10.50
SO-14	8.55	8.75	SO-20	12.60	13.00
SO-16	9.80	10.00	SO-24	15.20	15.60
			SO-28		

FIG. 3.22 Outline drawing for JEDEC-standardized SOIC packages.

Japanese manufacturers produce a wider range of packages that unfortunately do not match the JEDEC outlines. Although leads are also on a 0.050-in (1.27-mm) pitch, body widths differ. They include 4.4 mm (0.173 in), 5.4 mm (0.213 in), 7.5 mm (0.295 in), and 9.4 mm (0.370 in). Recently, some Japanese companies have begun offering packages that conform to the JEDEC outline.

Although nearly all SOIC packages now manufactured employ gull-wing leads, there have been attempts to promote a J-lead version of this package called the *SOJ*. The protected lead configuration and larger body outline in relation to total package footprint make this an attractive alternative, but the overwhelming popularity of the gull-wing format has been difficult to overcome.

SMALL OUTLINE J-LEAD (SOJ) PACKAGE

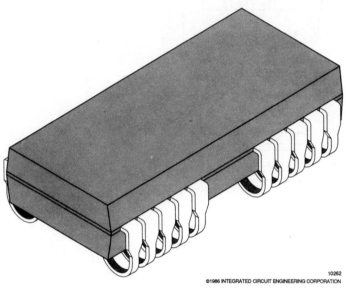

10262
©1986 INTEGRATED CIRCUIT ENGINEERING CORPORATION

FIG. 3.23 SOJ package for 1-megabit and 4-megabit DRAM memories. (Used by permission. Copyright 1985 Integrated Circuit Engineering Corporation.)

The one area where SOJ packages have become dominant is for large dynamic random access memory (DRAM) products of 1- and 4-megabyte capacity (Fig. 3.23). The large die size dictates the use of a 26-lead package, of which only 20 leads are actually used. By eliminating the center three leads on each side, additional area on the board can be used for conductor routing.

3.4.2 Plastic leaded chip carrier (PLCC)

This product was developed to meet the need for a low-cost plastic package for higher lead-count devices. As illustrated in Fig. 3.24, it employs J-leads on 0.050-in (1.27-mm) centers in a quad configuration. In the square outline used for most digital and linear ICs, the lead count is divided equally among all four sides. A rectangular outline is preferred for memory chips because it more closely matches the geometry of the silicon chip.

The JEDEC MO-047 drawing defines outlines for square packages with lead counts of 20, 28, 44, 52, 68, 84, 100, and 124 leads. The MO-052 drawing covers rectangular packages with 18, 22, 28, and 32 leads. One complication is the existence of two sizes of 18-lead rectangular packages. The smaller outline (Fig. 3.25a) was developed for 64k dynamic random access memory (DRAM) chips. When 256k DRAMS were introduced, they also needed an 18-pin package but were too large to fit into the outline for the 64k chip. A

FIG. 3.24 Internal construction of PLCC package. (Courtesy of Philips Export B.V., Electronic Components and Materials Division.)

package with an extended outline (Fig. 3.25b) was developed to meet this need. The design of the extended version is such that both packages can be accommodated by a single land pattern design with extended lands in the long direction (Fig. 3.26).

3.4.3 Quadpack

Gull-wing quadpacks (Fig. 3.27) have been used by Japanese manufacturers since the mid-1970s. Various configurations have been developed in response to unique product needs, so few standards currently exist. The package is oriented toward applications with lead counts of 44 and above. Lead pitches include 1.25 mm, 1.0 mm, 0.8 mm, 0.6 mm, and 0.5 mm.

The primary advantage of the quadpack lies in its high-density capability. With a 0.6-mm lead pitch, package interconnectivity is improved over the PLCC by a factor of two. In addition, the use of gull-wing leads facilitates visual inspection of solder joints.

The quadpack has several limitations. The combination of fine lead pitch and gull-wing configuration makes it particularly susceptible to damage in handling. Leads are often protected during shipping by placing each package in its own carrier at a significant cost increase over tube or tape-and-reel packaging. Specialized automatic placement equipment must then be used in the assembly process.

Another problem relates to overall package thickness. Body heights of about 2.5–3.0 mm (0.100–0.120 in) are commonly used, compared to about

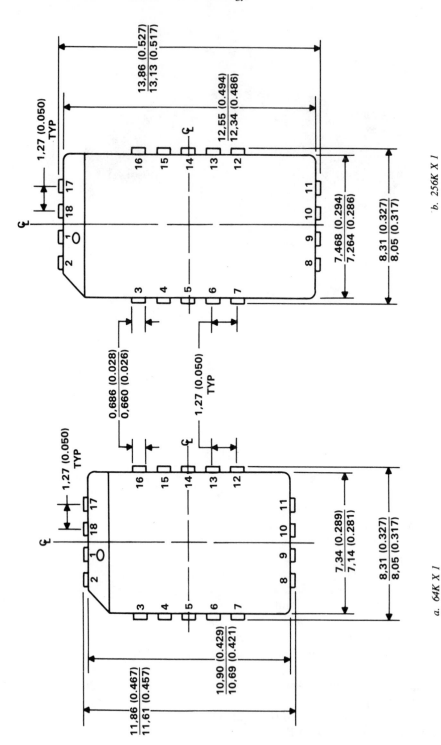

FIG. 3.25   PLCC outline drawings for 64K and 256K DRAMs. (Used by permission. Copyright 1984 Texas Instruments, Inc.)

a. 64K X 1

b. 256K X 1

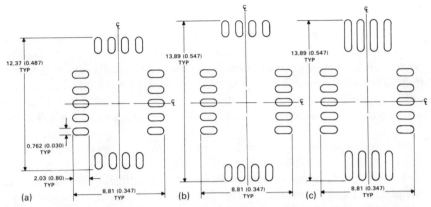

FIG. 3.26 Land patterns for rectangular PLCC packages: a. 64K DRAM, b. 256K DRAM, c. Composite land pattern. (Used by permission. Copyright 1984 Texas Instruments, Inc.)

FIG. 3.27 Gull-wing quadpacks. These 60-lead packages have an 0.8 mm lead pitch and are an early example (circa 1980) of surface mount technology in a pocket computer. (Photograph by the author.)

4.4 mm (0.175 in) for the PLCC. The thinner body of the quadpack is more susceptible to cracking during temperature cycling, especially in larger package sizes. Because of these limitations, the quadpack has not yet found a large market outside Japan.

3.4.4 Leadless ceramic chip carrier (LCCC)

This package has been developed under the direction of the US military for use in extreme environments. It is of ceramic construction with a soldered or frit-sealed lid that protects the device in a true hermetically sealed environment. Instead of contacting the board via external leads, metallized contacts are fabricated directly on the ceramic material. This reduces the manufacturing cost of the package and improves high-frequency electrical performance.

Four package variations with leads on 0.050-in (1.27-mm) centers have been established in JEDEC standards MS002 through MS005 (Fig. 3.28). Two of the four families are designed for socket mounting. Leadless Type A, defined in MS002, is intended for lid-down mounting. In this configuration, the die is mounted in contact with the top surface of the package, permitting efficient use of an external heat sink. Leadless Type B, defined in MS003, is designed for lid-up mounting when heat dissipation is not a primary concern.

Leadless Type C is similar to Type B except for corner configuration. This package can either be socket mounted or soldered directly to the board; it is produced in standard terminal counts of 16, 20, 24, 28, 44, 52, 68, and 84 contacts. Leadless Type D has a recessed lid and is intended for lid-down mounting directly on the board. It is available in 28, 44, 52, 68, 84, 100, 124, and 156 terminal versions. Both Type C and Type D can be mounted on land patterns that are nominally interchangeable with the PLCC format.

Two families of 0.040-in (1.0-mm) pitch packages are also defined by JEDEC standards. The MS009 drawing covers multilayer packages with 16 to 32 leads, while MS014 covers single-layer packages with 16 to 96 leads.

The leadless configuration of these packages can cause problems when mounted directly to an organic printed wiring board because of the substantial difference between the coefficient of thermal expansion for ceramic and that of epoxy-glass composite. Large stresses can build up in the solder joints

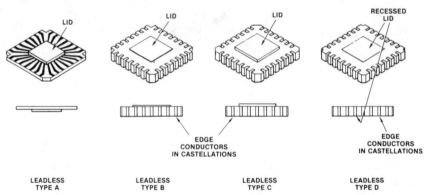

FIG. 3.28   JEDEC leadless chip carrier styles. (Published with permission of the Institute for Interconnecting and Packaging Electronic Circuits (IPC).)

as the assembly is cycled through its full operating temperature range, leading to premature failure of the joints. A number of techniques that address this problem are described in Chapter 6.

3.4.5 Leaded ceramic chip carrier (LDCC)

One way to solve the thermal cycling problems of LCCCs is to attach leads to the package. This introduces a compliant element that can absorb the stress without degrading the joint. As illustrated in Fig. 3.29, two outlines for this

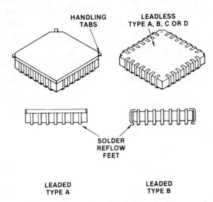

FIG. 3.29   JEDEC leaded chip carrier styles. (Published with permission of the Institute for Interconnecting and Packaging Electronic Circuits (IPC).)

package configuration have been standardized by JEDEC. The Leaded Type A family defined in MS006 and MS007 includes leads as an integral part of the package. Actual lead configuration is optional, but the J-lead version is commonly used. The Leaded Type B (MS008) consists of a Leadless Type A, B, C, or D package to which leads have been attached after fabrication. Again, actual lead configuration is not specified.

Leaded chip carriers have both advantages and disadvantages when compared to leadless chip carriers. These are summarized in Table 3.3.

3.4.6 Advanced package configurations

The size of an IC package is rarely dictated by the size of the internal die. The limiting parameter is usually the space necessary to fan out the leads to the required pitch. As lead counts continue to grow, the 0.050-in lead pitch becomes extremely inefficient. Although PLCC and LCCC package outlines have been defined for lead counts well above 100 pins, such packages are difficult to manufacture and consume an excessive amount of board space. A practical limit to maximum package size seems to occur when the length of the package reaches about 25–32 mm (1.0–1.3 in) along a side. For a package with 0.050-in lead pitch, this limit is reached at about 84 leads. For

Consideration	Leadless CCs	Leaded CCs
Thermal expansion match to P/I structure	Critical	Less critical
Removal and replacement	Comparatively easy with special tools	Less risk of damaging P/I structure
Solder joint inspection	Difficult	Less difficult
Flux removal after soldering	Difficult	Less difficult
Socket compatible	Yes (except Type C)	Yes (except Type B)
Lead length (CC-land pattern)	Minimal	Moderate (inductance greater)
Conductive cooling	Good, with direct heat conduction path. (Lower profile height)	Poor. (Higher profile height)
Preparation for soldering	Solder coating of terminals required	None except for solder coating as required for solderability
Self centering	Usually	Rarely
Flexure of P/I structure	Critical	Less critical

TABLE 3.3   Chip carrier application considerations. (Published with permission of the Institute for Interconnecting and Packaging Electronic Circuits (IPC).)

higher pin counts, package size must be reduced by adopting a finer lead pitch.

The quadpack was the first to exploit the higher density possible with tighter spacing, but its unprotected gull-wing lead format has discouraged widespread use. Several improved outlines are currently in development. None are yet widely available, and it is uncertain which will evolve into usable standards. The descriptions that follow are intended to illustrate industry trends rather than endorse specific outlines. It is likely that some of these packages will undergo considerable modification before being made commercially available.

Plastic quad flatpack

The existing quadpack offers advantages that many users find attractive. Lead pitches to at least 0.60 mm (0.024 in) are possible, greatly improving packing density compared to the PLCC. The gull-wing lead format is preferred for visual inspection of the completed solder joint. Two serious disadvantages, however, have limited its usage: leads are easily damaged, and the thin body outline is prone to cracking.

To avoid the problems of the quadpack while using a similar configuration, a group of US manufacturers has proposed the package shown in Fig. 3.30. It has gull-wing leads on a 0.025-in (0.63-mm) pitch and accommodates lead counts from 44 to 244 leads. A prominent feature is the inclusion of "bumpers" at the corners to protect the leads. This permits packages to be

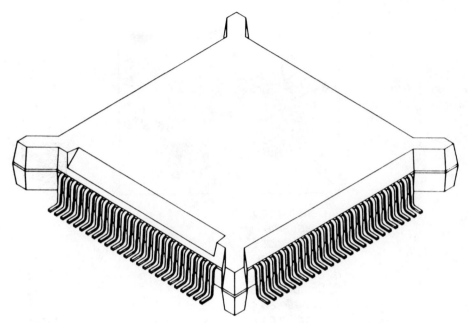

FIG. 3.30 JEDEC-registered plastic quad flatpack. (Reprinted with permission from the September 15, 1986 issue of *Computer Design*, copyright 1986, PennWell Publishing Company, Advanced Technology Group.)

transported in tape-and-reel or tube formats without damage to the leads. Except for the ears, body dimensions are identical to those of the PLCC.

C-Quad[6]

This package, shown in Fig. 3.31, incorporates several advanced concepts. It employs ceramic construction, which provides hermeticity, high reliability, and good thermal characteristics. The ceramic housing is based on low-cost CERDIP technology, resulting in an overall package cost roughly comparable to post-molded plastic packages. The C-Quad also incorporates an I-lead format that assures precise lead coplanarity and protection against handling damage. The leads are not bent to a full 90° angle but flare outward slightly to allow packages to be stacked for shipping. Relatively simple tubes can then be used for transporting the devices and feeding them to the placement machine.

The C-Quad is based on the concept of fixed body size rather than fixed lead pitch. With only three body sizes, lead counts from 28 to 148 leads are achieved by varying lead pitch. For example, the 1.200-in (30-mm) body size serves as an 84-lead, 124-lead, or 148-lead package depending on whether a 0.050-in, 0.030-in, or 0.025-in lead pitch is used. This approach reduces the range of tooling necessary for packages of different lead counts.

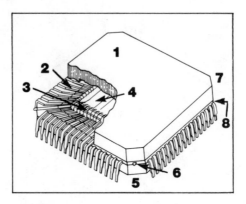

1/ Ceramic cap
2/ Leadframe
3/ Wire bonds
4/ Silicon chip
5/ Ceramic base
6/ Singulation point
7/ Chamfered corner design of
    ceramic cap and base
8/ Glass seal

FIG. 3.31   C-quad package. (Reprinted with permission. J. C. Walker, Northern Telecom Canada, "A Novel Low Cost Hermetic Leaded Chip Carrier Technology," presented at the 1984 Annual Conference of the IEPS.)

TapePak™

This package (Fig. 3.32) has been proposed for very high density applications up to about 300 leads per package. Like the C-Quad, the TapePak also makes use of the fixed body-size concept. Lead pitch ranges from 0.5 mm (0.020 in) for low pin counts to 0.28 mm (0.011 in) for the highest counts.

At such fine lead pitches, an ordinary package with preformed leads would be unable to maintain acceptable coplanarity during handling. The TapePak avoids this concern; leads are cut and formed as part of the placement process in a manner analogous to the cut-and-clinch step in automated through-hole assembly. Until this step, the leads are protected by a plastic carrier ring. This ring is molded around the lead frame coincident with the molding of the package body.

Besides protecting the leads, the carrier ring provides another benefit. It is possible to design the lead frame such that leads fan out to 0.050-in centers at the outside of the carrier ring. Devices can then be electrically tested using conventional probe fixture techniques. Since probing is done outside the ring, the critical lead surfaces remain undamaged by probes.

The TapePak also uses an advanced lead frame technology. Instead of

FIG. 3.32   TapePak package. (Used by permission. National Semiconductor, Inc.)

wire bonding the device pads to the lead frame, the frame itself is bonded to the device. This approach, known as *tape automated bonding* (TAB), is illustrated in Fig. 3.33. TAB technology reduces cost and improves reliability by eliminating one set of interconnections within the package.

Chip-on-board (COB)

Various techniques have been devised for mounting bare semiconductor die directly onto organic printed wiring boards. These include chip-and-wire bonding, TAB, and flip-chip attachment. Few standards currently exist for devices or mounting processes. Chip-on-board technology is mainly used in very high volume applications which can justify the effort to develop an entire manufacturing process.

The two most common COB processes are chip-and-wire and TAB. These two processes are briefly described in the following paragraphs.

Chip-and-wire[7]

This approach is basically an extension of chip-and-wire hybrid technology using organic printed wiring boards. The bare semiconductor die is adhesively mounted directly onto the board by way of a suitable adhesive. Wire bonds are used to electrically connect the die to the board. The bonded chip is usually protected by application of a conformal coating; when true hermeticity is required, a separate lid can be used.

Several considerations differentiate chip-and-wire assembly on printed wiring boards from similar techniques on hybrids. The most important is the much lower maximum temperature capability of the substrate. Wire bonds on ceramic substrates usually employ gold wire bonded to the substrate with either a thermocompression or a thermosonic process at temperatures between 200–350 °C. Most organic materials cannot tolerate such high temperatures, making both material selection and bonding technique extremely important.

Polyimide board materials are generally preferred because of their relatively high glass transition temperatures. With polyimide boards, gold wire can be reliably bonded to the pads using a thermosonic process at temperatures around 150 °C. When using ordinary epoxy-glass boards, gold wire cannot be used. Instead, aluminium wire is ultrasonically bonded at room temperature.

TAB[8]

In TAB technology, a tiny etched lead frame serves as the interconnection between semiconductor die and printed wiring board. The basic TAB process is illustrated in Fig. 3.33. A number of lead frames are contained in a long roll of gold-plated copper tape. Semiconductor chips are attached to the frames by an *inner-lead bonding* process. Inner-lead bonds are formed by thermocompression bonding the lead to the die metallization. A special tool is used to form all bonds simultaneously. After inner-lead bonding, the chips are protected from mechanical damage by encapsulating them in a conformal epoxy coating.

The chips on tape are now ready for assembly to the printed wiring board via an *outer-lead bonding* process. Chips are bonded in a sequential fashion. Each chip is first positioned over the corresponding land pattern and excised from the tape. The actual outer lead bond can be made in one of several ways. For lead pitches of about 0.5 mm (0.020 in) or larger, it is common practice to use a standard solder paste and reflow sequence. For finer pitches, the resolution of screen-printed solder paste is not adequate to prevent excessive bridging during reflow, so other techniques must be employed. In one method, solder is plated onto the pads of the board land pattern. After the component is positioned, the solder is reflowed using a high-power laser system. In another approach suitable for high-temperature substrate materials, the leads are thermocompression bonded to the land pattern with a tool similar to that used for inner-lead bonding.

In most cases the lead frame is rigid enough to support the device without the need for additional adhesive. If high thermal or electrical conductivity between chip and board is essential, the die can be mounted with thermally or electrically conductive epoxy.

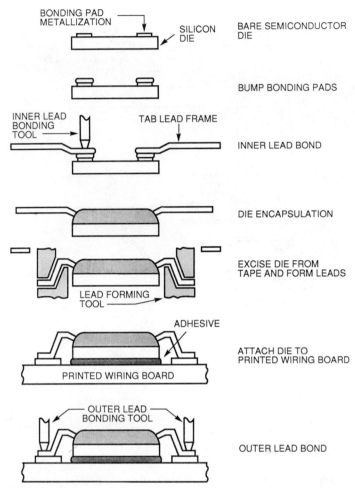

FIG. 3.33   Sequence of operations in a representative TAB manufacturing process.

Two variations of the inner-lead bonding process exist. In the first, known as the *bumped-chip* method, thick gold bumps (approximately 0.25 mm high) are plated onto the IC bonding pads (Fig. 3.34a). The raised pads permit the tape leads to be bonded to the device without interfering with the device metallization. In the second, known as the *bumped-tape* method, the bumps are included on the tape leads (Fig. 3.34b). This approach permits the use of die having standard thin film pad metallization.

TAB technology has not yet gained widespread acceptance because neither TAB-bonded chips nor TAB equipment are readily available. It is primarily used in high-volume applications where the high cost of process development can be amortized over a large number of units. It is also being investigated as a potential solution for the interconnection of high lead-count VLSI devices to printed wiring boards.

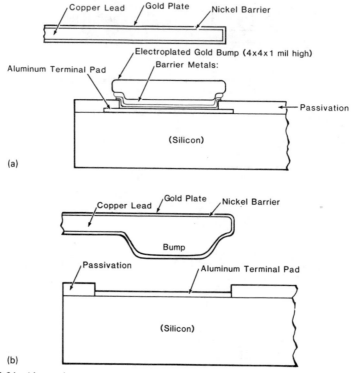

FIG. 3.34 Alternative approaches to TAB processing: a. bumped chip, b. bumped tape. (Used with permission of Mesa Co.)

3.5 IC PACKAGE SELECTION CRITERIA

With the large number of integrated circuit package styles available, it is important that component engineers understand how to specify an appropriate packages for any device type. Improper selection can result in unnecessary cost increases, limited availability, and reduced assembly process yields. The considerations that enter into the selection process include:

Reliability

It is first necessary to determine the system reliability requirements: operating and nonoperating environmental extremes, acceptable failure rates, and any other specialized demands. This information can then be used to determine whether hermetic packages or plastic packages should be used.

Hermetic ceramic packages have inherently higher reliability than equivalent plastic packages, but actual performance is so dependent on device type, operating conditions, and specific manufacturing techniques, that it is impossible to quantify this difference in a general sense. Plastic does not provide an effective moisture barrier and so the risk of corrosion in humid environments is greater. Post-molded plastic packages also place mechanical stresses on the die and wirebonds during thermal cycling. As a result, plastic packages are generally restricted to commercial operating environments.

Recent improvements in die passivation and plastic molding technology have narrowed this reliability difference (Section 3.1.5), so some applications that would formerly have required the hermetic package may now find plastic acceptable. For operation at extreme temperatures or in hostile environments, hermetic packages continue to be preferred.

Cost

Post-molded plastic packages are less expensive than hermetically sealed units and should be considered in industrial and consumer applications. When high reliability is essential, ceramic packages may be necessary.

Whenever possible, the industry-preferred package style for a given device should be selected. The SOIC, for instance, is the standard plastic package for many types of digital components with 20 or fewer leads, while the PLCC is preferred above 28 leads. Selection of these packages will assure a ready supply of parts from multiple manufacturers.

Package size

The physical size of various surface mount packages is shown in Fig. 1.7. For plastic packages of about 24 leads and less, the SOIC is most efficient. Above this range, the PLCC gains the advantage. Beyond about 84 leads, the 1.25 mm (0.050-in) lead pitch of the PLCC loses efficiency, and a finer pitch is necessary. Gull-wing quadpacks or the improved plastic quad flatpack may be used in this region.

When hermeticity is necessary, the choice narrows to either leadless or leaded ceramic chip carriers. If the components are to be mounted onto a standard organic printed wiring board, leaded chip carriers are recommended. If ceramic or controlled-expansion materials are to be used, either leaded or leadless chip carriers may be used.

REFERENCES

1. Kastner, M. and Melville, P. *SMD Thermal Considerations*, Signetics Corp., 1986.
2. Shepard, Jeffrey. "Component Comments," *Electronic Engineering Times*, Apr. 9, 1984, p. 61.
3. Naumchik, P. *SMD Reliability Data*, Signetics Corp, 1986.
4. Roesch, W. J. "Surface Mount Digital Package Reliability," Presented at the *International Reliability and Maintainability Symposium*, Las Vegas, NV, Jan. 1986.

5. Ganci, L. "Surface-mounting SOT-23 packages successfully," *Electronic Products*, Mar. 1985.
6. Walker, J. "A Novel Low Cost Hermetic Leaded Chip Carrier Technology," Presented at *1984 Annual Conference of the International Electronics Packaging Society*, Oct. 1984.
7. Ginsberg, G. L. "Chip and Wire Technology: the Ultimate in Surface Mounting," *Electronic Packaging and Production*, Aug. 1985, pp. 78–83.
8. Brown, D. B. and Freedman, M. G. "Is There a Future for TAB?" *Solid State Technology*, Sept. 1985, pp. 173–175.
9. Walker, R. J. "Reliability of Surface Mount Components and Assemblies," Presented at *Electro/86*, Boston, MA, May 1986.
10. Lau, J. and Rice, D. "Solder Joint Fatigue in Surface Mount Technology: State of the Art," *Solid State Technology*, Oct. 1985, pp. 91–104.
11. Fogle, J. "Thermal Management of Discrete SMT Devices," Motorola Corporation.

4

Connectors and electromechanical devices

Advances in electromechanical devices such as connectors, relays, sockets, and switches have traditionally followed rather than led other component technologies. This has again been the case in the conversion to SMT. Compared to the state of standardization for passive and active components, electromechanical devices lag far behind.

A combination of technical and market factors has contributed to this situation. Surface mount solder joints, for example, are not well suited for the severe mechanical stresses seen by connectors and switches. Moreover, housings molded from traditional thermoplastic materials tend to distort when exposed to reflow soldering processes. Concern over technical uncertainties coupled with limited product availability has led to weak market demand for these products. Without the incentive of a strong market opportunity, many component suppliers have been hesitant to invest heavily in surface mount product development programs.

The situation is currently undergoing rapid change. As end-users wholeheartedly convert from through-hole to surface mount, they increasingly discover that the only remaining through-hole components are the electromechanical devices. Faced with the prospect of supporting an entire through-hole assembly line for these few devices, they are strongly lobbying for new surface mountable product families. Component suppliers are now responding, and as a result, new products are regularly being introduced. This chapter reviews the current status of these products, particularly emphasizing solutions to those technical obstacles that have most hindered development.

4.1 CONNECTORS

Printed circuit edge connectors epitomize the technical problems of converting electromechanical devices from through-hole to surface mount technology. They are often large, bulky devices that are awkward to handle with automatic equipment. They must withstand repeated insertions and withdrawals without physical damage. In many cases they also serve as the sole form of mechanical support for the printed wiring board. Solutions to these problems typify the directions being considered for all electromechanical devices.

4.1.1 Solder joint stresses

Tin-lead solder does not provide a high degree of mechanical support. Through-hole solder joints are inherently much stronger than their surface mount equivalents both because of the larger joint cross section and because of the mechanical support provided by the lead inserted in the via hole. This is an especially important consideration for connectors, which must withstand large mechanical stresses. The types of stresses normally seen by connectors include the following:[1]

- thermal shock in the initial soldering process
- temperature cycling during operation
- insertion and withdrawal forces
- torsional forces
- vibrational forces

Thermal shock and high soldering temperatures are an unavoidable part of the surface mount assembly process. Connectors must be manufactured from materials that are undamaged by exposure to these extremes. Connector solder joints, like all surface mount joints, must also survive exposure to the temperature cycles and mechanical vibrations that characterize a typical operating environment. Furthermore, they must withstand linear and torsional forces encountered during mating and unmating of the connector.

	Forces Acting on Individual Contacts
INSERTION FORCE— Pin into Typical Receptacle:	275 grams max
WITHDRAWAL FORCE— Pin from Typical Receptacle:	200 grams max
FORCE TO PEEL OFF SOLDER TAIL (Vertical Direction):	900 grams min
FORCE TO SHEAR OFF CONTACT (Horizontal Direction):	1800 grams min

TABLE 4.1   Forces acting on a single connector contact. (Used by permission. J. Spickler, DuPont Connector Systems.)

The mechanical forces encountered during mating and unmating are far higher than those generated by thermal cycling. As shown in Table 4.1, the strength of a typical surface mount solder joint is still far in excess of the average insertion and withdrawal force. The real risk comes not from insertion forces, but rather from shear and torsional forces. Connector insertion is largely a manual process, and it is virtually impossible for an operator not to exert at least a small sideways force when inserting the edge connector into its receptacle. The leverage developed across the length of the printed wiring board can be enough to break off a connector that is held only by its solder joints.

4.1.2 Connector design factors

Four factors have been identified as being critical to connector design. These are:[2]

- lead configuration
- plastic molding compound
- mechanical support
- lead finishes

Lead configuration

The most important factor in a connector lead is that it have a measure of compliance. Obviously, a compliant lead is more forgiving of differences in thermal expansion between the connector and board, but it also serves as a cushion against insertion stresses.

Both gull-wing and J-lead configurations can be used. At present, few connectors use the classic J-lead configuration, in which the lead is rolled under the component body, because such joints are difficult to visually inspect. (Well-formed joints are especially important for connectors because of the high mechanical stresses encountered.) Some connectors use a lead with a "J" shape but which extends outward in the manner of a gull-wing lead (see Fig. 4.1).

The need to visually inspect the solder joint can actually make a surface mount connector larger than its through-hole counterpart. The leads, rather than exiting underneath the body and into the board, must extend outward. The additional real estate consumed by this design can sometimes be offset by using the area on the bottom of the board under the connector for conductor routing or even for placing other surface mount components.

Some connectors incorporate a floating contact design that allows each contact in a long row to seek its own level, as illustrated in Fig. 4.2. This can be important when mounting a long connector to a board with a significant degree of warpage. For shorter connectors, it is less important.

FIG. 4.1   Surface mount connector employing inverted J-leads to permit visual inspection of the joints. (Photo by the author.)

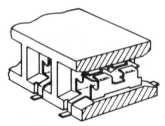

FIG. 4.2   Connector design employing floating contacts. Each contact floats separately to compensate for variations in board planarity across the length of the connector. (Used by permission. DuPont Connector Systems.)

Plastic molding compound

Traditional thermoplastic materials have relatively low melting points and are not suited for exposure to surface mount reflow processes. High temperature thermoplastics are available, but they by necessity have higher melting temperatures. This makes processing more difficult and expensive.

Physical properties for several high-temperature thermoplastics are summarized in Table 4.2. PET polyester has been used by several manufacturers for some product lines. It is acceptable when processing temperatures remain below 225 °C and there is no mechanical loading of the plastic during

Plastic Resin Material	Coefficient of Thermal Expansion (10/°C)	Heat Deflection Temperature @ 264 psi (°C)
Polyphenylene sulfide (PPS) (glass- and mineral-filled)	20	260
Polyetherimide (PEI) (30% glass-filled)	19.8	210
Polyamide (nylon) (33% glass-filled)	15–20	250
PBT polyester (30% glass-filled)	25	220
PET polyester (30% glass-filled)	29	224
Epoxy (60% glass-filled)	11–50	110–260

TABLE 4.2 Coefficients of thermal expansion and heat deflection temperatures of selected plastic molding compounds

reflow. For higher temperatures or when terminals are preloaded by the connector body, a polyphenylene-sulphide (PPS) material may be necessary. Nylon has attractive physical properties but may not be compatible with cleaning solvents used on the assembly line.

Mechanical support

With few exceptions, connectors should not depend on the solder connections as the only means of mechanical support. Additional support can be provided in a number of ways. Mounting ears such as shown in Fig. 4.3 are advised for connectors that must withstand large physical stresses (for example, a connector directly accessible to the end user). The connector can be mounted on the board by way of rivets, press-fit or heat stake clips, or nuts and bolts.

Some connectors include plastic protrusions directly on the connector body. These can be inserted through holes in the board and heat-staked to hold the connector in place. Another approach is to attach the connector with epoxy or similar adhesive. Disadvantages of adhesive are that it is messy and subject to variations in operator technique. It also lacks compliance, making it unsuitable when the coefficient of thermal expansion of the connector body does not closely match that of the printed wiring board.

Short connectors that are not subject to repeated matings may not need additional mechanical support, relying instead only on the strength of the solder joints. When using this approach, it is very important that no mechanical load be exerted on the connector. It should not, for example, be used as the sole means of mechanical support for a board, especially in high-vibration environments.

FIG. 4.3 Use of mounting ears to provide additional mechanical support. (Used by permission. DuPont Connector Systems.)

Lead finishes

To ensure adequate joint strength, the plating finish of the connector leads must be highly solderable. Poor solderability not only causes problems during production but also reduces the strength of the soldered joints. Eutectic tin-lead finishes offer the highest solderability, but other finishes perform with nearly equal results. Refer to Sect. 5.9 for a more complete discussion of lead termination finishes.

4.1.3 Connector types

Various families of surface mount printed wiring board connectors are now on the market, and more are being introduced all the time. Activity is currently underway within EIA to standardize connector families, with initial results expected sometime in 1988. Families presently available include both vertical and horizontal edge card connectors, "D"-subminiature headers, and audio jacks. Representative offerings are pictured in Fig. 4.4.

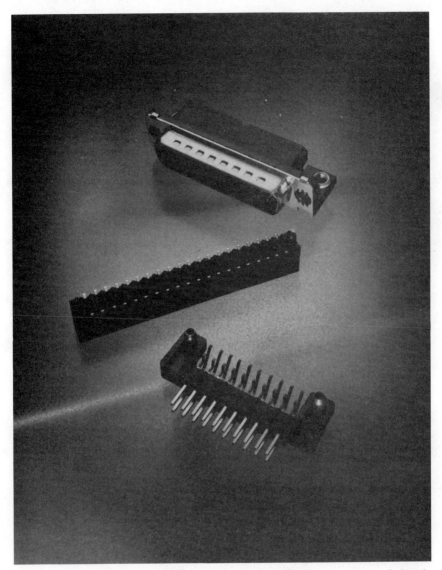

FIG. 4.4. Representative SMT connectors. Top to bottom: RS-232 connector, vertical card connector, horizontal header. (Courtesy AMP Incorporated.)

4.2 IC SOCKETS

Sockets for integrated circuits have a number of uses. During engineering development, they permit ICs to be rapidly changed so that circuit performance over a large number of components can be evaluated. In production, they are often used for custom ROM (read-only memory) chips or ASICs (application-specific integrated circuits) that must be individually confi-

FIG. 4.5 Socket to adapt surface mount integrated circuit for through-hole mounting. (Photograph by the author.)

gured based on exact customer specifications. Whenever ICs must be rapidly and routinely changed, IC sockets are desirable.

Surface mount sockets come in two styles. The first, designed for through-hole insertion, is used to adapt a surface mount IC for through-hole mounting (see Fig. 4.5). This is attractive when the benefits of the surface mount package (such as small size and reduced parasitic reactances) are desired on a board that would otherwise be totally through-hole. Rather than developing an entirely new assembly line to mount just one surface mount device, the existing through-hole line can be used to build the entire board.

The second type of socket, shown in Fig. 4.6, is itself designed for surface mounting. It fits roughly the same footprint as the original package, so if designed properly, the board can accept either the IC or the socket interchangeably. These sockets are frequently used for custom ROM chips during early production runs. Because firmware programs within the ROMs are often still undergoing revision even during early production, it is advantageous to rapidly replace ROMs as the new firmware becomes available. Once the firmware has stabilized, the sockets can be eliminated to reduce cost and improve reliability.

Since sockets do not form metallurgical bonds with the component leads

FIG. 4.6 Surface mount IC socket. The socket land pattern is identical to that of the original IC so sockets used in early production runs can be eliminated without requiring a change in board design. (Used by permission. AMP, Inc.)

but rather depend strictly on mechanical contact, they are not as reliable as a soldered connection. Contacts can corrode in high-humidity environments, and mechanical contact can be interrupted during shock or vibration. Furthermore, sockets are expensive, costing from a few dollars to fifteen dollars or more for high pin count devices. For these reasons, they are not advised for all components. They should be used only when their advantages outweigh their disadvantages.

FIG. 4.7   Burn-in socket. (Photo by the author.)

Sockets for production or prototype environments normally do not experience repeated insertions and withdrawals. The contacts of these sockets will reliably survive only a few insertions before the plating is worn away. Sockets used in component test or burn-in systems must withstand repeated insertions. Their designs must be much more robust. A typical product that employs a zero-insertion-force concept is pictured in Fig. 4.7. The top portion of the socket, when manually depressed, spreads the contacts apart and allows the component to drop into place. When released, the contacts close to complete the electrical circuit. Such sockets can withstand thousands of insertions before they must be replaced.

4.3 TEST CLIPS

Test clips are essentially sockets that clip onto the leads of a surface mount component while it remains soldered to the board. They provide convenient access points for test probes during troubleshooting or circuit evaluation. Representative products are shown in Fig. 4.8.

When using test clips, the clearances around components must be larger than would otherwise be required. A typical spacing requirement is 25.4 mm (0.100 in) between leads of adjacent components. When several clips must be simultaneously attached to adjacent components, even larger clearances may be required.

(a)

(b)

FIG. 4.8   Test clips for surface mount ICs: a. SOIC, b. PLCC. (Used by permission. Electronic Specialty Products, 3M Corporation.)

4.4 SWITCHES AND RELAYS

Many SMT switches and relays are nothing more than through-hole designs whose leads have been re-formed for surface mounting. Product designs are governed primarily by physical restrictions, such as the size of the switch actuator or the rated current through the contacts, so SMT offers few inherent advantages over through-hole mounting. The primary motivation for making the conversion is to maintain process compatibility with the remainder of the components on the board. Representative products are illustrated in Fig. 4.9.

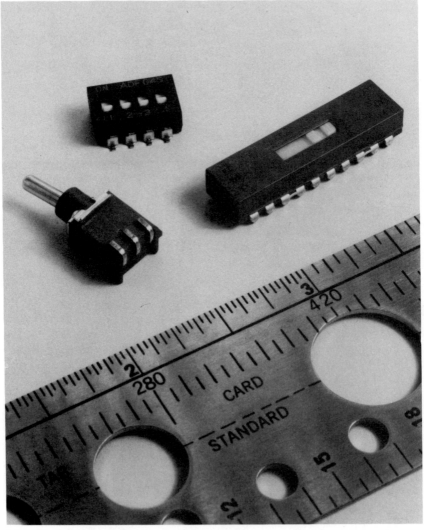

(a)

(b)

FIG. 4.9   Surface mount electromechanical devices: a. Switches, b. Relay. (Photos by the author.)

REFERENCES

1. Brearley, D. "The Connector/PCB Interface; Key to Success in Surface Mounting of Connectors," *Proceedings of NEPCON/West '85*, Anaheim, CA, Feb. 1985.
2. Spickler, J. *Connector Design for Surface Mounting*, Du Pont Connector Systems, Camp Hill, PA, Jan. 1987.

5

Solder materials and solderability

Soldering of surface mount assemblies is performed primarily with tin-lead alloys. Such alloys, known as *soft solders*, melt in the range from about 180–240 °C, considerably lower than hard-solder alloys used in brazing applications. Although composed primarily of tin and lead, small amounts of other metals are sometimes added to modify physical properties of the alloy.

5.1 TIN-LEAD PHASE DIAGRAM

The physical properties of a tin-lead alloy depend on the percentages of tin and lead it contains. The temperature behavior of such alloys as a function of mass percentages of tin and lead is shown in the phase diagram of Fig. 5.1. The melting point of pure tin is labeled A; that of pure lead is labeled B. At temperatures above the line defined by points BCA all alloy compositions are liquid. This is known as the *liquidus* line. At temperatures below the line BECDA, the *solidus* line, all alloy compositions are solid.

Between these two lines, both solid and liquid coexist. This is the plastic region and consists of lead-rich and tin-rich crystals together with liquid tin-lead. The exact composition of the liquid and solid portions is a function of temperature and alloy composition. Soldering operations must always be performed above the liquidus line, and the maximum operating temperature of the finished assembly must always be kept well below the solidus.

The alloy with composition 61.9% tin and 38.1% lead by weight, indicated by Point C, is especially important in electronics. This is the *eutectic* composition, characterized by the absence of a plastic region. Instead, this alloy transforms directly from solid to liquid at a temperature of 183 °C. Many manufacturers represent the alloy 63% tin/37% lead as the eutectic

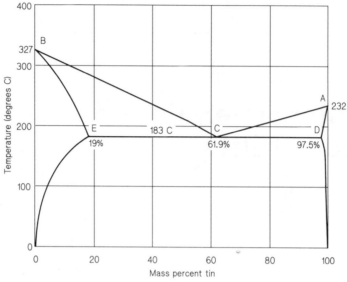

FIG. 5.1   Tin-lead phase diagram. (Adapted from *Constitution of Binary Alloys*, copyright 1958, McGraw-Hill Book Company.)

composition, and from a practical perspective there is little difference in properties for alloys in the range 60–63% tin.

5.2 SOLDER ALLOYS

Solder alloys for electronics applications must maintain carefully controlled compositions and purity levels. Excessive amounts of such metals as zinc, iron, gold, copper, and aluminium can be detrimental to the performance and reliability of the finished joints. In the United States, the document most often cited for controlling these properties is Federal Specification QQ-S-571, issued by the US Government. Table 5.1, excerpted from this document, lists those alloys of particular importance in surface mount applications. There are also several other useful alloys not covered in QQ-S-571. These are presented in Table 5.2.

The nomenclature used within QQ-S-571 to designate specific alloy compositions is widely used. For example, the designation Sn63 defines an alloy with nominal 63% tin and 37% lead, while the designation Sn62 specifies an alloy with nominal 62% tin, 36% lead, and 2% silver.

Alloys other than those specified in QQ-S-571 are generally identified by the weight percentages of their major constituents. The alloy of 90% tin and 10% lead, for example, is designated 90Sn/10Pb.

Alloy Designation	Sn	Pb	Weight Percentages Sb (max)	Bi (max)	Ag	Cu (max)	Fe (max)	Zn (max)	Al (max)	As (max)	Cd (max)	All Other (max)	Melting Range Solidus (°C)	Liquids (°C)
Sn63	62.5 to 63.5	Remainder	.20 to .50	.25	.015 max	.08	.02	.005	.005	.03	.001	.08	183	183
Sn62	61.5 to 62.5	Remainder	.20 to .50	.25	1.75 to 2.25	.08	.02	.005	.005	.03	.001	.08	179	179
Sn60	59.5 to 61.5	Remainder	.20 to .50	.25	.015 max	.08	.02	.005	.005	.03	.001	.08	183	191
Sn96	Remainder	.10 max	—	—	3.6 to 4.4	.20	—	.005	—	.05	.005	—	221	221
Sb5	94.0 min	.20 max	4.0 to 6.0	—	.015 max	.08	.08	.03	.03	.05	.03	.03	235	240

TABLE 5.1 Solder alloys for surface mount applications (From Fed. Spec. QQ-S-571)

Alloy Composition (Weight Percentage)	Melting Range	
	Solidus (°C)	Liquidus (°C)
62.5Sn/36.1Pb/1.4Ag	179	179
90Pb/10Sn	275	302
80Au/20Sn	280	280
75Pb/25In	250	264
50Pb/50In	180	209
25Pb/75In	156	165
90Sn/10Pb	183	215
95Sn/5Pb	183	220

TABLE 5.2   Other useful solder alloys

5.2.1 Selection process

The most important parameter to be considered in selecting a solder alloy is the maximum operating temperature of the joint. Since tensile strength drops exponentially as temperature approaches the solidus point, a generous margin must be maintained between these two temperatures—typically by at least 50 to 75 °C. Other important selection parameters include mechanical strength, vibration resistance, thermal cycling performance, and metallurgical compatibility with components and boards. Some of the more useful alloys are described in the paragraphs that follow.

A. Tin-lead alloys

Most surface mount soldering is performed with these solders. Eutectic tin-lead solder, Sn63, and the near-eutectic Sn60 have a solidus point of 183 °C and are suitable for continuous operation to about 125 °C. They are especially popular for soldering components with non-precious metal surfaces to the copper traces of organic-base printed wiring boards.

Alloys with below 50% tin are rarely used in SMT because of poor wetting characteristics. Solders with high tin content, such as 90Sn/10Pb and 95Sn/5Pb, are often used to provide solderable terminations on components. Such alloys exhibit acceptable wetting characteristics and are relatively easy to apply by plating.

B. Tin-lead-silver alloys

Ordinary tin-lead solders are not recommended for soldering to component terminations containing silver. Silver dissolves rapidly into tin-lead solder, a phenomenon known as *scavenging* or *leaching*. At worst, the termination will totally dissolve into the solder, leaving behind an unsoldered joint. Even if this does not happen, enough silver may dissolve to significantly reduce the strength of the termination and resultant reliability of the joint.

The addition of a small amount of silver into the solder (1.4–2%) significantly reduces this tendency. The Sn62 alloy with 2% silver or the exact eutectic with 1.4% silver are often used for soldering to silver-bearing component terminations. The added silver also improves the strength and creep resistance of the solder. However, these alloys are invariably more expensive than ordinary tin-lead solders.

C. Lead-indium alloys

These alloys, although not widely used, exhibit properties that are attractive in certain surface mount applications. Lead-indium solders of various compositions do not leach gold as rapidly as does eutectic tin-lead.[1] This makes them attractive for use on gold-bearing surfaces. Indium also retains plasticity down to extremely low temperatures, a potential benefit when soldering materials with significantly mismatched coefficients of thermal expansion. These alloys are, however, extremely sensitive to halide corrosion. For this reason, assemblies soldered with lead-indium alloys are normally protected within a hermetically sealed package.

D. Tin-silver alloy

The eutectic composition Sn96 is especially useful as a high temperature solder. It has a melting point of 221 °C, just above the boiling temperature of standard vapor phase soldering fluids. It can therefore be used to solder components that must subsequently withstand vapor phase reflow. Tin-silver alloy exhibits excellent wettability and higher joint strengths than tin-lead solders.

E. Other alloy compositions

With a solidus temperature of 235 °C, the tin-antimony composition Sb5 is another useful high-temperature solder. It provides high creep strength at temperatures up to 100 °C. At the other extreme, tin-indium solders are low melting-temperature alloys with solidus temperatures in the range 118–130 °C. Their primary usage comes as the last solders used in sequential operations where previously soldered joints must not re-melt during subsequent steps.

5.3 SOLDERABILITY

It is not enough to carefully specify and maintain the soldering process; strict control must also be exercised over the quality of the incoming material. The

term *solderability* is used to describe the ability of a component termination*
to be wet by solder during a specific soldering operation. It is a function of
the exact process and materials employed; a termination may exhibit acceptable solderability for some processes but not for others.

The solderability of a surface is characterized by the degree to which it
wets and forms a metallurgical bond with the solder. The degrees of wetting
can be classified as follows:

- *Non-Wetting*. In this case, no metallurgical bond is formed and the
  interface between the solder and the surface remains distinct. Assuming
  the joint has actually reached melting temperature, this is indicative of a
  surface coated with an oxide layer or other contaminant. It typically
  occurs when the flux used to promote soldering cannot adequately remove the surface contamination, either because the oxide layer is too
  thick or the flux is not sufficiently active.
- *Wetting*. The surface energy of a clean metallic surface is higher than that
  of molten solder.[2] Under these circumstances, the solder will wet the
  surface and form a metallurgical bond at the interface. As wetting proceeds, a thin intermetallic layer grows at the interface, forming the basis
  of a reliable joint.
- *Dewetting*. The intermetallics that grow at the interface are tin-rich
  compounds that draw their tin from the tin-lead solder. As tin is consumed from the solder, it leaves behind lead-rich regions with relatively
  poor solderability. If left at temperature long enough, the extent of these
  regions will be sufficient to cause the solder to recede from previously
  wetted regions,[3] a phenomenon called *dewetting*.

  Dewetting can also occur when a thin solderable layer is totally dissolved into the solder, exposing the non-wettable surface underneath.
  This is a major concern when soldering to precious metal terminations
  that rapidly dissolve in tin-lead solder.

Poor component solderability is a major cause of defects in reflow-
soldered surface mount assemblies. In the wave soldering process, the
joint is washed by an essentially infinite supply of solder. Small amounts of
contamination are quickly diluted and carried away. The reflow process
does not provide this cleansing operation; contaminants that are present on
the component terminations will remain in the completed joint.

5.4 SOLDERING FLUXES

The purpose of a flux is to promote wetting by removing oxides and other
contaminants from the surfaces to be joined. Ideally, a flux should be highly

---

* A component termination is the portion of the component that makes electrical contact
with the printed wiring board: the leads of a leaded device or the metallized ends of a device
without separate leads.

active at soldering temperatures and totally inactive at normal equipment operating temperatures; it would then be unnecessary to remove the flux after soldering.

Such an ideal flux does not exist, and real fluxes are a compromise between activity at soldering temperatures and inactivity at operating temperatures. Fluxes can be divided into two general categories: *solvent-soluble* fluxes and *water-soluble* fluxes. Solvent-soluble* fluxes are designed for removal in chlorinated or fluorinated hydrocarbon solvents, while water-soluble fluxes are designed for aqueous removal.

5.4.1 Solvent-soluble fluxes

These fluxes are normally based on a pine-tree rosin known as colophony. Since pure colophony is a very mild reagent, various additives may be included to increase flux activity. Synthetic fluxes derived from certain organic compounds are also included in this category.

Solvent-soluble fluxes are designed for removal with fluorinated or chlorinated hydrocarbon solvents (Chapter 13). Cleaning in aqueous solutions is less effective and not generally recommended. Fluxes activated with ionic halides should be cleaned in a blend of polar and non-polar solvents to ensure complete removal of ionic residues (see Chapter 13).

A. Rosin fluxes

Several types of rosin-based flux are defined in Federal Specification QQ-S-571 and Military Specification MIL-F-14256 (see Table 5.3). Based on level of activity, they are:

Type R
This is the lowest activity flux and consists of pure-water white rosin (colophony) dissolved in an alcohol thinner. Because of its relatively weak cleaning action, it is suitable only for use with highly solderable surfaces. It can be used to cleanse gold surfaces but is not considered aggressive enough for copper, tin, or tin-lead surfaces. The residue is essentially inert at room temperature, so Type R flux need not be removed after soldering. (In fact, rosin coatings are often used to preserve printed wiring board solderability during storage.)

Type RMA (Rosin-mildly activated)
Increased activity can be achieved by adding a small amount of a suitable organic compound. Federal Specification QQ-S-571 does not specify what compounds should be used but rather the chemical and electrical tests that an RMA flux must pass. Amine hydrochlorides, polybasic carboxylic acids,

* Strictly speaking, water is a solvent, but within the electronics industry, the term *solvent* is customarily reserved to describe organic-based solvents.

Flux Type	Additives	Resistivity of Water Extract (ohm–cm)	Chlorides Bromides Test[2]	Copper Mirror Test[3]
R	None	100,000	No discoloration of Silver Chromate Test Paper	No removal of Copper Film
RMA	Non-chlorinated	100,000	No discoloration of Silver Chromate Test Paper	No removal of Copper Film
RA	Non-chlorinated[1]	50,000	Not Specified	Not Specified

Notes:
1. Unspecified in MIL-F-14256
2. Chlorides/bromides test consists of applying 1 drop of flux to silver chromate test paper for 15 seconds, then removing with isopropanol.
3. Copper mirror consists of a vacuum-deposited film of pure copper on a glass sheet. Thickness is such as to permit $10 \pm 5\%$ transmission of light at 5000 Angstroms wavelength.
   Approximately 0.05 ml flux is applied to the copper and left for 24 hours at 23 °C. Surface is examined after cleaning in isopropanol.

TABLE 5.3   Rosin flux classes (Per Fed. Spec. QQ-S-571 and Mil. Spec. MIL-F-14256)

and allylic organic halides have all been used as activators. RMA flux is suitable for use with many easily solderable materials such as copper, gold, and tin-lead solders. Its residue is generally considered inert and so removal is optional. In fact, incomplete removal may do more harm than good. As long as the activator is bound in the rosin, its corrosive effect is inhibited. If the rosin is partially dissolved in an inadequate cleaning process, the activator may be dispersed across the surface, accelerating corrosion.

Type RA (Rosin-activated)

The additives in Type RA fluxes are more aggressive than those used in RMA fluxes. Again, Federal Specification QQ-S-571 defines the tests the flux must pass, rather than the specific chemical composition of the activator.

The additional activity of these formulations makes them suitable for soldering to metals that are not readily solderable with Types R and RMA fluxes. Their primary use, however, is to speed the wetting of easily solderable metals and thereby reduce defect levels in the soldering process.

Because of their increased activity levels, RA fluxes should be completely removed after soldering. If left on the surface of the board, they can promote long-term corrosion, especially in humid environments.

Type RSA (Rosin-superactivated)

This classification is not formally part of the military specification but is commonly used to define fluxes with even higher activity than RA fluxes. As with Type RA, their residues must be completely removed to reduce the likelihood of long-term corrosion.

B. Synthetic fluxes

Rosin-based fluxes are a complex combination of naturally occurring products. The exact composition of colophony varies depending on the geographical location from which it was obtained, previous climatic conditions, etc., making reproducibility from lot to lot extremely difficult to achieve. Rosin also tends to polymerize at soldering temperatures, leaving residues that are not easily removed.

Synthetic activated (SA) fluxes were first developed in the late 1970s as a way to address the problems with rosin fluxes. SA fluxes are based on mono- and di-isooctyl phosphate compounds combined with various additives to improve flux activity and facilitate removal of residues.[4] They are not yet covered in the QQ-S-571 document but are being considered for future revisions.

Initial indications are that SA fluxes provide activity levels similar to organic acid fluxes but with lower residual ionic contamination levels. They are available both in liquid form for wave soldering applications and as solder paste. Because their compositions can be accurately controlled, SA and less active SMA fluxes are likely to grow in importance in the coming years.

5.4.2 Water-soluble fluxes

These fluxes are typically organic acids with much higher activity than rosin fluxes. (The more corrosive types derived from organic halides and inorganic salts are not normally used in electronic applications.) Organic acid (OA) fluxes have been especially popular in wave soldering processes where low defect levels must be maintained across materials with wide variations in solderability. Historically it has been easier to increase the activity level of the flux than to address the solderability problems of incoming materials.

The flux need not actually contain water, and other solvents such as alcohols or glycols are more often used. These solvents, as compared to water, are less likely to spatter at soldering temperatures. As their name implies, water-soluble fluxes are removed with aqueous cleaning processes, and because of their high activity level, thorough cleaning soon after soldering is essential.

5.4.3 Flux efficacy

The efficacy of a flux is a measure of its ability to promote the wetting of the surfaces to be soldered. It is a combination of the flux *activity* (its inherent ability to clean the surfaces) and its *stability* (the time over which it retains

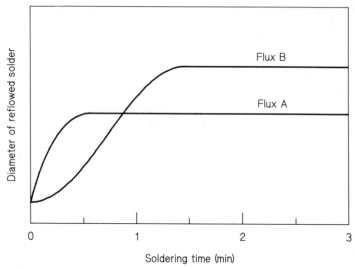

FIG. 5.2   Spread factor tests for two different fluxes. Flux A becomes active much more rapidly than Flux B, but Flux B ultimately achieves a greater area of spread.

activity at soldering temperatures). The efficacy of a particular flux depends on the specific soldering operation. A highly active flux that rapidly decays, for example, may be suitable for a wave soldering process lasting only a few seconds but not for a much slower reflow process. In the latter case, a flux that develops activity more slowly but retains that activity for an extended period would be preferred.

Flux efficacy is often measured by the Spread Factor Test (Section 5.7.5). By measuring the area of spread at different soldering times, the dynamic activity of the flux can be inferred. Figure 5.2 shows the results for two different fluxes at a specific soldering temperature. Flux A develops activity very rapidly but quickly decomposes. Flux B takes longer to activate but, given enough time, produces a greater area of spread. At a different test temperature, different results may be expected.

A frequently cited measure of flux activity is termed *acid number*. This is simply the number of milligrams of potassium hydroxide necessary to neutralize the free acids in 1 gram of the flux under specified test conditions. It is of limited use since fluxes of widely different activity can have similar acid numbers.

5.5 CAUSES OF SOLDERABILITY PROBLEMS

Components can experience soldering problems for a variety of reasons. Predominant causes are described next.

5.5.1 Oxidation

Most solderability problems are caused by oxidation on the surface of the materials to be soldered. Ordinarily, the flux used during soldering breaks up and disperses this oxide, but if the layer is unusually thick, the flux may not be sufficiently active to do an adequate job.

Tin-lead surface finishes are often preferred for surface mount component leads because they are not likely to grow tenacious oxide layers; rosin-based fluxes will remove ordinary levels of growth. Tin-lead finishes also retain adequate solderability even after extended storage. When used on component terminations, the tin-lead finish is applied over the base metal either by electroplating or by dipping the leads in a bath of molten solder.

Simply specifying a tin-lead surface finish will not guarantee a solderable component. Particularly with plated finishes, it is necessary to carefully control the initial manufacturing process. If the base metal of the component termination is not properly prepared prior to plating, a layer of oxide can remain on its surface. Although this surface is not itself solderable, the solderable top coating can still be electroplated over it. In this case, the component as received from the manufacturer will be visually acceptable, but when it is subsequently soldered, the electroplated coating will recede from the base, resulting in a non-wetted joint.

5.5.2 Contamination

The range of contamination possible on a component termination is virtually unlimited. Unwanted metallic or organic residues can sometimes be deposited during electroplating processes. Bits of fibrous material, silicones, or plasticizers can be left from packaging materials. Fingerprints are always possible if human intervention is necessary anywhere in the process. Any of these contaminants, in large enough quantities, will degrade solderability.

5.5.3 Porous solder coating

Porosity in the termination finish will permit oxide growth on the underlying surface, causing a non-wetting condition at the interface between the layers. Electroplated coatings are particularly susceptible to this phenomenon. Unlike solder-dipped finishes, electroplated tin-lead is not a true solder alloy. Instead, individual nodules of tin and lead grow over the base, the ratio being determined by plating parameters. If the process is not carefully controlled, porosity can occur at the boundaries between individual grains. Although initial solderability may be acceptable, it will degrade rapidly as oxide growth occurs.

5.5.4 Improper joint metallurgy

Certain metal systems are poorly suited for surface mount technology. Terminations with exposed precious metal surfaces, for example, should generally be avoided. Gold and silver are highly soluble in tin-lead solder; this leads to rapid leaching of the termination metal into the solder. If enough of the termination is dissolved, the joint may not have adequate mechanical strength. Underlying layers (such as on multilayer ceramic capacitors) may also become exposed, degrading electrical reliability. In addition, high concentrations of gold (above about 1%) in tin-lead solder will significantly change its properties, leading to brittle or visually unacceptable joints. Fig. 5.3 illustrates the problems that can occur when soldering directly to precious metal electrodes on ceramic capacitors.

(a)

(b)

FIG. 5.3 Dissolution of termination metal into solder: a. Joint protected with a nickel barrier, b. Unprotected joint. (Used by permission. J. Hagge, "Critical Component Requirements for Vapor Phase Soldering Leadless Components on Circuit Board Assemblies for Military Electronics," *IEEE CHMT-6, No. 4.* Copyright 1983 IEEE.)

5.5.5 Solder coating grain structure

It has recently been discovered that the solderability of unreflowed plated finishes may be related to grain structure. Dense platings with small grain size (approximately 0.5 μm mean intercept distance) have been found to match the solderability of solder-dipped finishes. Finishes with larger grain structures (3.0 to 4.5 μm mean intercept distance) have reduced solderability.[5] Fig. 5.12 illustrates the sensitivity of solderability to grain size.

5.5.6 Thin top coating

During the soldering process, a portion of the surface of the component termination dissolves into the solder. This dissolution and formation of intermetallic compounds is an essential part of the soldering process. However, if the solderable surface is too thin, it may be totally consumed during the process. The solderability of the termination then depends on the properties of the base metal; since the solderable coating was originally applied to promote solderability, it is unlikely that the base will solder equally well. Dewetting and loss of mechanical strength are typical problems in this situation.

5.5.7 Wicking

This is primarily a problem with J-lead components that have been reflow soldered in a vapor phase system. It occurs when the component lead reaches reflow temperature before the circuit land. The solder paste is drawn by wetting forces up the lead, leaving little behind to form the joint. A typical example is shown in Fig. 5.4.

The factors that contribute to wicking are not well understood. Lead coplanarity and solder volume variations have been suggested as potential contributing factors. Because the problem occurs much more often in vapor phase reflow than in infrared reflow, it is also apparently related to the dynamics of heating. Vapor phase ovens operate through a process of condensation, which is a surface-heating phenomenon. Portions of the assembly with low thermal mass (the component leads) are likely to heat faster than portions with larger thermal mass (the board). The large thermal gradients that occur within the process exacerbate this problem.

Thermal gradients in infrared furnaces are less severe, and a larger portion of energy is transmitted via direct radiation, so even heating is more likely. In addition, many solder pastes are excellent absorbers of infrared energy. This combination of factors tends to improve the distribution of heat throughout the joint, making wicking less likely.

Wicking can be minimized by adding a preheat stage to the vapor phase system. A preheat step that permits the boards to enter the vapor zone at a temperature of at least 125 °C is generally considered adequate.

FIG. 5.4   Solder wicking. Solder has climbed up the second lead of this PLCC. The amount remaining is insufficient to form a reliable joint. (Photograph by the author.)

5.6 SOLDERABILITY SPECIFICATIONS

Component solderability specifications fall into two general classes. The first is comprised of *tests* designed to predict how well components will solder in production. The second defines *specifications* for acceptable component termination materials and manufacturing processes.

If existing solderability tests could accurately predict how well components would solder during the production process, users would not need to control the physical design of the parts. Manufacturers could adopt various design approaches as long as the resultant components pass these acceptance tests. Unfortunately, the ideal test does not yet exist, and data from real tests does not always correlate with actual production results. To minimize the risk of receiving unacceptable parts, many users strictly control the range of permissible termination finishes.

5.7 SOLDERABILITY TESTS

Various tests have been developed to qualitatively or quantitatively measure solderability. *Qualitative tests* are based on visual criteria, while *quantitative tests* measure actual wetting characteristics. All solderability tests, regardless of their specific nature, attempt to measure two basic properties:

(a) The initial wettability of the termination;
(b) The extent of dewetting that occurs during the soldering process.

In conjunction with a suitable artificial aging process, such as described in Section 5.8, solderability tests can also predict the performance of a termination after an extended storage period.

Of the many solderability tests that currently exist, only two show promise for surface mount components. The *Dip Test* provides a rapid and inexpensive qualitative measure of solderability, but it is highly subjective. The *Wetting Balance Test* yields quantitative results, but it is slower and more costly to perform. Two other tests, the *Globule Test* and the *Rotary Dip Test*, are sometimes used to measure the solderability of printed wiring boards but are not suitable for components. The *Area of Spread Test* is frequently used to measure flux efficacy.

5.7.1 Fluxes for solderability testing

Since a solderability test should detect even relatively subtle soldering problems, the flux used in the test should be of low activity. For incoming inspection testing and initial qualification of a new component supplier, nonactivated Type R rosin flux is recommended. This flux is adequate to promote wetting of tin or tin-lead surfaces without decreasing the sensitivity of the test; more active fluxes will mask low-level problems. On-line production testing can be performed with the flux normally used in production, often a Type RMA or Type RA composition. This provides an adequate indication of how the components will actually perform in the production process.

5.7.2 Dip Test

The simplest way to test a component termination for solderability is to immerse the termination into a pot of molten solder, withdraw it, and visually examine the degree of wetting. A skilled operator can determine the percentage of wetted area, the degree of dewetting or leaching, and the extent of contamination of the parts.

In addition to testing component terminations, the Dip Test is suitable for printed wiring boards. Although it is possible to perform the test manually, a mechanized approach is preferred. Unfortunately, even with automated equipment, the test depends on a highly subjective visual interpretation of the results.

The Dip Test, using the equipment of Fig. 5.5, is described in MIL-STD-202 Method 208. Similar tests are described in MIL-STD-883 Method 2003, IPC-S-804, and IPC-S-805. In each case, the test methods are similar. The acceptance criteria, however, may vary slightly. None of these tests specifically covers surface mount components, but it is relatively simple to extrapolate to include these devices. The following test, adapted from MIL-STD-202, Method 208, and IPC-S-805, can be used for many types of leaded and leadless surface mount components. Of particular note is the temperature of the solder bath, 215 °C. This temperature is lower than that used for through-hole tests (245 °C) and is representative of actual temperatures encountered in reflow soldering.

Dip Test for Surface Mount Components

1. *Apparatus*

   (a) *Solder pot*. A solder pot of sufficient size to contain at least 1.5 kg of solder shall be used. This apparatus shall be capable of maintaining the solder at the temperature specified in 3(d).

   (b) *Dipping device*. A mechanical dipping device capable of controlling the rates of immersion and emersion of the terminations and providing a dwell time (time of total immersion to the required depth) in the solder bath as specified in 3(d) shall be used. A suggested dipping device is shown in Fig. 5.5.

   (c) *Optical equipment*. An optical system having a magnification of ten diameters shall be used.

2. *Materials*

   (a) *Flux*. The flux shall conform to Type R of Federal Specification QQ-S-571.

   (b) *Solder*. The solder shall be composition Sn60 or Sn63 of Federal Specification QQ-S-571 or 60B or 63B of ASTM-B32.

   (c) *Flux remover*. The flux remover shall be isopropyl alcohol. Other flux removal solvents may be used provided that they remove the flux residues and do not damage the component body or finish materials.

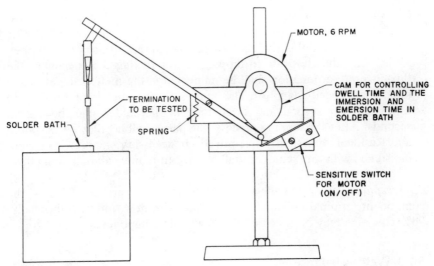

FIG. 5.5   Apparatus suggested in MIL-STD-202, Method 208, for dip testing of component leads.

3. Procedure. The test procedure shall be performed on the number of terminations specified in the applicable procurement document. During handling, care shall be exercised to prevent the surface being tested from being abraded or contaminated by grease, perspiration, etc. The test procedure shall consist of the following operations:

  i.   Proper preparation of the terminations as described in 3(a);
 ii.   Aging of all specimens per 3(b);
iii.   Application of flux per 3(c);
 iv.   Immersion of the terminations into molten solder per 3(d);
  v.   Examination and evaluation of the tested portions of the terminations upon completion of the solder dip process per 4.

(*a*) *Preparation of terminations.* No wiping, cleaning, scraping, or abrasive cleaning of the terminations shall be performed. Any special preparation of the terminations, such as bending or reorientation prior to the test, shall be specified in the individual specification.

(*b*) *Aging.* Prior to the application of flux and subsequent solder dips, all specimens assigned to this test shall be subjected to accelerated aging. It is recommended that this aging consist of a 24-hour exposure to steam, as described in Section 5.8.1.

(*c*) *Application of flux.* Flux Type R as specified in 2(a) shall be used. Terminations shall be immersed in the flux, which is at room ambient temperature, to the minimum depth necessary to cover the surface to be tested. The surface to be tested shall be immersed in the flux for a minimum of 1 second. Drain and blot the termination prior to immersion.

(*d*) *Solder dip*. The molten solder shall be stirred with a clean stainless steel paddle to assure that it is at a uniform temperature of $215° \pm 5°C$. Dross and burned flux shall be skimmed from the surface of the molten solder immediately prior to dipping. After fluxing the specimen, the flux-covered termination shall be immersed in the molten solder to the same depth specified in 3(c). The immersion and emersion rates shall be 25 ± 6 mm per second and dwell time in the solder shall be 5 ± 0.5 seconds. After the dipping process, the parts shall be allowed to cool in air. Residual flux shall be removed. If necessary, a soft clean cloth moistened with flux remover shall be used to remove all remaining flux.

4. Acceptance criteria. Unless otherwise specified, at least 95% of the component termination should be covered with new solder. (Optionally, 90% coverage may be specified for small chip components.)

5.7.3 Wetting balance

This method provides quantitative results that are well suited for analyzing the basic properties of the component termination. As with the Dip Test, it can also be used for characterizing the solderability of substrates.[6] Commercial machines such as illustrated in Fig. 5.6 are readily available, although their application to surface mount components is not well developed.[7,13]

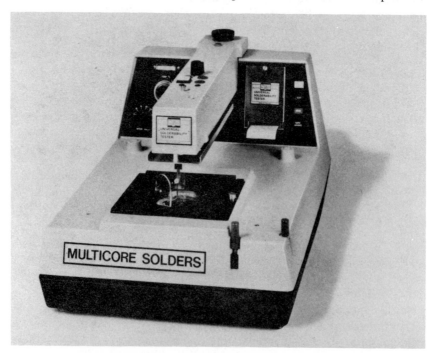

FIG. 5.6   Commercial wetting balance. (Used by permission. Multicore Solders, Inc.)

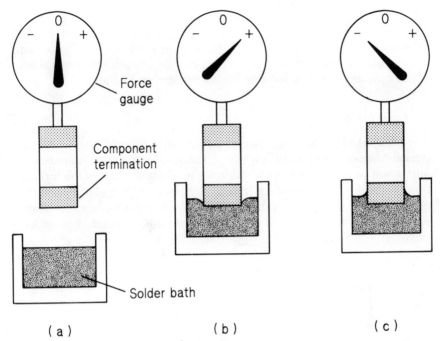

FIG. 5.7 Operation of the wetting balance: a. initial position, b. termination immersed in solder, wetting not yet started, c. wetted termination.

The operation of the wetting balance* is illustrated in Fig. 5.7. The component to be tested is suspended from a force gauge above a pot of molten solder (Fig. 5.7a). By raising the solder pot, the termination is immersed into the solder. Initially, the temperature of the termination is too low to promote wetting. As shown in Fig. 5.7b, the component displaces some of the solder, resulting in a net upward force on the gauge. Then, when the termination wets, surface tension pulls the component down into the pot (Fig. 5.7c). The dynamic force curve thus indicates the solderability of the termination.

A. Buoyancy

When the component being tested is lowered into the solder pot, it displaces some of the molten solder. The displaced solder exerts an upward force that counteracts the downward pull due to surface tension. For accurate results, this buoyancy force must be subtracted from the total force. This is often accomplished semiautomatically within the machine. The operator first calculates the immersed volume of the termination and enters this information into the computer controller. When the test is subsequently initiated,

* The wetting balance is sometimes called a meniscograph, although that term is legally a trademark of the General Electric Company of the United Kingdom.

the machine automatically weighs the part and calculates a net buoyancy force. This force is automatically subtracted from the measurement. The calculation makes certain assumptions, such as density of the solder and homogeneity of the termination, but is accurate enough for practical use. Specific details are included with the equipment instructions.

B. Force curves

The graph of Fig. 5.8 demonstrates three possible force curves. Curve A is typical of a sample that wets properly. The force starts upward, indicating initial non-wetting, but quickly reaches a maximum. Then as the termination wets, the force descends rapidly, crossing zero and exponentially approaching a maximum negative value. The time to the zero-crossing is typically less than 1 or 2 seconds, and equilibrium is reached in under 5 seconds.

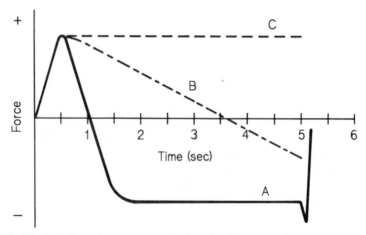

FIG. 5.8 Wetting balance force curves: a. ideal wetting, b. poor wetting, c. non-wetting.

The plot of Curve B represents a sample that exhibits poor wetting. The peak upward force occurs similar to that of Curve A, but the decline is much slower. In many cases the net force may not reach zero during the test period. Even when the net force does go negative, the zero-crossing may not occur for many seconds and equilibrium may not be reached during the time of the test.

Curve C illustrates a non-wetting condition. The force reaches the peak value and does not noticeably decline for the duration of the test.

Other possible curves are shown in Fig. 5.9. Fig. 5.9a demonstrates dewetting. In this case, the equilibrium force slowly increases, indicating a reduction in surface tension force. This is most often a result of leaching of the termination into the solder. It can also occur when the solderable coating

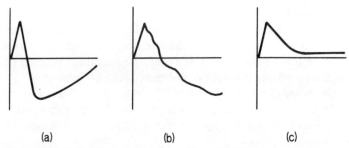

<table>
<tr><td>(a)</td><td>(b)</td><td>(c)</td></tr>
</table>

FIG. 5.9 Possible wetting balance curves: a. rapid wetting followed by dewetting, b. unstable wetting, c. large buoyancy force.

on the termination is extremely thin; as intermetallic formation consumes the coating, the less solderable base layer is exposed.

Fig. 5.9b illustrates instability in wetting. Contamination or irregularities in the termination metal are likely causes of this phenomenon.

The effect of a large buoyancy force is shown in Fig. 5.9c. In this case, the downward force due to surface tension is not enough to overcome the buoyancy of the component. Normally, the effects of buoyancy are calculated and corrected prior to the start of the test.

C. Testing of surface mount components

Wetting balance tests are today performed almost exclusively with commercial equipment. Unfortunately, the applicability of the test to surface mount components is not well established. Chip capacitors have been successfully tested but the method has been reported to be inadequate for flatpacks.[8] Problems in testing SMCs include the following:

(1) Small net force
Because of the small physical sizes of surface mount component terminations, net force readings are correspondingly diminished. In some cases, the readings can tax the resolution of the available equipment.

(2) Short termination length
An immersion depth of 2 mm to 4 mm is standard for through-hole component leads. Most surface mount components do not have this much available termination length. The minimum length of a chip capacitor termination, for example, is 0.25 mm, while the maximum is only 0.75 mm. As a result, both the immersion depth and rate of immersion must be adjusted.

The optimal immersion depth varies by device type. Leaded devices such as SOICs and quadpacks can use an immersion depth of 1 mm. Chip components should be tested with a near-zero immersion depth—0.1 mm or less. At most, one-half of the termination should be below the level of the solder.

The theoretical wetting curve for components with very short termination lengths may be different than for through-hole devices. The solder may wet to the top of the termination before reaching equilibrium, thus truncating the maximum force reading. In this event, the maximum reading depends more on the termination length than on wetting characteristics.

The immersion rate will also differ. The rate specified for through-hole devices, 25 ± 6 mm per second, is too large—rapid immersion creates waves on the surface of the pot that masks wetting effects. More reasonable rates are 1–5 mm per second.

(3) Buoyancy

With through-hole components, the buoyancy force is rarely significant. However, many surface mount components have large buoyant forces, complicating the measurements. Integrated circuits and other post-molded plastic packages are especially troublesome in this respect. Particularly with J-lead devices, it is often necessary to immerse a portion of the component body when measuring the solderability of the leads. In this case, the buoyancy force can be many times larger than the wetting force.

(4) Thermal heat sinking

The proximity of the component body to the termination increases the thermal heat sinking effect, extending the time required for the termination to come to temperature. The shape of the resultant curve can therefore be expected to differ significantly from historic curves for through-hole devices.

D. Test details

The wetting balance tests described in published standards have been developed for through-hole components and are not directly applicable to surface mount devices. When suitably modified, however, existing procedures can serve as the basis for new tests appropriate for these devices. The following test, adapted from MIL-STD-883, Method 2022, can be utilized for many component types.

Wetting Balance Test For Surface Mount Components

1. Apparatus

(*a*) *Wetting balance.* An apparatus capable of measuring the wetting force of component terminations shall be used. It shall include a solder bath consisting of at least 750 grams of Sn63 or Sn60 solder. Bath integrity can be maintained either by periodic assay or by routine replacement after every 50 hours of immersion time. For reflow soldered components, the temperature of the bath should be $215 \pm 5\,°C$. Components to be wave soldered may be tested at $235 \pm 5\,°C$.

2. Materials

(*a*) *Flux*. The flux shall conform to Type R of Federal Specification QQ-S-571.

(*b*) *Solder*. The solder shall conform to Type S, composition Sn60 or Sn63, of QQ-S-571.

3. Procedure

(*a*) *Sample preparation*. Means should be taken to protect the component from fingerprints and other sources of contamination. The terminations should not be cleaned, wiped, or scraped prior to testing.

(*b*) *Flux application*. Immerse the components in the flux for several seconds, then drain. Conduct the test immediately after flux application.

(*c*) *Immersion*. The immersion rate should be 1 mm per second for chip components and 5 mm per second for leaded devices.

4. Acceptance criteria. The following criteria can be used to determine the acceptability of the termination.

(a) The net force becomes and remains negative within 2 seconds of initial contact between termination and solder;

(b) The plot of net force versus time contains no abrupt discontinuities or reversals of slope later than 1 second after initial contact between termination and solder;

(c) The net force after 3 seconds is at least 25% of that obtained on a perfectly wetted reference component.

5.7.4 Resistance to dissolution of metallization

This test is used to examine the extent to which terminations dissolve during the soldering process. It is applicable to components, such as chip resistors and capacitors, that have a solderable coating applied over a precious metal base layer.

The test uses the same equipment and test methodology as the Dip Test of Section 5.7.2. The conditions of the test are changed to accelerate the rate of dissolution. Recommended conditions (per EIA-186-9F) are as follows:

Solder temperature: $260 \pm 5\,°C$
Dwell time: 30 ± 1 second

Acceptance criteria are based on the amount of metallization lost during the test. The combined loss from all dewetted areas should not exceed 10% of the total electrode area, with no individual area exceeding 5%. In addition, the internal electrodes should not be exposed.

Resistance to dissolution can be measured quantitatively with the wetting balance. Using the same test conditions described above, any reduction in the equilibrium wetting force is indicative of dewetting. No industry-wide specifications have yet been developed, but a 10% reduction in force is suggested as an acceptance limit.

5.7.5 Other test methods

Several other test methods have been used to characterize the solderability of through-hole components and boards. None of these is particularly well suited for the testing of surface mount components, although some can be used on printed wiring boards and ceramic substrates. Some of the more common tests include:

A. Globule method

In this technique, a small droplet of solder is heated above the melting point. The termination to be tested (ideally the cylindrical wire of a through-hole component) is fluxed and positioned over the center of the globule (Fig. 5.10a). When the wire is lowered into the globule, the solder remains bisected until wetting occurs (Figs. 5.10b and 5.10c). The length of time required to wet is determined either visually or automatically to give a relative measure of solderability.

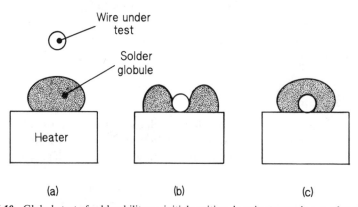

FIG. 5.10   Globule test of solderability: a. initial position, b. prior to wetting, c. after wetting.

This test is best suited to components with extended leads. Although in principle it is possible to test gull-wing surface mount devices, the complexities resulting from small, closely spaced leads make the practicality of the technique questionable.

B. Rotary dip method

This method, primarily suited for testing solderability of printed wiring boards, is described in ANSI/IPC-S-804 and IEC 68-2-20. A 25-mm square sample of the board is suspended from a motor-driven arm that pivots over a bath of molten solder. The specimen is oriented horizontally such that its underside is immersed to a depth of about 1.0 mm when the arm pivots. Care must be taken to prevent solder from flowing over the top surface of the board during the test. The speed of rotation of the arm is adjusted so that the specimen is immersed into the solder for 3.0 ± 0.5 seconds.

After dipping, the sample is visually inspected for solder coverage. A standard requirement is that 95% of the surface exhibit good wetting. In addition, all plated holes should be wetted to the extent that solder is visible on the land around the top of the hole.

C. Spread-factor test

This test is used to measure flux activity. Operation of the test is best understood by examining Fig. 5.11. A known quantity of solder is placed on a copper surface having a controlled thickness of oxide. After a measured amount of flux is applied, the solder is reflowed. The extent to which the solder spreads is a function of the activity of the flux. If no oxide were removed, wetting would not occur and (in the absence of gravity) the solder would form a perfect sphere of diameter D. The higher the activity of the flux, the more oxide is removed and the lower the height, H, of the solder bump.

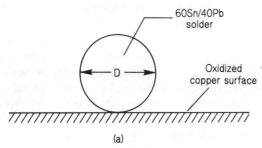

(a)

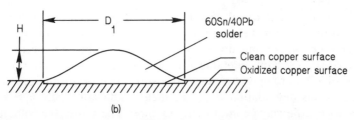

(b)

FIG. 5.11   Spread factor test. In (a), the flux was not active enough to remove the copper oxide. The molten solder does not wet the surface and instead forms a ball of diameter D. In (b), the flux has removed some of the copper oxide. The solder wets the surface, spreading out to diameter D_1 and height H.

A measure of flux activity can be calculated by the ratio of D to H, called the *spread factor*.

Spread factor = $((D-H)/D) \times 100$

The diameter, D, can be calculated from the weight of the solder, W, and its density, ρ:

$$D = 1.2407 \sqrt[3]{W/\rho}$$

A standard test for liquid flux is described in MIL-F-14256. A coupon 2 inches square is cut from 0.005-in (0.13-mm) thick electrolytic copper and cleaned in 10% fluoroboric acid. It is then oxidized for a predetermined length of time: 1 hour at 150 °C for Type R flux and one hour at 205 °C for Type RMA flux. An amount of Sn60 solder weighing 0.500 ± 0.025 grams is placed on the coupon along with 0.10 ± 0.005 grams of flux. The solder is reflowed for 6 minutes in a circulating-air oven at 205 °C. A spread factor of 80 or more is considered acceptable.

The spread factor test is also suitable for testing solder pastes.[9] A simple stencil can be made from a steel washer with an inside diameter of 0.200 in (0.51 mm) and a height of 0.025 in (0.63 mm). Solder paste is applied through the stencil onto the coupon by use of a spatula. The stencil is carefully removed, leaving a controlled quantity of paste. Paste should be dried according to the manufacturer's instructions and then reflowed per the above schedule. Flux is removed in a solvent, such as hot trichloroethane, followed by a rinse in isopropyl alcohol.

The weight of the coupon must be measured to the nearest microgram before and after application of the paste and again after reflow and flux removal. The weight of the solder is calculated and spread factor determined as above. The weight–percent metal of the solder can also be calculated from the weight of the coupon before and after flux removal. (A procedure for estimating spread factor by measuring only the diameter of the reflowed solder is described in Section 9.4.5.)

5.8 AGING

Many termination materials exhibit a very high degree of solderability immediately after manufacture. Only after the components have been stored for a period of time do noticeable differences begin to occur. Oxidation, corrosion, and intermetallic diffusion products cause the terminations to lose solderability upon extended exposure to the atmosphere. For some materials, this degradation becomes measurable after only a few days; others show little change after many months. Therefore, the solderability test must account for the effects of normal storage conditions on the performance of the parts.

It is typical within the industry to store components and boards for extended periods prior to assembly; durations of 6 to 12 months are common. Since it is obviously impractical to wait for such an extended term prior to testing, some means must be undertaken to accelerate the effects of storage. A comprehensive survey of techniques for accelerated aging was conducted by an IPC Task Group.[10] The group reviewed literature references to a number of techniques ranging from 1 hour of steam aging to a month or more of damp heat. The appropriateness of a given technique was found to depend on the metallurgy of the termination and expected cause of degradation. For tin–lead surfaces, oxidation is the primary concern. With precious metal surfaces, diffusion may be of greater importance.

The IPC Task Group recommended 20 to 24 hours of steam aging as the preferred method for accelerated aging of tin–lead surfaces. This duration was considered to be the best representation of 1-year shelf life under normal conditions. Considerable evidence was amassed in support of this position.

The group was unable to find sufficient documentation to take a definitive stand on coatings other than tin–lead and referred instead to the methods delineated in the IEC Standard 68-2-20. The IEC standard calls for 16 hours of dry heat aging at 115 °C when diffusion is the primary cause of degradation and steam aging when the mechanism is unknown.

Subsequent work by other researchers indicates that a shorter steam aging duration may be nearly as effective as the 24-hour test recommended by IPC.[13] The US military has adopted an 8-hour test, and other investigations support the efficacy of shorter times. Fig. 5.12 shows the result of one recent study that indicates that wetting times as measured by the wetting balance are unchanged after about 10 hours of aging. However, the applicability of these results across a wide range of termination varieties is still unproven, so the 24-hour test is preferred when the exact correlation is unknown.

5.8.1 Steam Aging

In this test, the components are suspended in a saturated steam zone above vigorously boiling water for a specified period of time. The test apparatus is relatively simple to construct, and if a 24-hour duration is used, the test can be started on one day and terminated at the same time on the subsequent day.

A. Apparatus

The apparatus should be constructed of materials that do not contaminate the test samples. Stainless steel or borosilicate glass are recommended materials. Means should be provided to prevent excessive pressure build-up, assure continuous boiling, and maintain an adequate water level.

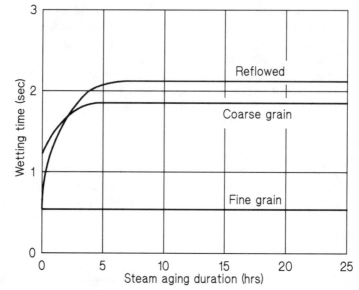

FIG. 5.12 Wetting characteristics for several plated solder lead finishes. The finishes tested included as-plated coarse-grain and fine-grain Sn60 solder and reflowed Sn60 solder on copper-clad steel wires. Lead-rich and tin-rich regions were approximately 0.5 μm diameter for fine-grain solder, 4 μm diameter for coarse-grain solder, and 2.5 μm for reflowed solder. (Adapted from A. Geiger, "Solderability of Capacitor Lead Wires," presented at the 10th Annual Soldering/Manufacturing Seminar Proceedings, China Lake, CA, 1986.)

B. Component location

Condensate should drip freely back to the supply water without striking other samples. Samples should be oriented such that they are freely exposed on all surfaces to the steam and of sufficient height above the water to prevent direct contact with splashing or turbulent water..

C. Test method

Parts should be suspended in the steam zone in the manner described for the specified period of time. The steam temperature should be within 6 °C of the local boiling point. After steam exposure, the parts should be allowed to air-dry prior to solderability testing. Oven baking should be used only if this is a normal step in the production process prior to soldering.

5.8.2 Dry heat aging

This method is suggested for solderable coatings in which intermetallic diffusion is the primary cause of degradation. Specimens are placed in a clean, dry container and kept at an elevated temperature for a specified period of time. There is no consensus on the appropriate time and temperature to simulate 1-year normal storage. The IEC, in its document 68-2-20 Test "T" Soldering, recommends 16 hours at 155 °C. The IPC Task Group suggested that 4 hours at 155 °C was more appropriate but acknowledged the lack of adequate information to make a firm recommendation. It is likely that the appropriate duration is a function of the exact materials being tested. In the absence of additional data, the 16-hour test documented by IEC is suggested for aging gold or silver coated terminations.

5.9 SPECIFYING COMPONENT TERMINATION MATERIALS

There is no universal agreement as to what constitutes the ideal surface mount component termination. The literature contains many references to the subject, often with conflicting results. In part, this may be due to differences in the soldering processes used and in the criteria used to measure acceptability. It is also likely to be influenced by factors not yet completely understood. For example, as discussed in Section 5.5.5, grain structure in electroplated finishes is now known to have an important influence on solderability. Since this factor is rarely considered in published work, its effect on experimental results is impossible to determine.

The following criteria, summarized in Table 5.4, are generally considered important for component solderability. As discussed in the following paragraphs, however, there are conflicting opinions regarding some recommendations. Additional experimental work is necessary to resolve these differences.

1. Tin–lead surface finish

The solderable surface of a termination should consist of a tin–lead coating. Compared to many other materials, tin–lead alloy exhibits excellent wetting characteristics. It also melts during the soldering process, becoming indistinguishable from the external solder.

Although a pure tin finish is sometimes used because it is easy to plate, such a coating is not generally recommended. A phenomenon called *tin whiskers* can cause reliability problems with a pure tin surface. Tin whiskers occur because internal stresses in the plated tin are relieved by the growth of tiny filaments that can extend to several millimetres in length. As the filaments grow, they can short across adjacent conductors. The addition of a small amount of lead (2–4%) is effective in preventing whisker growth.

Another problem with pure tin is that it gradually turns to an amorphous powder below about 13 °C. This phenomenon, called *tin pest*, occurs slowly and is not normally a problem in electronic applications. However, it can be of concern in certain situations.

Requirement	Advantages	Disadvantages	Comments
Tin–Lead finish	* Provides metallurgical compatibility with solder		* Near-eutectic alloys have best compatibility
Solder–Dipper finishes	* Long shelf life * Eutectic alloy coating	* Expensive * Poor control of surface geometry	
Electroplated finishes	* Good control of surface geometry * Low cost compared to dipping	* Tin–Lead ratio is sensitive to plating parameters * Susceptibility to oxidation	* Fine-grain platings retain solderability longer than coarse-grain platings
Reflow of plated finishes	* Alloys Tin–Lead plating * Reduces porosity * Provides feedback on solderability of base metal	* Adds cost * Reduces control of surface geometry	* Conflicting evidence regarding efficacy of this technique
Barrier layer over precious metals	* Improves leach resistance	* Adds cost	
Storage in inert environment	* Minimizes oxidation	* Requires careful control of environment	* Will not correct preexisting problems

TABLE 5.4   Surface finish recommendations for surface mount components

2. Dipped vs. electroplated finishes

Eutectic tin–lead alloy as deposited by dipping the terminations in a pot of molten solder is generally considered to provide the highest degree of solderability. However, solder-dipping is not always a practical solution. The process must often be performed manually, increasing both the expense and variability of coating. Even when performed automatically, the geometry of the resulting finish may not be desirable. Molten solder forms a meniscus with thick deposits at the center of the surface and thin layers at the edges. As a result, it may be difficult to control overall part dimensions to the required accuracy.

Component manufacturers often prefer electroplated tin–lead because of the greater control that can be exercised over the process. There is considerable disagreement regarding what constitutes the most desirable finish.

Commonly used tin–lead ratios include 60–40, 63–37, 85–15, 90–10, 95–5, 96–4, 98–2, and pure tin. In general, the higher the tin content, the easier it is to control plating parameters. Conversely, tin–lead ratios near the eutectic point exhibit better solderability than higher ratios.[3]

3. Reflow of plated finishes

Some specifications call for plated finishes to be reflowed, or "fused," as part of the component manufacturing process. The intent is to alloy the solder, provide a denser coating, and eliminate voids. Reflowing also serves as a test to insure that the solder will wet the base metal. However, there is considerable disagreement over the efficacy of this approach. The additional processing steps increase component cost, making it unpopular with manufacturers. And while some technical papers indicate that solderability is improved by reflowing the plating, others report opposite results. Additional experimental work in carefully controlled conditions is necessary to resolve this conflict.

4. Protection of precious metal electrodes

Components such as chip resistors and ceramic capacitors often use precious metal electrodes to contact the active component elements. Since gold and silver dissolve rapidly in tin–lead solder, these electrodes must be protected by a barrier between the electrode and the solderable surface. The barrier, which must have low solubility in tin–lead solder, is usually nickel at least 50

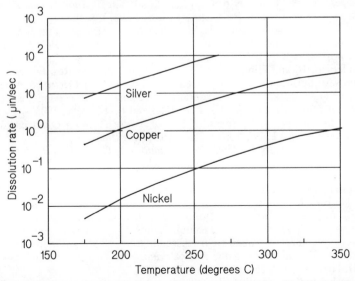

FIG. 5.13 Dissolution rates of several metals in molten Sn60 solder. (Used by permission. Copyright 1982, *Brazing & Soldering*, Wela Publications.)

microinches thick. Copper has occasionally been used and other materials have also been investigated.

Figure 5.13 shows the dissolution rates for silver, copper, and nickel in 605n/40Pb solder. This graph clearly shows the improvement afforded by a nickel or copper barrier between the precious metal layer and the solder.

5. Inert environment

An approach that is sometimes used to preserve solderability is to store components in an inert environment such as nitrogen or argon. Although this will retard any additional oxide growth, it will not reverse any oxidation that has already occurred. To be successful, the environment must be controlled continuously from initial manufacturer until the parts are ultimately soldered.

REFERENCES

1. Slattery, James A. and White, C. E. T. "A primer on the use of solder creams in hybrid assembly," *Electronic Packaging and Production*, Oct. 1981.
2. Klein Wassink, R. J. *Soldering in Electronics*, Electrochemical Publications, Ayr, Scotland, 1984, pp. 13–14.
3. Hagge, J. K. and Davis, G. J. "Ageing, Solder Thickness and Solder Alloy Effects on Circuit Board Solderability," *IPC Technical Review*, Nov. 1984, pp. 13–23.
4. Kenyon, W. G. "Synthetic Activated (SA) Flux Technology: Development, Commercialization, Benefits and Future Applications," *Proceedings of the Sixth Annual Electronics Packaging Conference*, Nov. 1986, pp. 204–281.
5. Geiger, A. "Solderability of Capacitor Lead Wires," *10th Annual Soldering/ Manufacturing Seminar Proceedings*, China Lake, CA, 1986.
6. Cooper, R. O. and Monahan, E. M. "The Characterization of the Solderability of Thick Film Conductors Using a Meniscograph," *Proc. of 1984 International Symposium on Microelectronics*, Sept. 1984.
7. Anderson, B. and Hinch, S. "Solderability and Process Resistance Requirements for Surface Mount Components," *Proceedings of Electro/86*, May 1986.
8. Davy, G. and Skold, R. "Solderability Testing for Receiving Inspection," *Circuits Manufacturing*, Part 1, Feb. 1985 and Part 2, Mar. 1985.
9. Rice, D. and Wells, B. *Spread Factor of Solder Paste on Oxidized Copper*, Hewlett-Packard Laboratories, Palo Alto, CA, 1986.
10. *Accelerated Aging for Solderability Evaluations*, IPC Technical Report IPC-TR-464, Institute for Interconnecting and Packaging Electronic Circuits, Lincolnwood, IL, April 1984.
11. Mather, J. C. and Hagge, J. K. "Kinetics of Intermetallic Compound Formation and of Base Metal Dissolution into Molten Solder During Vapor Phase Soldering," *Brazing and Soldering*, No. 3, Autumn 1982, pp. 29–32.
12. Hagge, J. "Critical Component Requirements for Vapor Phase Soldering Leadless Components on Circuit Board Assemblies for Military Electronics," *IEEE Transactions on Components, Hybrids and Manufacturing Technology*, Vol. CHMT-6, No. 4, Dec. 1983, pp. 443–454.
13. Stracchino, K., and Wun, K., "Surface Mount Component Solderability," *Proceedings of SMART IV*, Los Angeles, Jan. 1988.

Part III
Design

6

Assembly design and reliability

As with through-hole technology, the reliability of a surface mount assembly is a strong function of its initial design. Solder joint design, material selection, and layout techniques all contribute to reliability. This chapter describes those factors that influence the design of solder joints and choice of substrate materials. Factors that must be considered in the layout of circuitry are discussed in Chapter 7.

6.1 THE SURFACE MOUNT SOLDER JOINT

In surface mount technology, the solder joint serves as both the electrical and the mechanical interface between component and substrate. The reliability of the assembly thus depends directly on the integrity of the joint over the entire life of the assembly.

Fig. 6.1 illustrates the two categories of surface mount solder joints: *leadless* and *leaded*. In the leadless design, metallized portions of the component body are soldered directly to the substrate. In the leaded approach, leads extending out from the body of the component are soldered to the board.

6.1.1 Solder joint failure modes

Failures of surface mount solder joints are caused by three primary factors:

- thermal cycling
- power cycling
- mechanical flexure

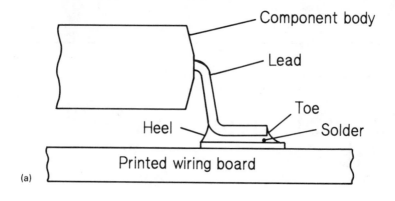

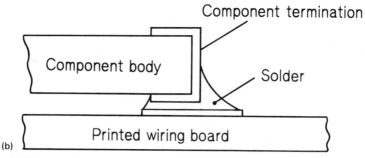

FIG. 6.1   Solder joint configurations: a. Leaded. b. Leadless.

The most important concern for either leaded or leadless joints is fatigue failure of the solder due to thermal cycling.[1] The problem arises when the coefficient of thermal expansion (CTE) for the component is different from that of the board. As the ambient temperature varies, the two expand at different rates, creating a strain at the interface. If the strain is large enough, the yield strength of the solder will be exceeded, causing it to experience plastic deformation. Over a number of temperature cycles, this deformation will accumulate until the joint fractures. The number of cycles to failure is inversely proportional to the amount of plastic strain in each cycle.[2]

A related failure mode is that of power cycling.[3,4] In this mode, a temperature difference between the device and board caused by device power dissipation creates a stress at the joint. The effect is only significant for high-power devices, particularly during turn-on transients. The temperature of the device can rise much more quickly than that of the board, causing significant strains even in assemblies with otherwise matched CTE materials.

The third failure mechanism is due to mechanical flexure of the board. This is not usually as severe a problem because of the large amount of flexure necessary to seriously impact the joint. It is mainly a problem in assemblies subjected to high levels of vibration, such as aircraft or certain types of ground vehicles. Vibration-related problems are usually easily solved by increasing board rigidity or improving the overall system design.

6.1.2 Leadless joints

Leadless joints are employed in many types of passive components and in leadless chip carrier packages. They have two primary benefits:

- low component manufacturing cost
- low parasitic reactances

Both advantages are a direct result of the lack of external leads. Leads add electrical length that increase parasitic inductance and capacitance. Extra manufacturing steps are needed to attach the leads, invariably increasing costs.

The primary disadvantage of leadless joints is their susceptibility to fracturing. Stresses due to differences in CTE between component and board must be absorbed totally within the solder. As shown in Fig. 6.2, the low yield strength of eutectic tin-lead solder results in large plastic deformations at relatively low stresses.

The difference in absolute linear expansion between the board and small leadless passive components is low even if the difference in CTE is large. For this reason, there is little reliability risk with passive devices. Large ceramic chip carriers, on the other hand, represent a significant risk—particularly over the full military operating temperature range of −55 to +125 °C.

For this reason, direct attachment of ceramic chip carriers to ordinary organic printed wiring boards is now discouraged except in the most benign

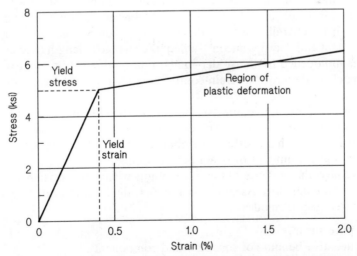

FIG. 6.2   Stress-strain relationship for Sn60 solder. (From Ref. 2. Used by permission.)

thermal environments. Instead, techniques to reduce the stress in the joints must be employed. These generally take one of two approaches: constraining the expansion of the board to more closely match that of the chip carrier or adding a measure of compliance to disperse the stress across a larger interface than just the solder. Each approach is described in more detail later in this chapter.

6.1.3 Leaded joints

One way to add compliance is to attach leads to the device. The flexible leads absorb most of the strain due to differential expansion between component and board, so the amount absorbed in the solder can be kept below its elastic limit.

Post-molded plastic IC packages include leads as a natural part of the device manufacturing process. In the case of ceramic chip carriers, additional processing steps are required. Ceramic *leaded* chip carriers are now available but have not gained a large market share. Much more attention has been placed on developing board materials and assembly processes that are compatible with the leadless packages.

The use of leaded chip carriers does not automatically eliminate problems due to joint fracture. An IEEE task force has found that if the leads are not sufficiently compliant, the joints can still fail.[5] As long as adequate compliance is maintained, however, the approach is extremely effective.

6.1.4 Solder joint stresses

The stress/strain relationship for a surface mount solder joint is quite complex. It has been analyzed theoretically in a number of studies (see, for example, Refs. 6, 7, and 8). Because of the low elastic modulus of tin–lead solder, it is generally assumed that the expansion and contraction of the component and board is unconstrained; the change in length over temperature is unimpeded by the solder joints. Failure due to thermal expansion mismatch is therefore a strain-controlled rather than a stress-controlled phenomenon.

Consider, for example, the two solders shown in Fig. 6.3. Both solders fail at the same applied load, but solder 2 exhibits a larger extension at failure. Solder 2 would exhibit better performance in thermal cycling because it can absorb a larger amount of strain before failing.

In reality, the presence of the solder joints will cause a certain amount of out-of-plane bending. As shown in Fig. 6.4, deformation can be classified into three distinct modes:

1. pure shear
2. negative bending of substrate and component
3. positive bending of substrate and component.

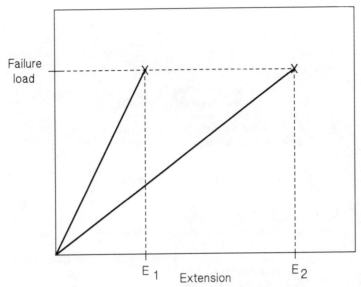

FIG. 6.3 Extension at failure for two different solders. (Adapted from Ref. 15. Published with permission of the Institute for Interconnecting and Packaging Electronic Circuits (IPC).)

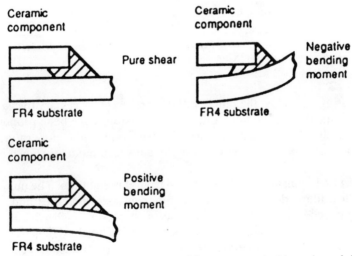

FIG. 6.4 Possible stresses due to CTE mismatch between ceramic chip carrier and glass-epoxy substrate material. (Published with permission of the Institute for Interconnecting and Packaging Electronic Circuits (IPC).)

Steady-state thermal expansion mismatch produces primarily a pure shear deformation, but a small amount of bending can be expected. Power cycling produces larger bending moments.

Fatigue life can be predicted by modified forms of the Manson-Coffin equation for low-cycle fatigue. This relation predicts, as a function of several

$$N_f = \tfrac{1}{2} \left(\frac{\Delta\gamma}{2\epsilon'_f} \right)^{(1/C)}$$

where

N_f = mean cycles to failure
ϵ'_f = fatigue ductility coefficient ≈ 0.325
C = fatigue ductility exponent
$\quad = -0.442 - 6 \times 10^{-4}\bar{T}_s + 1.74 \times 10^{-2}\ln(1 + f)$
$\Delta\gamma$ = shear strain range

$$= \frac{L}{\sqrt{2h}} \; \Delta(\alpha\Delta T)_{ss} \times 10^{-4} \text{ in percent}$$

and

$\Delta(\gamma\Delta T)_{ss}$ = in plane steady-state thermal expansion mismatch
$\quad = \alpha_s(T_s - T_o) - \alpha_c(T_c - T_o)$
α_c, α_s = coefficients of linear thermal expansion for SMC, and PCB respectively
T_c, T_s = temperatures of SMC and PCB respectively
T_o = power off, steady-state temperature, °C
$\bar{T}_s$ = mean cyclic solder joint temperature, °C
f = cyclic frequency, $1 \le f \le 1000$ cycles/day
L = chip carrier size
h = standoff height

FIG. 6.5   Modified Manson-Coffin equation for low-cycle strain fatigue. (From Ref. 1. Used by permission. Hewlett-Packard Company.)

contributing variables, the number of thermal cycles necessary to cause the joint to catastrophically fail. A number of versions have been proposed to include such influences as frequency of cycling, maximum temperature, and dwell time at maximum temperature. An advanced model is shown in Fig. 6.5.

Several relationships can be observed from this equation. The number of cycles to failure decreases as the component size increases and as the differential coefficient of thermal expansion increases. Cycles to failure can be increased by increasing the component standoff height. Higher vibration frequencies, smaller temperature excursions, and lower maximum temperatures also tend to increase the fatigue life.

6.2 PACKAGING AND INTERCONNECTION STRUCTURES

The printed wiring board or ceramic substrate on which components are attached is a primary influence on the performance, cost, and reliability of the finished assembly. The general term packaging and interconnecting structure (or more simply, P/I structure) has been defined by IPC to describe any substrate and associated wiring used for the purpose of mounting electronic components.

Packaging and interconnecting structures can be classified into several categories. Those with application in surface mount technology are:

- organic-based substrate
- metal core substrate
- compliant layer materials
- ceramic substrate

Within each of these major categories is a range of alternative materials. Table 6.1 summarizes the physical properties of the various materials, while Table 6.2 lists some of their advantages and disadvantages.

Reliable assembly design

The primary reliability consideration in choosing a material for the P/I structure is the need to minimize the impact of thermal expansion mismatch between the component and substrate. It is not usually a simple matter of selecting the material whose CTE most closely matches that of the components because different components may have widely varying expansion coefficients. Furthermore, the effect of power cycling may be an additional complication. Reliable assembly design depends on a complete understanding of the capabilities and tradeoffs of the various available substrate materials.

6.3 ORGANIC-BASED MATERIALS

Organic printed wiring boards range from inexpensive materials suitable for general-purpose use to exotic composites designed for highly specialized applications. The term *organic* is used rather loosely, as these materials often include other than organic materials. The term *polymer* board is sometimes used to describe these materials.

The ordinary laminates listed in Table 6.3 are compatible with small leadless components and larger leaded chip carriers. Special purpose materials must be employed for use with leadless ceramic chip carriers, particularly over large operating temperature extremes.

6.3.1 Fabrication processes

Conductor traces can be formed on the substrate material either through the traditional *subtractive* process or the more recent *additive* process. The subtractive process uses a laminate pre-clad with copper on one or both sides (depending on whether conductors are to be etched on one or both sides). In

Material Properties (Note 1)

Material	Glass Transition Temperature (°C)	XY Coefficient of Thermal Expansion (PPM/°C) (Notes 3,4)	Thermal Conductivity (W/M°C)	XY Tensile Modulus (PSI × 10^{-6})	Dielectric Constant (At 1 MHz)	Volume Resistivity (Ohm-cm)	Surface Resistivity (Ohms)	Moisture Absorption (Percent)
Unit of measure								
Epoxy Fiberglass	125	13–18	0.16	2.5	4.8	10^{12}	10^{13}	0.25
Polyimide Fiberglass	250	12–16	0.35	2.8	4.8	10^{14}	10^{13}	0.35
Epoxy Aramid Fiber	125	6–8	0.12	4.4	3.9	10^{16}	10^{16}	0.85
Polyimide Aramid Fiber	250	3–7	0.15	4.0	3.6	10^{12}	10^{12}	1.50
Polyimide Quartz	250	6–8	0.30		4.0	10^{9}	10^{8}	0.50
Fiberglass/Teflon	75	20	0.26	0.2	2.3	10^{10}	10^{11}	1.10
Thermoplastic Resin	190	25.30		3–4	10	10^{13}	NA	
Alumina	NA	8.0	44.0	8.0	10	10^{16}		
Beryllia	NA	4.2–9.4	200–400		5.8			
Aluminium (6061 T-6)	NA	23.6	200	10	NA	10^{6}		NA
Copper (CDA 101)	NA	17.3	400	17	NA	10^{6}		
Copper-Clad Invar (Note 2)	NA	3–6	150XY/20Z	17–22	NA	10^{6}		NA

Notes:

1. These materials can be tailored to provide a wide variety of material properties based on resins, core materials, core thickness, and processing methods.
2. The X and Y expansion is controlled by the core material and only the Z axis is free to expand unrestrained, where the Tg will be the same as the reinforced resin system used.
3. When used, a compliant layer will conform to the CTE of the base material and to the ceramic component, therefore reducing the strain between the component and P&I structure.
4. Figures are below glass transition temperature, are dependent on method of measurement and percentage of resin content.

NA—Not applicable.

TABLE 6.1 P&I structure material properties. (Adapted from Ref. 16. Published with permission of the Institute for Interconnecting and Packaging Electronic Circuits (IPC).)

the double-sided process (Fig. 6.6), all via holes are first drilled and coated with a thin layer of electroless copper. A negative resist is applied and exposed such that the resist covers the areas of unwanted copper. An electroplated layer of copper is deposited to build up the vias and increase the conductor thicknesses. A layer of tin or solder is plated over the exposed copper conductors to serve as an etch resist. After removal of the negative resist, the unwanted copper is etched away.

In the additive process, conductors are pattern-plated onto a bare laminate material. Several proprietary processes have been developed that are either *fully additive* (conductors built entirely from electroless copper) or *semiadditive* (electrolytic copper plated over a thin layer of electroless copper).[9] A typical fully additive process (Fig. 6.7) begins by drilling all via holes in the laminate. The laminate is sensitized to promote a strong bond with the electroless copper and a negative resist is applied. After the resist is exposed and developed, electroless copper is plated onto the laminate in a high-speed process. The negative resist need not be stripped off, and by leaving it in place, a nearly flush surface can be obtained.

The additive process is capable of producing finer pattern geometries than the subtractive process. Several hazardous chemical steps can be eliminated and the process can be used on materials such as molded or extruded thermoplastics. The subtractive process is somewhat less expensive and generally produces conductors with higher adhesion strength to the laminate.

Solder mask

To reduce the chance for solder bridging between conductors during the soldering process, conductors are generally covered with a permanent solder mask that exposes only the component land patterns. The mask is frequently an epoxy resin that can be applied one of two ways. *Dry-film masks* are photosensitive films, from about 0.025–0.075-mm (0.001–0.003-in) thick, that are laminated to the finished board. Standard photolithographic techniques are used to open windows in the mask at the locations of the component lands. *Liquid masks* are screen printed or roller-coated layers that tend to be thicker than dry-film masks. Screen printed masks are not photosensitive, so land patterns are defined by the configuration of openings in the screen.

Solder mask registration accuracy for surface mount boards is more critical than for through-hole boards. The mask must not intrude onto the component lands but must fully cover adjacent conductors—especially those routed between closely spaced integrated circuit lands. Screen printing is not usually adequate to achieve the required level of registration accuracy, and so photographically defined masks are preferred. It is sometimes incorrectly assumed that only dry-film masks are photosensitive and liquid masks are always screen printed. In reality, several liquid photosensi-

ORGANIC BASE SUBSTRATE

Type	Major Advantages	Major Disadvantages	Comments
Epoxy Fiberglass	Substrate size, weight, reworkable, dielectric properties, conventional board processing.	Thermal conductivity, X, Y and Z axis CTE.	Because of its high X-Y plane CTE, It should be limited to environments and applications with small changes in temperature and/or small packages.
Polyimide Fiberglass	Same as Epoxy Fiberglass plus high temperature Z axis CTE, substrate size, weight, reworkable, dielectric properties.	Thermal conductivity, X and Y axis CTE, moisture absorption.	Same as Epoxy Fiberglass.
Epoxy Aramid Fiber	Same as Epoxy Fiberglass, X-Y axis CTE, substrate size, lightest weight, reworkable, dielectric properties.	Thermal conductivity, X and Y axis CTE, resin microcracking, Z axis CTE, water absorption.	Volume fraction of fiber can be controlled to tailor X-Y CTE. Resin selection critical to reducing resin microcracks.
Polyimide Aramid Fiber	Same as Epoxy Aramid Fiber, Z axis CTE, substrate size, weight, reworkable, dielectric properties.	Thermal conductivity, X and Y axis CTE, resin microcracking, water absorption.	Same as Epoxy Aramid Fiber.
Polyimide Quartz (Fused Silica)	Same as Polyimide Aramid Fiber, Z axis CTE, substrate size, weight, reworkable, dielectric properties.	Thermal conductivity, X and Y axis CTE, Z axis CTE, drilling, availability, cost, low resin content required.	Volume fraction of fiber can be controlled to tailor X-Y CTE. Drill wearout higher than with fiberglass.
Fiberglass/Aramid Composite Fiber	Same as Polyimide Aramid Fiber, no surface microcracks, Z axis CTE, substrate size, weight, reworkable, dielectric properties.	Thermal conductivity, X and Y axis CTE, water absorption, process solution entrapment.	Resin microcracks are confined to internal layers and cannot damage external circuitry.
Fiberglass/Teflon® Laminates	Dielectric constant, high temperature.	Same as Epoxy Fiberglass, low temperature stability, thermal conductivity, X and Y axis CTE.	Suitable for high speed logic applications. Same as Epoxy Fiberglass.
Flexible Dielectric	Light weight, minimal concern to CTE, configuration flexibility.	Size.	Rigid-flexible boards offer trade-off compromises.
Thermoplastic	3-D configurations, low high-volume cost.	High injection-molding setup costs.	Relatively new for these applications.

NON-ORGANIC BASE Alumina (Ceramic)	CTE, thermal conductivity, conventional thick film or thin film processing, integrated resistors.	Substrate size, rework limitations, weight, cost, brittle, dielectric constant.	Most widely used for hybrid circuit technology.
SUPPORTING PLANE			
Printed Board Bonded to Plane Support (Metal or Non-Metal)	Substrate size, reworkability, dielectric properties, conventional board processing, X-Y axis CTE, stiffness, shielding, cooling.	Weight.	The thickness/CTE of the metal core can be varied along with the board thickness, to tailor the overall CTE of the composite.
Sequential Processed Board with Supporting Plane Core	Same as board bonded to supporting plane.	Weight.	Same as board bonded to supporting plane.
Discrete Wire	High-speed interconnections. Good thermal and electrical features.	Licensed process. Requires special equipment.	Same as board bonded to low-expansion metal support plane.
CONSTRAINING CORE			
Porcelainized Copper Clad Invar	Same as Alumina.	Reworkability, compatible thick film materials.	Thick film materials are still under development.
Printed Board Bonded With Constraining Metal Core	Same as board bonded to supporting plane.	Weight, internal layer registration.	Same as board bonded to supporting plane.
Printed Board Bonded to Low Expansion Graphite Fiber Core	Same as board bonded to low expansion metal cores, stiffness, thermal conductivity, low weight.	Cost.	The thickness of the graphite and board can be varied to tailor the overall CTE of the composite.
Compliant Layer Structures	Substrate size, dielectric properties, X-Y axis, CTE.	Z axis CTE, thermal conductivity.	Compliant layer absorbs difference in CTE between ceramic package and substrate.

TABLE 6.2 Packaging and interconnecting structure comparison. (Published with permission of the Institute for Interconnecting and Packaging Electronic Circuits (IPC).)

NEMA Grade	Material	Minimum Flexural Strength (KPSI)	Max. Continuous Operating Temperature (°C)	Coefficient of Thermal Expansion (ppm)		Water Absorption (0.062″ Mat'l) (%)
				Lengthwise	Crosswise	
XXXP	Phenolic paper	10.5	125	12	17	1.0
FR-2	Phenolic paper	10.5	105	12	25	0.75
FR-3	Epoxy paper	16	105	13	25	0.65
G-10	Epoxy glass	50	130	10	10	0.25
G-11	Epoxy glass	50	170	10	15	0.25
FR-4	Epoxy glass	50	130	10	15	0.25
FR-5	Epoxy glass	50	170	10	15	0.25
—	Polyimide glass	40	260	10	12	1.0

TABLE 6.3   Typical properties of commonly used organic printed wiring boards

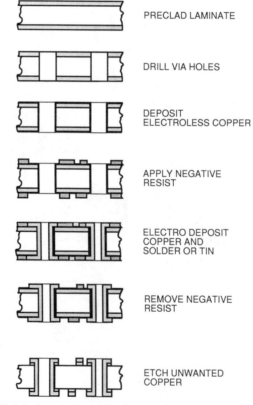

PRECLAD LAMINATE

DRILL VIA HOLES

DEPOSIT ELECTROLESS COPPER

APPLY NEGATIVE RESIST

ELECTRO DEPOSIT COPPER AND SOLDER OR TIN

REMOVE NEGATIVE RESIST

ETCH UNWANTED COPPER

FIG. 6.6   Steps in the subtractive plated through hole process.

tive masks have been developed with performance capabilities similar to or better than dry-film materials.

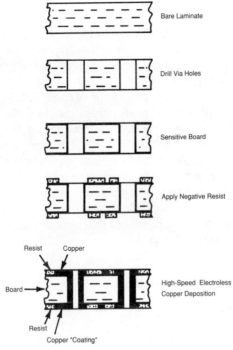

FIG. 6.7   Steps in the additive plated through hole process.

Solder-mask-over-bare-copper (SMOBC) process

Solder mask applied over solder-coated conductors can be a problem during circuit assembly. The solder melts during the component soldering process, causing the mask to wrinkle and blister. Portions of the mask can flake off the board, permitting flux to penetrate under the mask where it is not easily removed. This residual flux can eventually cause corrosion and reduced insulation resistance.

A variation of the subtractive process, *solder-mask-over-bare-copper* (SMOBC), has been developed in part to overcome this problem. In one version of this process, the solder or tin etch resist used in the conventional subtractive process is stripped away after the conductors are defined, exposing the underlying copper. A protective solder mask is applied over the board so that only the component land patterns are exposed. To protect the land patterns from oxidation prior to assembly, the board is either dipped in a bath of tin–lead solder (*selective solder coating*) or covered with an organic anti-oxidant.

The SMOBC process with selective solder coating has become popular for surface mount assemblies because of the highly solderable nature of the resulting boards. Selective solder coating can also be used on boards produced by the additive process.

6.3.2 Paper-based materials

Paper-reinforced phenolic and paper-reinforced epoxy substrate materials are heavily used in the Far East for consumer-oriented products. Their primary advantage is low cost; the physical properties of these laminates are relatively poor. They have poor dimensional stability, poor flexural strength, and twice the moisture absorption of epoxy–fiberglass materials.[10]

The least expensive material in this classification is the paper–phenolic NEMA grade XXXP. Somewhat better physical properties and a measure of flame-retardancy can be obtained with FR-3 paper–epoxy material.

Paper-based materials have rather limited application in SMT. They are best employed when low cost is of primary importance. Surface mount components should be restricted to passive devices and low-pin-count ICs. Because of their relatively poor physical properties, they are not recommended for reflow soldering processes that expose the boards to elevated temperatures for extended periods.

6.3.3 Epoxy–fiberglass materials

These materials are used in a wide variety of printed wiring board applications ranging from low-cost consumer to high-reliability military environments. They generally exhibit a good balance between physical properties and cost. Leaded surface mount components up to at least 32×32 mm (1.25×1.25 in) can be reliably mounted. Leadless components larger than about 9×9 mm (0.350×0.350 in) are not generally recommended unless additional compliance is introduced into the joint.

Epoxy–fiberglass materials come in several grades. The most common is the NEMA grade G-10 or its fire-retardant equivalent, FR-4. For higher operating temperatures, FR-5 material can be used.

6.3.4 Polyimide–fiberglass materials

Fiberglass-reinforced polyimide has a slightly lower coefficient of thermal expansion than epoxy–fiberglass, better thermal conductivity, and can withstand higher temperatures. It is primarily used in assemblies that must withstand temperatures higher than can be tolerated by epoxy–fiberglass. A typical application would be as a substrate for chip-on-board technology when the outer-lead bonds are made by thermocompression or thermosonic wirebonding. It is also recommended if large thermal excursions will occur when removing and replacing defective components.

The expansion coefficient of polyimide–fiberglass is still considerably higher than that of ceramic, so component restrictions similar to epoxy–fiberglass must be observed. The cost of polyimide material is higher than epoxy–fiberglass, limiting its use to those applications where it produces a substantial benefit.

6.3.5 Aramid-fiber materials

By using an aramid fiber in place of fiberglass in the laminate, a board material with a low coefficient of thermal expansion can be produced. Manufactured by DuPont under the tradename Kevlar®, this fiber has a negative expansion coefficient of about -2 ppm/°C. By appropriate choice of the volume fraction of Kevlar to epoxy, a composite can be produced with an expansion coefficient similar to ceramic (in the range of about 3–7 ppm/°C). In this sense, the Kevlar acts as a constraining core.

Kevlar has been used with both epoxy and polyimide resins. Either laminate is suitable for use with high pin-count leadless devices over extreme temperature ranges. Thermal cycling tests conducted at Martin–Marrietta Aerospace[11] showed no solder joint failures on 84-pin LCCCs after 333 cycles from -55 to $+125$ °C.

Kevlar materials have a number of problems that have limited their application to date. One problem is the high cost of the laminate, three to four times that of epoxy–fiberglass. Potentially more serious are the manufacturing problems that have been encountered. Kevlar is not easy to machine with conventional techniques. Difficulties in both cutting and drilling have driven some users to employ expensive CO_2 lasers for these purposes.

Laminates also exhibit a phenomenon called microcracking. Small cracks that form in the laminate propagate through the conductors, causing catastrophic open circuits. The phenomenon is thought to arise because of poor adhesion between the Kevlar and the epoxy, and work is underway to address the problem.

A final concern is that of moisture absorption. Kevlar readily absorbs moisture, and if not dried prior to processing the laminate, it could lead to delamination. Moisture retention can also be a reliability problem because of reduced volume-resistivity of the laminate.

Recent improvements have led to combining a fiberglass mat with a non-woven Kevlar-reinforced resin system. The machining characteristics of this laminate are improved, and by confining the Kevlar to internal layers, microcracking at the board surface can be contained.

6.3.6 Other organic-based materials

A number of other resin systems have been developed for special applications. Polyimide-quartz is a high-temperature laminate that is compatible with conventional PWB processing. Its high cost (10 to 15 times that of epoxy–fiberglass) is a major disadvantage.

Teflon®–fiberglass composites exhibit a low dielectric constant and low loss up to very high frequencies, making them popular for RF and microwave applications. Because of their very high expansion coefficients (approximately 20 ppm/°C), they are only recommended for use with small leadless components. Fortunately, this is not normally a serious restriction in high-frequency work.

Injection-molded thermoplastics are receiving increased attention as a low-cost alternative to conventional board materials. Because of the considerable expense involved in mold fabrication, they are normally viable only in extremely high-volume applications.

Flexible printed wiring boards can be used with a wide range of surface mount components. Typical applications include cameras and handheld calculators in which IC quadpacks are soldered to a single flexible board containing all the internal electronics for the product.

6.4 CONSTRAINING CORE MATERIALS

By bonding an organic printed wiring board to a low-expansion metal core, the CTE of the resulting laminate can be artificially constrained to match that of ceramic chip carriers. To balance the forces, printed wiring boards are bonded on both sides of the core, as shown in Fig. 6.8.

Materials that can be used in the core include copper-clad Invar, copper-clad molybdenum, and Alloy-42. Graphite is sometimes used where high thermal conductivity at low weight is required.

The core can be either electrically isolated (Fig. 6.8) or electrically functional (Fig. 6.9). In either case, the core serves as a board stiffener and heat sink. In the electrically functional approach, the core also serves as the power and/or ground plane of the circuit.

Fabrication of metal-core materials is considerably more complex than conventional board processes. The core material must first be drilled at the

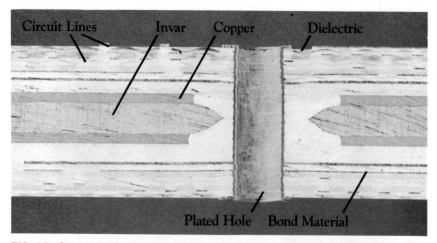

FIG. 6.8 Copper-clad Invar board construction. (Courtesy of Texas Instruments Incorporated.)

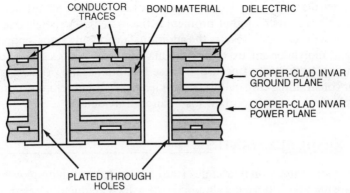

FIG. 6.9 Constraining core substrate with electrically-functional core material.

locations of all via holes. The holes are then back-filled with resin. Previously fabricated multilayer organic boards are then carefully registered to the core and bonded with a rigid adhesive. After lamination the via holes are redrilled (to a smaller diameter so they do not short to the core) and plated using conventional techniques.

Alternatively, the multilayer boards can be bonded to the core after all component assembly has been completed. This simplifies the assembly process because components can be mounted to both sides of the final board while using only single-sided component-assembly techniques. It also eliminates the risk of damaging the lamination adhesive during the solder reflow cycle. However, the lamination process is more complex, and plated via holes cannot be used to connect both sides of the board. Instead, a more cumbersome wraparound edge connector must be used.

The approximate CTE of the composite structure can be found from the following equation:[11]

$$a = \frac{2a_1 + \dfrac{t_2 E_2}{t_1 E_1}\, a_2}{2 + \dfrac{t_2 E_2}{t_1 E_1}}$$

where a = CTE of composite

t_1 = thickness of organic PWB (assumed both sides equal)
t_2 = thickness of metal core
a_1 = CTE of organic PWB
a_2 = CTE of metal core
E_1 = modulus in tension of PWB
E_2 = modulus in tension of metal core

A major disadvantage of these approaches is the extreme weight of the finished assembly. The weight penalty can often be mitigated by using the printed wiring board as a structural member in place of an additional mechanical support. Another problem is the increased expense due to the difficulty in processing. Besides the additional processing steps, copper-clad Invar and molybdenum are difficult to machine and call for special drilling and cutting techniques. Because of these limitations, the primary application for constraining core materials is for leadless ceramic chip carriers when small physical size is important (as in aircraft avionics).

6.5 CERAMIC SUBSTRATES

Surface mount functional modules (see Section 1.2) often employ ceramic substrate materials, typically alumina or beryllia. Conductors, resistors, and certain capacitors can be fabricated directly on the substrate by way of thick film process technology.

A major advantage of alumina is that its CTE matches that of ceramic chip carriers. Its thermal conductivity is higher than that of organic materials, making it preferable for high power-dissipation components. In addition, because many of the resistors are incorporated onto the substrate, overall assembly cost is reduced and electrical performance improved.

A fundamental disadvantage is the relatively small maximum substrate size, about 125×125 mm (5×5 in). The brittle nature of ceramic materials precludes larger sizes. Ceramic substrates are much heavier than epoxy–fiberglass material, particularly in the increased thicknesses necessary to prevent larger substrates from fracturing. The high dielectric constant ($\epsilon_r = 10$ for alumina) limits its use in high-speed circuitry. The thick film conductor materials tend to leach rapidly in tin–lead solder, making repair of defective components difficult. Although the cost of smaller substrates is similar to that of organic boards, costs increase rapidly in the larger sizes.

6.6 COMPLIANT LAYER MATERIALS

Compliance can be introduced into the joint in two ways. In the first, a flexible layer on the surface of the printed wiring board serves as a buffer between component and board (Fig. 6.10). In the second, the clearance between component and board is artificially increased to reduce the strain in the joint.

Boards with a compliant surface layer absorb the strain of differential expansion by allowing the component land patterns to "float" on the surface. In one implementation of this technique, a rubber nitrile blend is applied as the top layer of an ordinary FR-4 board.[12] Circuits produced in this manner and mounted with ceramic chip carriers have withstood 1000 thermal cycles from $-55\,^{\circ}\text{C}$ to $+125\,^{\circ}\text{C}$ with no solder joint failures. However, since via holes must penetrate the compliant layer, they are subjected to stresses that could lead to failure due to barrel cracking.

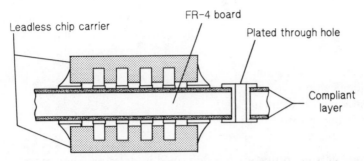

FIG. 6.10 Compliant layer board with leadless components mounted on both sides.

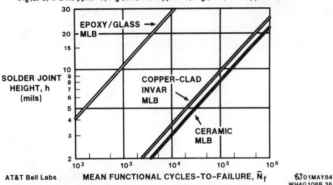

PREDICTED MEAN FUNCTIONAL CYCLES-TO-FAILURE
FOR 850 MIL SQUARE CHIP CARRIER
(L = 850 mils, T_{CC} = 50°C, T_S = 45°C, T_0 = 25°C, f = 1 c/d, α_{CC} = 5.5 ppm/°C,
α_S (E/G) = 21.5 ppm/°C, α_S (CCI) = 8.6 ppm/°C, α_S (CER) = 5.5 ppm/°C, $\bar{\mathcal{F}}$ = 1.29)

FIG. 6.11 Plot of predicted mean functional cycles-to-failure for 0.850-in square chip carrier. (Used by permission. W. Engelmaier, "Fatigue Life of Leadless Chip Carrier Solder Joints During Power Cycling," *IEEE CHMT-6, No. 3*, copyright 1983.)

Compliance can also be added by increasing the standoff height between the chip carrier and board. As shown in Fig. 6.11, raising the chip carrier even a small amount can considerably increase the number of cycles to failure. One technique involves placing solder-coated copper balls at each of the component lands. Another makes use of solder columns held inside a disposable frame.[13] These approaches essentially imitate the benefits afforded by leaded chip carriers and have a similar set of advantages and disadvantages. However, such processes are generally very labor-intensive and add considerable additional cost to the finished product.

6.7 IMPACT OF ASSEMBLY PROCESS ON RELIABILITY

Reliability in design is only half the battle. If sound practices are not followed in manufacturing, even the best-designed product will exhibit a high failure rate in the field. The pervasive impact of manufacturing on product reliability is evidenced by the number of factors that have a significant effect:

- solder alloy selection
- solder volume
- component placement
- soldering process
- flux removal

Manufacturing processes are described in detail in Chapters 8–15. The following discussion highlights those factors with particular impact on reliability.

6.7.1 Solder alloy selection

The solder alloy used to form the joints must be fully compatible with the materials to be joined. It must not dissolve the solderable surface on either the component or substrate and must not form brittle or unstable intermetallic compounds. The finished joint must exhibit enough compliance to survive repeated temperature and power cycles. Metal systems that might degrade over time, such as certain indium-bearing solders, must be avoided.

Under normal circumstances, eutectic tin-lead solder is recommended for general-purpose soldering to the base metals found in electronic systems. Eutectic tin–lead–silver or tin–silver alloys should be used on silver-bearing surfaces.

Gold should be avoided as a surface finish on solderable component terminations. Gold is highly soluble in tin–lead solder and quantities above about 1% cause the formation of brittle intermetallic compounds that are easily fractured. In addition, the high cost of gold is an incentive to use layers as thin as 0.13–0.25 μm (5–10 μin) thick. Coatings this thin are insufficient to preserve the solderability of the termination by protecting the underlying metal against corrosion.

If gold-coated terminations cannot be avoided, the gold should be totally removed before soldering. This can be done by tinning the terminations in a pot of molten tin–lead solder immediately prior to use. The only time that gold should remain in the terminations is when soldering to gold-bearing conductors on thick film circuits. In this case, a compatible solder, such as eutectic gold–tin, is indicated.

6.7.2 Solder volume

The amount of solder at the joint must be sufficient to provide adequate mechanical strength without being so great as to reduce the compliance of the joint. Considering its importance in the reliability of the finished assembly, relatively little has been published regarding the optimum solder volume necessary to form a reliable surface mount joint. Work conducted at Bell Telephone Laboratories[14] has determined that for SOT-23 transistors soldered to PtPdAg thick films, an amount of solder between 0.6 and 2.0 mg per connection is optimum. Most other published information simply defines visual acceptance criteria without providing the supporting data necessary for justification.

Visual inspection of the completed joint, while beneficial, can only give a gross indication of joint reliability. Voids internal to the joint or problems in visually inaccessible areas can have a serious impact on reliability without being visually detectable. Reliability testing or X-ray analysis of the joints offers improved inspection capability but is rarely practical on the production floor. The best approach is to exercise tight control over the manufacturing process.

The workmanship criteria presented in Appendix A describes limits of acceptability for a number of types of joints. Considerable experience has shown that joints which lie within these bounds are less likely to fail than those which exceed these limits. It is not possible, however, to insure that such general specifications are optimum in all situations.

6.7.3 Component placement

The component placement operation impacts reliability in several ways. Poor placement accuracy is a primary concern—adequate joint strength cannot be achieved if a large portion of the termination extends beyond the corresponding circuit land. Problems can also arise due to mechanical misadjustment of the placement machine. Excessive downward pressure by the placement tool can fracture sensitive components such as ceramic capacitors. Similarly, misadjusted centering jaws can chip the component body or bend leads beyond coplanarity limits.

6.7.4 Soldering process

The soldering process, by its very nature, exposes assemblies to large temperature extremes that can damage both components and board materials. Damage can occur from one or more of three basic causes:

- large temperature gradient
- high maximum temperature
- extended time at elevated temperature

All surface mount soldering processes suffer from one or more of these concerns. Large temperature gradients and extended time at temperature are of particular concern in the vapor phase reflow process. When using infrared reflow, the concerns are high maximum temperature and extended time at temperature. Wave soldering processes are susceptible to large temperature gradients and high maximum temperature.

Many components are comprised of materials with differing physical properties that react differently to thermal stresses. A plastic-encapsulated integrated circuit, for example, consists of a silicon die mounted on a copper lead frame and protected by an epoxy molding compound. Each of these materials has a different coefficient of thermal expansion. When the device is subjected to a severe temperature gradient, stresses due to differential thermal expansion may become large enough to crack the die or molding compound.

From a reliability standpoint, the ideal soldering profile would include a gradual rise to an intermediate temperature, a quick excursion above the reflow point to form the joints, and a gradual cooling phase back to room temperature (Section 11.1). No real process conforms exactly to the ideal, but certain measures can be taken to achieve a closer approximation.

The most important consideration is to include an adequate preheat step in the soldering cycle. Preheating accomplishes several beneficial results, including evaporation of volatiles, activation of the flux, and improvement in production throughput, but the primary reliability benefit is to reduce thermal shock. Preheating can be accomplished in a number of ways, and the actual technique is not as important as the fact that the step is employed.

The exact preheat temperature is not particularly critical; temperatures in the range of 100–150 °C are generally recommended. When reflowing a solder paste, it is important to distinguish the preheat step from the paste drying step. Paste drying is performed to drive off volatiles in the solder paste and should be tailored to the specific paste employed. Preheating is usually a separate step designed specifically to activate the flux and reduce thermal shock. Preheating is discussed more fully in Chapter 11 for reflow soldering and in Chapter 12 for wave soldering.

When reflow soldering via the infrared process, it is essential that individual temperature profiles be developed for each board type to be soldered. Infrared soldering is not an equilibrium process and actual board temperatures depend largely on the board's thermal mass and distribution of components. A temperature profile developed for one board type should not be used on another type without first confirming its suitability.

6.7.5 Flux removal

The extent to which a flux should be removed depends primarily on its activity level. Low-activity Types R or RMA rosin fluxes can safely be left on most boards. More active RA, RSA, SA, and OA fluxes must be completely removed.

The choice of flux removal process is critical. Water-based processes are generally discouraged. Water does not readily penetrate under surface mount components, so flux under the components may not be completely removed. It is possible to add a surfactant to the water to reduce surface tension, but this trades one problem for another. The surfactant must also be removed, normally in a final deionized water rinse. Again, it is difficult to penetrate under the SMCs, so although the flux may have been removed, surfactant left under the component may be equally detrimental.

For this reason, solvent cleaning of surface mount assemblies has gained popularity. The surface tension of fluorinated or chlorinated hydrocarbon solvents is much lower than that of water, so removal of flux under components is easier. In-line solvent cleaners with aggressive spray and immersion cycles generally are more effective than batch-mode vapor degreasers. Chlorinated solvent blends are more effective than fluorinated blends but may damage certain types of components. The solvent should include a combination of polar and nonpolar reagents to provide the most effective cleaning potential.

The choice of solvent has a direct impact on the type of flux that can be used. Highly active OA fluxes are not compatible with solvent-based cleaning systems and are rarely used in SMT production. Rosin-based RMA and RA fluxes are most popular because they are ideally suited for removal in a solvent cleaner. Synthetic activated fluxes are promising alternatives when a flux with even higher activity level is required.

It is important to note that incomplete cleaning may be more harmful than no cleaning at all, particularly with RMA flux. As long as the flux remains intact on the board, the activators are bound within the rosin where they cannot cause corrosion. If the flux is incompletely removed, these activators can be released onto the board. To prevent this problem, it is necessary to select a matched flux-solvent system and use an aggressive combination of spray and immersion cleaning cycles.

REFERENCES

1. Lau, J., and Rice, D. "Solder Joint Fatigue in Surface Mount Technology: State of the Art," *Solid State Technology*, October 1985, p. 91–104.
2. Lau, J., and Rice, D. "Effects of Standoff Height on Solder Joint Fatigue," *Proceedings of NEPCON West/86*, Anaheim, February 1986, p. 437–454.
3. Howard, R., Sobeck, S., and Sanetra, C. "A New Package-Related Failure Mechanism for Leadless Ceramic Chip Carriers (LC-3s) Solder Attached to Alumina Substrates," *Solid State Technology*, Feb. 1983, pp. 115–122.
4. Englemeier, W. "Fatigue Life of Leadless Chip Carrier Solder Joints During Power Cycling," *IEEE Transactions on Components, Hybrids and Manufacturing Technology*, Vol. CHMT-6, No. 3, Sept. 1983, pp. 232–237.
5. Kotlowitz, R. and Engelmaier, W. "Impact of Lead Compliance on the Solder Attachment Reliability of Leaded Surface Mounted Devices," *Proceedings of the Sixth Annual Electronics Packaging Conference*, San Diego, Nov. 1986, pp. 841–865.
6. Hagge, J. "Predicting Fatigue Life of Leadless Chip Carriers Using Manson–Coffin Equations," *Proceedings of the Second Annual International Electronics Packaging Conference*, 1982, pp. 199–208.
7. Engelmaier, W. "Functional Cycling and Surface Mounting Attachment Reliability," *Surface Mount Technology, ISHM Technical Monograph 6984–002*, International Society For Hybrid Microelectronics, Silver Spring, MD, 1984.

8. Shah, H. and Kelly, J. "Effect of Dwell Time on Thermal Cycling of the Flip-Chip Joint," *Proceedings of the ISHM Symposium*, International Society for Hybrid Microelectronics, 1970.
9. Messner, G., and Nakahara, H. "Additive Process in the U.S.—An Update," *Electronic Packaging and Production*, Dec 1984, pp. 54–61.
10. Coombs, C. *Printed Circuits Handbook*, McGraw-Hill Book Co., New York, 1979, pp. 2–24.
11. Love, G. "Development of Packaging and Interconnect Structures Used for Leadless Hermetic Chip Carrier Packaging," *International Journal for Hybrid Microelectronics*, Nov. 1982, pp. 300–306.
12. Markstein, H. "Surface Mount Substrates: the Key in Going Leadless," *Electronic Production*, March 1984, pp. 23–30.
13. Lyman, J. "Solder Columns Secure Chip Carriers to Epoxy," *Electronics* Sept. 16, 1985.
14. Panousis, N. T. and Kershner, R. C. "Solder Attachment of Leaded Components to Thick Film Hybrids," *IEEE Transactions on Components, Hybrids and Manufacturing Technology*, Vol. CHMT-4 No. 4, Dec. 1981, pp. 411–416.
15. Lee, T., Wiltshire, B. and Culver, D. "Joint Strength Analyis of Surface Mounted Components," *IPC Technical Paper IPC-TP-566*, Institute For Interconnecting and Packaging Electronic Circuits, Lincolnwood, IL, 1985.
16. *Surface Mount Land Patterns (Configurations and Design Rules), ANSI/IPC-SM-782*, Institute For Interconnection and Packaging Electronic Circuits, Lincolnwood, IL, Mar. 1987.

7

Design and layout guidelines

This chapter contains SMT assembly layout guidelines. It does not attempt to cover all design requirements but rather those aspects that directly relate to the use of SMT. Information in this chapter can be used to augment existing design guidelines for through-hole boards.

The information herein is generally applicable for automatic placement and soldering, although exact requirements may vary slightly depending on the specific assembly equipment used. Before undertaking any new board design, the precise capability of the manufacturing facility should be known and understood. Consultation with manufacturing engineering is essential, especially when using components or procedures outside the scope of this guideline.

7.1 PRINTED WIRING BOARD

This section contains guidelines for printed wiring board layout. It is applicable for both manual and automatic assembly methods.

7.1.1 Board size and construction

Printed wiring boards are manufactured in panels of various sizes. Several recommended panel sizes have been identified by IPC and published in ANSI/IPC-D-322. Table 7.1 summarizes the panel sizes, board sizes, and material utilization factors described in this document.

The 457 × 610 mm (18 × 24 in) panel is widely used. After allowance for plating and processing, the maximum usable board dimensions for this panel are approximately 405 × 560 mm (16 × 22 in). Exact dimensions vary depending on the specific equipment used for imaging and etching. Lowest

A	B	C	D	E	F	G
Panel Size mm (in)	Panel Area cm² (in²)	Quantity of Boards Per panel	Board Size mm (in)	Board Area cm² (in²)	Material Utilization $\frac{C \times E \times 100}{B}$	Notes & Restrictions
457 mm × 610 mm (18" × 24")	2788 cm² (432 in²)	1	406 mm × 559 mm (16" × 22")	2270 cm² (352 in²)	81%	1, 3, 4, 5, 6
457 mm × 533 mm (18" × 21")	2436 cm² (378 in²)	1	406 mm × 483 mm (16" × 19")	1961 cm² (304 in²)	80%	1, 3, 4, 5, 6
457 mm × 610 mm (18" × 24")	2788 cm² (432 in²)	2	267 mm × 406 mm (10.5" × 16")	1084 cm² (168 in²)	78%	1, 2
457 mm × 610 mm (18" × 24")	2788 cm² (432 in²)	3	178 mm × 406 mm (7" × 16")	723 cm² (112 in²)	78%	1, 2
457 mm × 533 mm (18" × 21")	2436 cm² (378 in²)	2	234 mm × 406 mm (9.2" × 16")	950 cm² (148 in²)	78%	1, 2
406 mm × 457 mm (16" × 18")	1855 cm² (288 in²)	1	356 mm × 406 mm (14" × 16")	1445 cm² (224 in²)	78%	1
457 mm × 533 mm (18" × 21")	2436 cm² (378 in²)	3	152 mm × 406 mm (6" × 16")	617 cm² (96 in²)	76%	1, 2
406 mm × 457 mm (16" × 18")	1855 cm² (288 in²)	2	196 mm × 356 mm (7.7" × 14")	698 cm² (109 in²)	76%	1, 2
356 mm × 457 mm (14" × 18")	1627 cm² (252 in²)	1	305 mm × 406 mm (12" × 16")	1238 cm² (192 in²)	76%	1
356 mm × 457 mm (14" × 18")	1627 cm² (252 in²)	2	196 mm × 305 mm (7.7" × 12")	598 cm² (93 in²)	74%	1, 2
305 mm × 457 mm (12" × 18")	1394 cm² (216 in²)	1	254 mm × 406 mm (10" × 16")	1031 cm² (160 in²)	74%	1
406 mm × 457 mm (16" × 18")	1855 cm² (288 in²)	3	127 mm × 356 mm (5" × 14")	452 cm² (70 in²)	73%	1, 2
305 mm × 406 mm (12" × 16")	1238 cm² (192 in²)	1	254 mm × 356 mm (10" × 14")	904 cm² (140 in²)	73%	1

Notes:
1. Using 25.4 mm (1″) borders.
2. Using 12.7 mm (0.5″) margins for test coupon (one per panel) and 0.25″ for margins without test coupons; rounding off to the next smallest 2.5 mm (0.1″) increment.
3. Exceeds normal auto–insertion limits.
4. Exceeds normal in-circuit test limits.
5. Exceeds normal bare board test limits.
6. Exceeds normal solder coating limits.

TABLE 7.1 Resultant board size recommendations as a function of panel size and material utilization. (Published with permission of the Institute for Interconnecting and Packaging Electronic Circuits (IPC).)

board costs are realized when the individual board sizes are optimized for full panel utilization.

The full panel is usually cut into subpanels for assembly processing. The two most common subpanels are half-panels and third-panels. Typical panel and subpanel relationships are shown in Figs. 7.1 and 7.2.

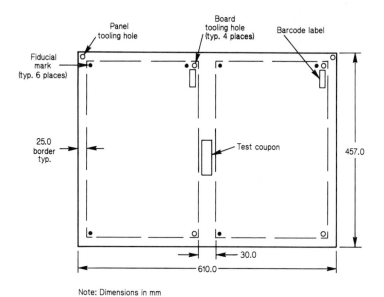

Note: Dimensions in mm

FIG. 7.1   Typical half-panel dimensions for 457 × 610-mm full panel.

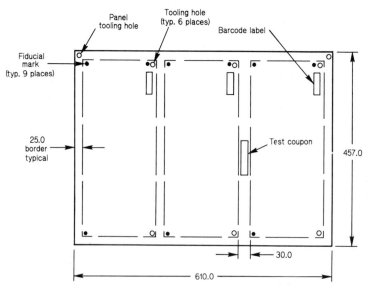

FIG. 7.2   Typical third-panel dimensions for 457 × 610-mm full panel.

7.1.2 Tooling holes

Accurately located tooling holes at the corners of the board are essential features. They are frequently used to align the board at both the screen printing and the component placement operations. At least two tooling holes are required at opposite corners along the longest side of the board (Figs. 7.1 and 7.2).

The recommended tooling hole diameter is 3.18 mm (0.125 in). Tolerance should be held to ±0.075 mm (±0.003 in). It is usually easier to maintain this tolerance with nonplated holes.

If the tooling holes are to be used as the primary reference feature for component placement, the center of the holes should be accurately located with respect to the artwork. Recommended tolerances are as follows:

±0.025 mm (0.001 in) if placing 0.050-in pitch ICs to 44-lead PLCCs

±0.075 mm (0.003 in) if placing only chip components

Because of accuracy limitations, tooling holes should not be used as the primary locating feature for fine-pitch chip carriers or PLCCs above 44 leads. Vision alignment is recommended for these devices.

7.1.3 Fiducial marks

Fiducial marks should be used when a machine vision system is used for board alignment. (Refer to Sect. 10.4.3 for a discussion of the principles of vision alignment.) A mininum of three fiducial marks should be employed at three corners of the board as shown in Figs. 7.1 and 7.2. If four marks are used they should be located asymetrically so that it is not possible to align a board that has been incorrectly oriented on the system.

The actual shape of the fiducials depends on the characteristics of the alignment system. Representative shapes are illustrated in Fig. 7.3. The best fiducial mark is one that has uniform brightness and high contrast compared to the background. Hot-air-leveled solder-coated fiducials are not recommended because the curved, highly reflective surface reflects a direct image of the light source. Depending on the exact orientation of the source and camera, the brightest spot on the fiducial may not represent its true center. This can confuse the vision alignment algorithm and cause it to miscalculate the position of the fiducial. Bare copper fiducials work best, but if hot-air-leveled marks must be used, the vision system should employ a highly diffuse illumination source.

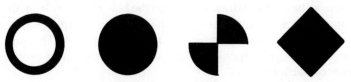

FIG. 7.3 Representative shapes of fiducial marks used by optical alignment systems.

7.1.4 Conductor routing

Conductor widths and spacings for SMT boards are generally smaller than for through-hole technology. When laying out boards that include components with 1.27-mm (0.050-in) lead pitch, a board technology capable of producing 0.2-mm (0.008-in) lines on 0.4-mm (0.016-in) pitch is recommended. This allows one conductor trace to be routed between adjacent IC leads. Smaller geometry board technologies are required for components with finer lead pitches.

Highest board yield is obtained by providing generous margins between actual conductor geometries and the process minimums. Small conductors should be employed only in those regions where they are actually needed. Wherever practical, conductors should be enlarged to 0.3-mm (0.012-in) width on 0.62-mm (0.025-in) pitch. This will reduce the number of defects due to variability in the board imaging and etching processes.

Conductor routing can also have a major impact on soldering yields. In general, anything that alters the symmetry of the land pattern is likely to increase the number of solder defects. For example, exposed conductors entering the component land pattern can act as solder thieves that draw solder away from the land. Several steps can be taken to avoid this problem (refer to Fig. 7.4):

- Reduce the width of a conductor at the point it enters the land area. Unless impacted by factors such as current-carrying capacity or board fabrication limitations, maximum width should be 0.4 mm (0.016 in) or half the width of the land, whichever is smaller.
- Lands that are connected to large conductor areas, such as ground or power planes, should be thermally isolated by a short length of conductor.
- Avoid entering lands at an angle. Whenever possible, conductors should enter from the center of the long side of the land.
- Protect traces with a solder mask that exposes only the land patterns. The mask prevents solder from wicking down the conductor and away from the joint. Solder mask should be used over traces running between IC leads to prevent solder bridges between conductor and land.

7.1.5 Via holes

Except as described in the following paragraphs, via holes should not be located within or immediately adjacent to a surface mount component land. A hole within the land will draw solder into the hole and away from the joint. A hole immediately adjacent to the land, even if protected by solder mask, can act as a heat sink to alter the rate at which the joint wets. This can lead to tombstoning of chip components. In extreme cases it can prevent proper formation of the joint.

A minimum conductor length of 0.5 mm (0.020 in) is recommended be-

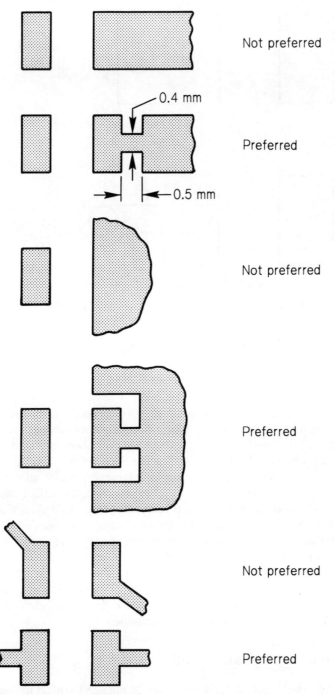

Not preferred

Preferred

Not preferred

Preferred

Not preferred

Preferred

FIG. 7.4 Examples of preferred and non-preferred conductor routing.

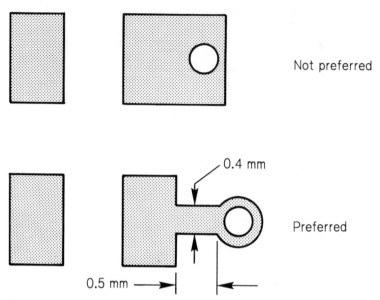

FIG.7.5   Example of preferred and non-preferred via hole placement.

tween the land and the hole. Refer to Fig. 7.5 for examples of acceptable and unacceptable design.

The one exception is that a via may be located within the land if the component is soldered by the adhesive attach/wave solder process and the hole has been completely filled with solder prior to assembly. The adhesive prevents component tombstoning and the filled via prevents solder wicking.

Via hole diameters should be made as large as possible to obtain highest board yields and lowest costs. For lowest cost, as-drilled diameters of 0.75 mm (0.030 in) or larger are recommended. As-drilled diameters to about 0.4 mm (0.016 in) can usually be obtained at slight additional cost, while smaller holes are considerably more expensive. The reliability of small holes can be improved by filling the holes with solder.

Avoid placing via holes directly under leadless components that sit flush on the board surface. Such vias can entrap flux that is not easily removed during cleaning. Via holes under leaded components such as SOICs or PLCCs are generally considered acceptable.

7.2 OVERALL BOARD LAYOUT

Overall board layout criteria are driven by the need to meet manufacturability, testability, and repairability requirements. The following guidelines should be observed.

7.2.1 Component orientation

All components should be laid out parallel to grid lines. Placement cycle time can be reduced by orienting all devices so as to minimize the need for rotation during placement. Polarized devices should be mounted with a consistent polarity orientation.

Wave soldered components should be oriented such that component terminations are fully exposed to the wave, as shown in Fig. 7.6. The orientation of reflow soldered components is less critical.

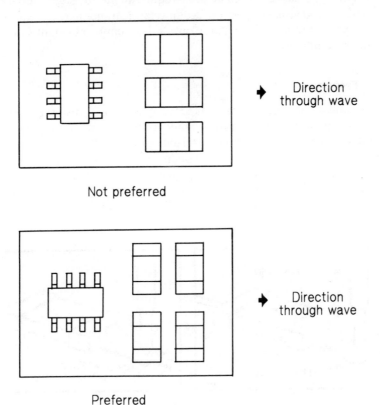

FIG. 7.6   Preferred and non-preferred component orientation for wave soldering.

7.2.2 Component density

The maximum component density is governed by the following criteria:

- component placement machine accuracy
- clearances required for repair equipment tooling
- clearances required for test probe access
- clearances for convection or forced air cooling
- clearances for visual inspection of solder joints

Since these factors are highly dependent on the specific assembly equipment employed, it is not possible to define universally applicable specifications. Information regarding the impact of test and repair is discussed in Chapters 14 and 15.

A convenient technique for specifying component clearances is to define, for each device land pattern, a "clear area" that must be free of components. The clearance between any two types of SMCs is determined by the larger of the two individual clearances. The recommended land patterns in this chapter include suggested clear area requirements to accommodate the needs of test and visual inspection. Additional clearance may be required by certain types of repair equipment. Consult the equipment manufacturer for specific recommendations.

7.2.3 Test points

When using in-circuit electrical tests to verify performance of the assembled board, adequate allowance must be made for test probes. It is not generally desirable to probe the component termination directly (Fig. 7.7c), as the pressure of the probe could force an open joint to make contact and appear to be functional. Direct probe contact could also damage the component. The recommended technique is to add a test pad to the conductor adjacent to the component, as shown in Fig. 7.7a. This pad should be solder coated to

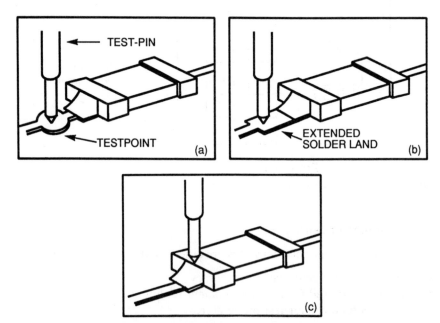

FIG. 7.7 Test probe locations: a. preferred, b. acceptable, c. not recommended. (Used by permission. Copyright 1986 Signetics Corporation.)

improve contact with the probe point. An acceptable (although not recommended) alternative is to extend the land, as shown in Fig. 7.7b. When using this approach, care should be taken to fully analyze all tolerances to insure that the probe never makes contact with the component or solder fillet.

Several other factors must be considered on boards to be tested on an in-circuit test system. These are described in Chapter 14.

7.3 COMPONENT LAND PATTERNS

Much energy has been expended in search of the "ultimate" land pattern to obtain the lowest solder defect rate. Many companies have developed proprietary land patterns that they consider optimum. Curiously, land patterns proposed within the literature show little agreement. Representative data can be found in Refs. 1, 2, 3 and 4. In the author's experience, the window of acceptable land pattern shapes for most components is rather broad. Other factors such as solder volume, soldering thermal profile, and component solderability have a much greater influence on defects than does the exact shape of the land pattern. However, the optimum land pattern shape for reflow soldering is generally different than that for wave soldering.

The relatively loose tolerances associated with many surface mount components have made it difficult to define a single land pattern that works equally well for components at either end of the tolerance range. One solution, advocated by IPC[1], is to define more restrictive component dimensions than allowed by the relevant EIA and IEC standards. Unfortunately, most component manufacturers are not readily equipped to build components to selectively tighter tolerances. A more practical approach is to optimize land patterns for the center of the range of sizes and accept slightly reduced yields with components near the size extremes. Tightened component tolerances will eventually be necessary to resolve this conflict.

7.3.1 Adhesive location for wave soldered components

When adhesive is used to attach a component, a dummy land, as shown in Fig. 7.8, should be placed under the component. This land reduces the effective component standoff height and controls the spread of adhesive. As

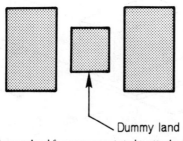

Dummy land

FIG. 7.8 Placement of dummy land for components to be attached with adhesive.

an alternative, a functional circuit trace may be routed under the component.

7.3.2 Standard land pattern formulae

For many component families it is convenient to represent land pattern geometries in terms of standardized formulae. These formulae can then be used to calculate pattern shapes for numerous components, including types for which no previous land pattern has been developed. Suggested formulae are presented in the relevant sections that follow.

7.3.3 Passive component land patterns

Land patterns for passive components can be found from the following formulae (see Fig. 7.9):

$$X = W_{max} - K \text{ (wave soldered)}$$
$$X = W_{max} + K \text{ (reflow soldered)}$$
$$Y = H_{max}/2 + T_{max} + K$$
$$G = L_{min} - 2T_{max} - K$$

where X = land width
Y = land length
G = gap between lands
W = width of component
H = height of component
L = length of component
T = termination length
K = 0.25 mm (0.010 in) for reflow soldered components
0.50 mm (0.020 in) for wave soldered components

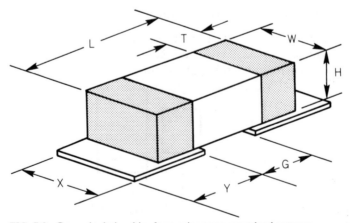

FIG. 7.9 General relationships for passive component land patterns.

The approximate formulae described above break down for extremely small components, such as 0805 capacitors and resistors. Use the specific dimensions provided in this section for these component types.

The recommended land patterns for chip resistors are shown in Table 7.2 and 7.3. Recommended land patterns for ceramic capacitors are shown in Tables 7.4 and 7.5.

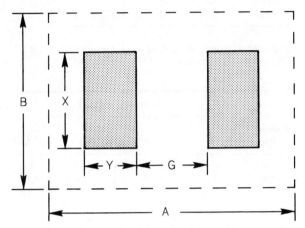

FIG. 7.10 Land pattern relationships for two-terminal passive devices.

Package Style	Dimensions (mm)				
	A	B	G	X	Y
0805	4.0	2.0	0.8	1.4	1.3
1206	7.0	2.5	1.8	2.0	1.3
1210	7.0	3.5	1.8	3.0	1.3

TABLE 7.2 Land pattern relationships for reflow soldered chip resistors (refer to Fig. 7.10 for definitions)

Package Style	Dimensions (mm)				
	A	B	G	X	Y
0805	4.5	2.0	0.8	1.0	1.5
1206	7.0	2.5	1.8	2.0	1.6
1210	7.0	3.5	1.8	3.0	1.6

TABLE 7.3 Land pattern dimensions for wave soldered chip resistors (refer to Fig. 7.10 for definitions)

Package Style	Dimensions (mm)				
	A	B	G	X	Y
0805	4.0	2.0	0.8	1.4	1.3
1206	7.0	2.5	1.8	2.0	1.7
1210	7.0	3.5	1.8	3.0	1.8
1812	8.5	5.0	3.2	3.7	1.8

TABLE 7.4   Land pattern dimensions for reflow soldered chip capacitors (refer to Fig. 7.10 for definitions)

Package Style	Dimensions (mm)				
	A	B	G	X	Y
0805	4.5	2.0	0.8	1.0	1.5
1206	7.5	2.5	1.8	1.3	2.0
1210	7.5	3.5	1.8	2.2	2.0
1812			See Note 1		

Note 1: Chip capacitors larger than 1210 are not recommended for attachment by wave soldering.

TABLE 7.5   Land pattern dimensions for wave soldered chip capacitors (refer to Fig. 7.10 for definitions)

It is suggested that tantalum capacitors and wirewound inductors be attached exclusively by reflow soldering. While it is possible to safely wave solder these devices, their tall outlines and protected leads are likely to promote solder shadowing (Section 12.4.2). Land patterns for reflow soldering are shown in Tables 7.6 and 7.7

Cylindrical MELF components can be wave soldered or reflow soldered. If reflow soldered, they should be adhesively attached to the board to prevent unwanted rolling of the parts. Horseshoe-shaped land patterns have

Package Style	Dimensions (mm)				
	A	B	G	X	Y
3216	5.0	2.0	0.8	1.4	2.0
3528	6.0	4.0	1.2	2.4	2.0
6032	9.0	4.0	3.2	2.4	2.4
7243	10.0	5.0	4.2	2.6	2.4

TABLE 7.6   Land pattern dimensions for tantalum capacitors (refer to Fig. 7.10 for definitions)

Package Style	Dimensions (mm)				
	A	B	G	X	Y
A	5.0	3.0	1.4	2.4	1.4
B	6.0	4.0	2.4	3.0	1.6

TABLE 7.7   Land pattern dimensions for wirewound inductors (refer to Fig. 7.10 for definitions)

sometimes been advocated as a way to prevent MELFs from rolling without the need for adhesive. The author's experience indicates that while this shape can be of some help, it is not a universal solution and should not supplant the use of adhesive. Recommended MELF land patterns are illustrated in Fig. 7.11.

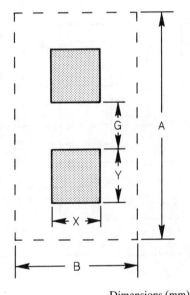

Device Type	Dimensions (mm)				
	X	Y	G	A	B
Resistor, 0.125 W	0.9	1.6	2.0	6.5	3.0
Resistor, 0.250 W	1.5	1.7	4.1	8.5	4.0
Diode, DO-213AA	1.1	1.6	2.0	6.5	3.5
Diode, DO-213AB	1.8	2.1	3.5	8.5	4.5

FIG. 7.11   Land pattern dimensions for cylindrical components.

7.3.4 Discrete semiconductor land patterns

The recommended land patterns for both the Japanese SC-59 and EIA TO-236 versions of the SOT-23 package are shown in Fig. 7.12. The land pattern for the SOT-89 (TO-243) package is shown in Fig. 7.13 and that for the SOT-143 (TO-253) in Fig. 7.14. The land pattern for the DPAK (TO-252) is shown in Fig. 7.15.

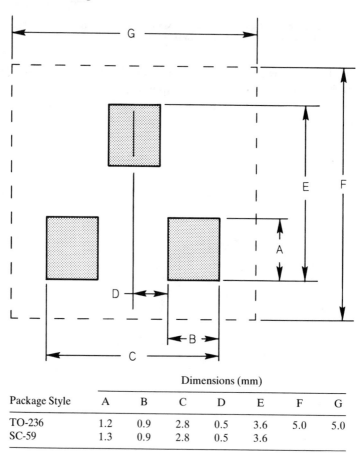

Dimensions (mm)

Package Style	A	B	C	D	E	F	G
TO-236	1.2	0.9	2.8	0.5	3.6	5.0	5.0
SC-59	1.3	0.9	2.8	0.5	3.6		

FIG. 7.12 Land patterns for SOT-23 packages.

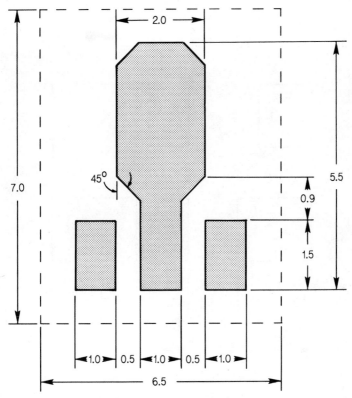

FIG. 7.13   Land pattern for SOT-89 (TO-243) package (dimensions in mm).

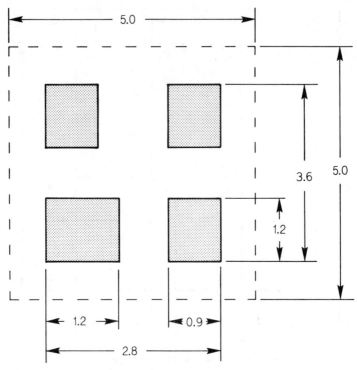

FIG. 7.14   Land pattern for SOT-143 (TO-253) package (dimensions in mm).

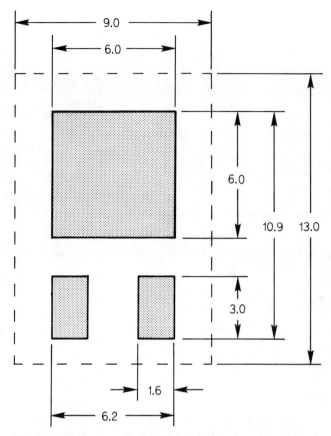

FIG. 7.15   Land pattern for DPAK (TO-252) package (dimensions in mm).

7.3.5 SOIC package land patterns

The land pattern geometry for SOIC components can be calculated from the following formulae:

$X = 0.60$ mm $(0.024$ in$)$
$Y = 1.80$ mm $(0.070$ in$)$
$G = A_{min}$

where X = land width
Y = land length
G = gap between the two rows of lands (see Fig. 7.16)
A = component body width

Land patterns for SOIC packages conforming to the EIA Standards MS-012 and MS-013 are illustrated in Fig. 7.16.

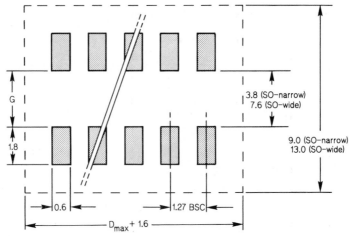

FIG. 7.16   Land patterns for SOIC packages conforming to JEDEC MS-012 and MS-013 outlines (dimensions in mm).

7.3.6 PLCC package land patterns

Land patterns for PLCC components can be claculated from the following formulae:

$$X = 0.60 \text{ mm } (0.024 \text{ in})$$
$$Y = 1.80 \text{ mm } (0.070 \text{ in})$$
$$W = E_{max} + K$$

where X = land width
Y = land length
W = distance between outer edges of opposing lands
E = distance between outer edges of opposing component leads
K = 0.75 mm (0.030 in)

Land patterns for PLCC packages conforming to EIA Registration MO-047 are illustrated in Fig. 7.17.

7.3.7 LCCC package land patterns

Land patterns for 0.050-in lead pitch LCCCs are the same as for PLCC packages. Since an LCCC is about 1.0 mm (0.040 in) smaller than a corresponding PLCC, the value for K is larger. When using LCCC outer dimensions, use the value $K = 1.75$ mm (0.070 in).

7.3.8 Gull-wing quadpacks

Land patterns for gull-wing quadpacks can generally be found from the following formulae (see Fig. 7.18):

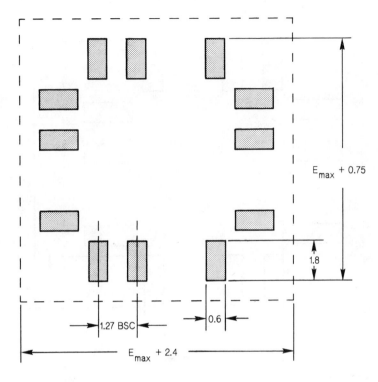

Note: E = component body width

FIG. 7.17   Land patterns for PLCC packages conforming to JEDEC MO-047 outline (dimensions in mm).

$$X = B_{max} + S$$
$$Y = F_{max} + K$$
$$W = E_{max} + 2K$$

where   X = land width
        Y = land length
        W = distance between outer edges of opposing lands
        B = component lead width
        F = length of component foot
        E = distance between outer edges of opposing component leads
        K = 0.4 mm (0.016 in)
        S = 0.1 mm (0.004 in)

7.4 OTHER DESIGN CONSIDERATIONS

Several considerations impact the testability and repairability of a surface mount board. Since the specific design guidelines depend on various equipment-related features, it is not possible to present general guidelines.

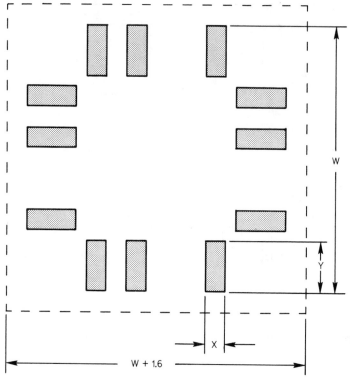

FIG. 7.18   Generalized land pattern relationships for gull-wing quadpacks (refer to text for formulae).

The impact of testing on board design is discussed in Chapter 14. Repair considerations are discussed in Chapter 15.

REFERENCES

1. *Surface Mount Land Patterns (Configurations and Design Rules), IPC-SM-782.* Institute for Interconnecting and Packaging Electronic Circuits, Lincolnwood, IL, Mar. 1987.
2. *SMD Substrate Design Guide*, Signetics Corp., Sunnyvale, CA, 1986.
3. *Guidelines for the Surface Mounting of Multilayer Ceramic Chip Capacitors, Component Bulletin No. 11.* Electronic Industries Association, Washington, DC, 1986.
4. Kress, E. "Solder Pad Geometry Studies for Surface Mount of Chip Capacitors," *Proceedings of the 35th Electronic Components Conference*, Institute of Electrical and Electronics Engineers, Inc., 1985.

Part IV
Manufacturing technology

8

SMT factories and process flows

All surface mount factories have similar goals: to produce high-quality products at low cost in volumes sufficient to meet demand. The approaches used to achieve these goals, however, differ depending on the types of products to be built. A subcontract manufacturing facility, for instance, must handle many different products in widely varying volumes from a multitude of customers. An automotive-electronics manufacturer may build only a few board types in quantities of tens or hundreds of thousands per month. While the subcontract facility must be designed for high flexibility, the automotive-electronics manufacturer needs high throughput and lowest possible manufacturing cost. Such diverse product requirements will clearly be reflected in the resulting factory designs.

This chapter discusses the considerations that enter into the design of an SMT factory. It begins with an overview of the various surface mount process flows, then examines technology and cost tradeoffs. Subsequent chapters describe the individual processes in greater detail.

The first step in designing an SMT factory must be to gain a clear understanding of customer requirements. Such factors as size of boards, number and type of components, production volumes, and anticipated future demands must be known prior to designing the factory. Table 8.1 presents a representative list of factors to be considered.

From this information, cost, quality, capacity, delivery and technology objectives for the line can be defined. The choices necessary to achieve these objectives are what "customize" the factory for its customer base. Representative objectives for several example factories are listed in Table 8.2. Once these are defined, the manufacturing engineer can configure a factory and process flow that best meets all objectives.

Factor	Effect on factory design
Maximum and minimum board size	• Size of production equipment
Number of different component types	• Placement machine feeder capacity
	• Stock room size
	• Equipment flexibility level
Types of components	• Process flow design
	• Placement machine accuracy requirements
Total component placements per month	• Required equipment speed
	• Number of machines
	• Extent of factory automation
Number of different board types per month	• Equipment flexibility level
	• Extent of factory automation
Extent of prototyping and pre-production activity	• Degree of CAD/CAM automation
	• Extent of factory automation

TABLE 8.1   Factors impacting factory design

8.1 PROCESS FLOW ALTERNATIVES

The two basic surface mount process flows are shown in Fig. 8.1. The Japanese-developed *adhesive attach/wave soldering* approach is often used when simple surface mount components must be added to a board with a high percentage of through-hole components. The *reflow soldering* approach, derived from traditional hybrid circuit assembly techniques, accommodates a wider range of SMCs and is preferred for soldering large numbers of integrated circuits.

8.1.1 Adhesive attach/wave soldering overview

This approach is a simple form of double-sided component mounting in which the through-hole components are inserted from the top of the board and the surface mount components (primarily small passive devices) are attached to the underside. The first step is to insert all through-hole components in a conventional manner. The board is then inverted and drops of adhesive are applied in the locations where SMCs are to be attached. The components are mounted and the adhesive cured to secure them rigidly to the board. After again inverting the board, it is wave soldered, forming both surface mount and through-hole solder joints simultaneously. During this process, the SMCs travel directly through the solder wave. A final cleaning step removes any remaining flux residues.

In the standard sequence, all through-hole devices are inserted prior to placing any surface mount components. Otherwise, stresses inflicted on the board, particularly by automatic insertion equipment, could fracture the adhesive and dislodge the SMCs.

	Factory size		
Parameter	Low volume	Medium volume	High volume
Capacity	• Under 2 million component placements per year	• 2–25 million component placements per year	• Over 25 million component placements per year
Manufacturing cost	• Cost is secondary to achieving technical capability	• Moderate cost which is competitive with that of similarly positioned competitive factories	• Lowest possible cost
Quality	• Solder joint defect levels under 10,000 ppm	• Solder joint defect levels under 1,000 ppm	• Solder joint defect levels under 100 ppm
Technology	• Semiautomated factory design • High setup times are acceptable • Technology access is primary concern	• Semiautomated factory design • Moderate setup times are necessary • High flexibility • State-of-the-art technology	• Fully automated factory design • Minimal setup times are necessary • Low flexibility • Technological capability is secondary to low cost
Delivery	• Rapid delivery of prototypes and low volume production demands	• Rapid response to changing customer demands	• Dependable delivery based on accurate forecasts • Limited ability to respond to rapid changes in demand.

TABLE 8.2   Representative factory objectives

8.1.2 Reflow soldering overview

This approach is preferred for more complex assemblies with a wide variety of SMCs. The first step is to apply solder paste to the board (typically by screen printing) in the locations of the surface mount component lands. SMCs are then mounted so that their terminations are immersed in the paste. The highly viscous paste holds the components in place prior to soldering without the need for additional adhesive. The joints are formed by melting the solder in a reflow oven. Upon cooling, residual flux is removed

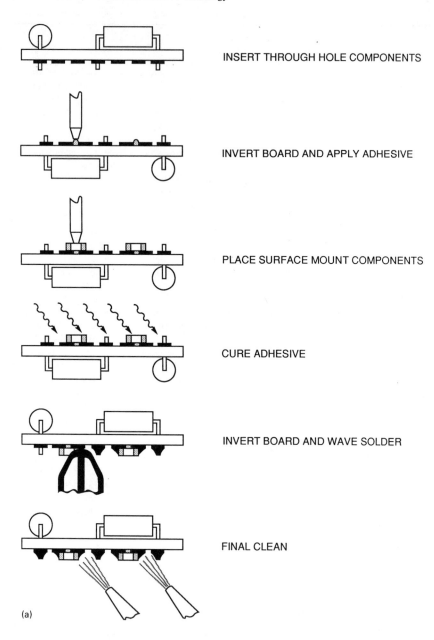

INSERT THROUGH HOLE COMPONENTS

INVERT BOARD AND APPLY ADHESIVE

PLACE SURFACE MOUNT COMPONENTS

CURE ADHESIVE

INVERT BOARD AND WAVE SOLDER

FINAL CLEAN

(a)

FIG. 8.1 Surface mount process flows: a. adhesive attach/wave soldering, b. Reflow soldering.

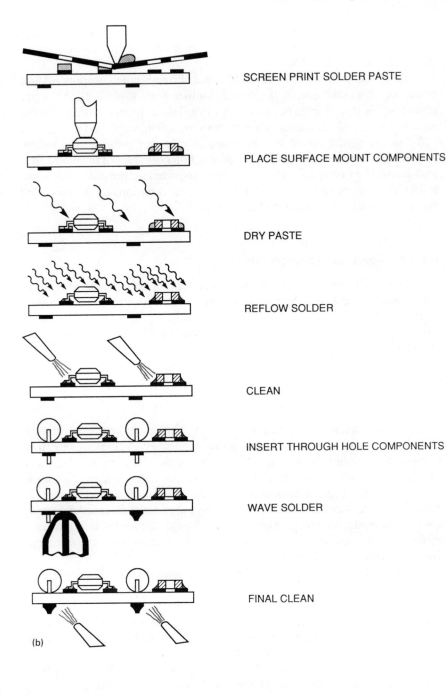

SCREEN PRINT SOLDER PASTE

PLACE SURFACE MOUNT COMPONENTS

DRY PASTE

REFLOW SOLDER

CLEAN

INSERT THROUGH HOLE COMPONENTS

WAVE SOLDER

FINAL CLEAN

(b)

in a suitable cleaning process. If through-hole components are necessary, they are added in a separate sequence of operations after the completion of the surface mount process.

In this process, both surface mount and through-hole components are placed on the same side of the board. Unlike wave soldering, SMCs are placed *before* inserting through-hole devices. This sequence is driven by the screen printer, which can only apply paste to a flat board surface.

By inverting the board and repeating the screen printing and reflow processes, it is possible to mount components on both sides of the board. It is also possible to combine reflow soldered topside components with wave soldered components on the underside. Several variations on double-sided surface mounting are described in Section 8.3.

8.1.3 Comparison of process flows

The technical capabilities of the two process flows are considerably different; each has advantages and disadvantages depending on specific product needs. Although it is not possible to precisely define when to use each process, some general guidelines, summarized in Table 8.3, are presented in the following paragraphs.

Adhesive attach/wave soldering

This process maximizes utilization of existing equipment and is therefore a low-cost, low-risk avenue for entering the technology. Automatic insertion equipment can continue to be used for the through-hole components, many of which may not be available in surface mount packages. The existing wave soldering machine may also be usable, although as described in Chapter 12, best results are normally obtained with a modified wave designed expressly for surface mount soldering. The process is best suited for soldering surface mount passive devices while retaining semiconductors and integrated circuits in through-hole formats.

Since the SMCs travel directly through the solder wave, they undergo a significant thermal shock. Chip resistors and capacitors are relatively unaffected, but sensitive semiconductors may be damaged. In addition, components with exposed metal surfaces, such as certain types of variable resistors and capacitors, will be mechanically damaged if solder is allowed to come in contact with functional metal surfaces.

Successful wave soldering depends on the molten solder coming into intimate contact with the joint. Devices with exposed terminations are easily wetted by the solder wave, but protected leads are much more difficult to access. J-lead devices such as plastic leaded chip carriers are particularly prone to exhibit skipped solder joints.

Process flow	Advantages	Disadvantages
Adhesive attach/ wave soldering	• Maximum utilization of existing through-hole assembly equipment • Low technical risk when used on passive components • Especially suitable for boards with a high percentage of through-hole components	• Components are exposed to large thermal gradients • Difficult to reliably solder large ICs • Difficulty in wetting all joints when components are closely spaced
Reflow soldering	• Suitable for soldering a wide variety of surface mount components • Thermal gradients more easily controlled • Process is insensitive to component geometries	• Requires heavy investment in new equipment and processes • More difficult to add through-hole components

TABLE 8.3 Comparison of process flows

Reflow soldering

This process is more versatile than the adhesive attach/wave solder option. Soldering temperature profiles can be precisely controlled, so thermally sensitive components can be reliably soldered. Because solder paste is applied directly to the joint, the process is less sensitive to lead configuration; J-lead devices can be soldered as easily as gull-wings.

The main drawback is that an entirely new set of processes must be developed and maintained. In a factory with a heavy investment in through-hole technology, the tradeoffs between using existing equipment and setting up a new line must be carefully analyzed.

8.2 MIXED ASSEMBLY TECHNOLOGY

Very few surface mount boards consist entirely of surface mount components. Invariably, a few components will not be available, or if available, cost considerably more than their through-hole equivalents. As a result, nearly all so-called SMT boards are actually *mixed assemblies* containing both surface mount and through-hole devices.

Mixed assembly technology is a natural part of the adhesive attach/wave solder process flow, but it is an additional complexity in reflow soldering. It can be added in one of two ways. The most common approach is to include a conventional through-hole line at the end of the SMT process. Alternatively, the leads of all through-hole devices can be formed into configurations that allow them to be surface mounted as an integral part of the SMT process flow.

8.2.1 Conventional through-hole approach

In this approach, through-hole components are conventionally inserted after all surface mount components have been soldered. Normal through-hole insertion processes are employed, so virtually any component compatible with standard through-hole insertion can be mounted on the mixed assembly. A typical product is pictured in Fig. 8.2.

Although technologically straightforward, the actual process flow is cumbersome. Two full production lines must be supported, one for surface mount and one for through-hole. Besides the increased floor space and cost of capital equipment, engineering support must be distributed across a larger base of process technologies.

8.2.2 All SMT approach

Considerable attention has been focused on full surface mount solutions to the mixed assembly problem. Generally this involves cutting or forming the leads of through-hole devices to permit surface mounting. A typical assembly is shown in Fig. 8.3.

FIG. 8.2 Mixed assembly with through-hole components inserted in conventional fashion.

FIG. 8.3 Mixed assembly using modified through-hole components. The leads on the 40-pin DIP have been trimmed, allowing it to be surface mounted simultaneously with the SMT components. (Photograph by the author. Board supplied by Micro Industries, Westerville, OH.)

Axial lead resistors and capacitors are surface mounted by forming their leads in gull-wing fashion, as shown in Fig. 8.4a. A flat surface is sometimes coined on the lead to increase the contact area and improve the visual inspectability of the solder joint. Dual-in-line packages can be surface mounted either by shearing to form I-lead joints or by forming them into a gull-wing configuration (Fig. 8.4b).

This approach simplifies the process flow because all devices can be attached in a single reflow process. Product designs can take better advantage of such SMT benefits as reduction in the number of via holes and

(a)   (b)

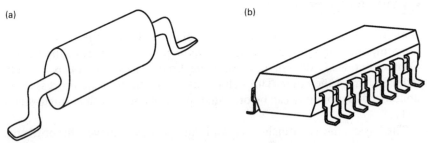

FIG. 8.4 Modification of through-hole components for surface mounting: a. axial-leaded component, b. DIP package.

freedom in inner-layer trace routing. As described in Section 8.3.2, the all surface mount approach has distinct advantages for double-sided component mounting.

Not all through-hole components can be surface mounted successfully. Unlike wave soldering, reflow soldering exposes the entire component to temperatures above the reflow point for an extended period (typically 30–60 seconds). Components that have internal solder connections, or those that use temperature-sensitive materials, can be damaged during reflow.

The flux removal process is another area of concern. Solvent cleaning offers advantages for surface mount assemblies, and most SMT products have been designed for compatibility with fluorinated and chlorinated solvents. Many through-hole products are not. For example, switches often employ lubricants that are dissolved in typical cleaning solvents. Some types of inductors are coated with solvent-soluble lacquers, and the internal electrodes of aluminum electrolytic capacitors are attacked by solvents. Components incompatible with surface mount soldering and cleaning processes must be hand-loaded and soldered as a final process step.

Surface mounting is impractical for larger, more massive through-hole components, such as transformers or filter capacitors. It is also discouraged for front panel control potentiometers, some classes of connectors, and other components that experience high mechanical stresses in operation.

Care must be taken when adapting through-hole components for surface mounting. The lead-forming process must be done in such a way as to minimize the potential for damage to the part. The worst approach is to use diagonal cutters to simply clip off the ends of the leads; mechanical shock transmitted along the lead can cause separation between the lead and the molding compound of plastic-encapsulated parts. This increases the potential for moisture penetration. In extreme cases the shock can break wirebonds internal to the device.

Lead forming and shearing should be performed with specially designed tooling. The tool should include a structure to support the leads and prevent mechanical stresses from being transmitted to the component body.

8.3 DOUBLE-SIDED SMT

A major advantage of SMT is its inherent ability to double the available area for component mounting by taking advantage of both sides of the board. Component leads do not penetrate the board, so each side is entirely independent of the other. Through the use of an appropriate process flow, double-sided mounting can be only slightly more complex than single-sided SMT.

The basic adhesive attach/wave soldering process achieves this objective automatically but is of rather limited value. Components must be segregated, with through-hole devices restricted to the top side and surface mount devices restricted to the underside. The range of surface mount components is also limited to those that can tolerate immersion in a solder wave.

The full benefit of double-sided technology comes from being able to attach surface mount components to both sides of the board. Various process flows have been developed to accomplish this result, and no single flow has achieved dominance. The most common approaches are described in the following sections.

8.3.1 Combined reflow/wave soldering

In this approach, diagrammed in Fig. 8.5, surface mount components are reflow soldered to the top of the board and wave soldered to the underside. The two processes are essentially independent.

In the process shown in Fig. 8.5, solder paste is first deposited on the top of the board. The surface mount components are then placed and reflow soldered. In most cases, this is followed by a solvent cleaning step. (If solvent cleaning is used after wave soldering, this step can usually be eliminated.) Through-hole components can then be inserted on the top side. After the board is inverted, adhesive is dispensed and the surface mount components are placed on the underside. The adhesive is cured, the board is again inverted, and the assembly is wave soldered. Finally, it is cleaned, inspected, and electrically tested.

A primary advantage of this approach is the ease with which all components, both surface mount and through-hole, can be mounted. Automatic insertion and wave soldering can be used and there is little need for hand assembly. Where a single-sided SMT reflow process has already been added to a through-hole line, it is a relatively easy addition.

Combined reflow/wave soldering is less flexible than other double-sided processes. The range of surface mount components that can be mounted to the underside is limited to passive devices and small active devices compatible with wave soldering. More complex packages, such as PLCCs or gull-wing quadpacks, must be grouped on the top of the board.

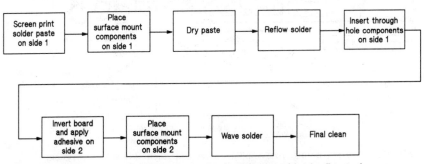

FIG. 8.5 Process flow for double-sided mixed assembly via combined reflow and wave soldering processes.

This process is best suited for analog circuitry and other products with a heavy concentration of discrete devices. It has been successfully used for years in the RF and video portions of video cameras, videotape recorders, and televisions. It is less effective for digital circuits such as memory or microprocessor boards, which consist primarily of integrated circuits.

A relatively new version of this approach is the so-called *single-pass* system. Although equipment design varies, the overall concept is to combine reflow and wave solder capability in a single machine. Boards are populated with both surface mount and through-hole components prior to soldering. Once all components are mounted, the assembly is successively reflow and wave soldered in a single machine.

One manufacturer's approach[1] is illustrated in Fig. 8.6. The machine consists of two sections: an initial wave soldering section followed by a forced-air convection reflow section. The wave soldering section includes a fluxer, top and bottom preheat stages, dual wave solder pot, and a hot-air jet to blow excess solder off the joints. The reflow section includes top and bottom IR preheat and a set of three low-pressure air jets that reflow the solder paste via thermal convection.

Single-pass soldering can be a benefit in certain situations. Double-sided surface mounting is easily achieved with the dual wave. In addition, the number of process steps is reduced compared to a typical dual-pass process flow. All else being equal, this will result in a lower total manufacturing cost.

Single-pass systems have several potential difficulties. Ordinarily, through-hole components must be inserted prior to SMT placement. Otherwise, the mechanical stresses encountered during automatic insertion could dislodge some of the SMCs. This sequence precludes the use of a screen printer for applying solder paste, so it must be dispensed via syringe. As

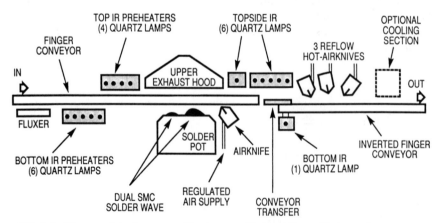

FIG. 8.6 Diagram of single-pass combined wave soldering/reflow soldering system manufactured by Hollis Automation Inc. (Reprinted from *Circuits Manufacturing* magazine. Copyright 1986 Miller Freeman Publications.)

described in Section 9.6, this is a much slower process, which can have a significant negative impact on overall line capacity.

Another concern is that through-hole components are subjected to the entire reflow temperature profile. Some component types are not designed to tolerate this temperature extreme and can be damaged by such exposure. This is of particular concern to components that employ tin–lead solder in their internal construction.

Finally, SMCs on the underside must be limited to packages compatible with wave soldering. Large integrated circuits and other temperature-sensitive devices are restricted to reflow soldering on the top of the board.

8.3.2 Double-sided reflow

Highest flexibility is obtained by reflow soldering components to both sides of the board. Any component that can be reflow soldered to the top of the board can also be reflow soldered to the bottom. It is also possible to include through-hole components, although this considerably increases the complexity of the process.

A number of process flow variations have been devised. In general they fall into one of the following two categories:

- double-pass reflow
- single-pass reflow

Double-pass reflow

The simplest implementation is to send the board through the process twice: once to mount all components on the top of the board and once to mount those on the underside (Fig. 8.7). Each pass is separate, and no link need exist between processes.

It is important to note that components soldered on the first pass travel through the second pass upside down. Initially it would seem that since they are held to the board only by way of the solder joints, they would fall off

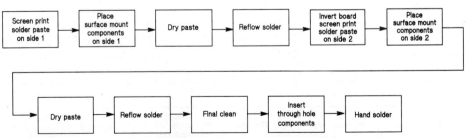

FIG. 8.7 Process flow for double-sided mixed assembly via double-pass reflow soldering process.

when this solder is reflowed a second time. Extensive theoretical analysis backed by practical experience has shown that for most components this is not true. Surface tension of the molten solder is more than adequate to hold them in place.

As a general rule, any small chip component or discrete semiconductor up to at least the SOT-89 package will be held securely by the molten solder. The same is true for SOICs and PLCC packages to about 28 leads. More massive PLCCs and gull-wing quadpacks are less reliably held in place. These devices should either be grouped on the second side of the board or secured in place with adhesive.

Single-pass reflow

The double-pass reflow process just described has two limitations. The first relates to the potential impact on component reliability. Components soldered on the first pass must undergo a second reflow, and each cycle through the process increases the risk of component damage. The second limitation is the complexity of the process flow. Boards must traverse the entire line twice. There is little opportunity to streamline production flow to reduce costs

To address these concerns, some companies have experimented with single-pass reflow.[4] A representative process flow is illustrated in Fig. 8.8. Solder paste is screen printed on the top of the board and the components are placed. The solder paste is dried *but not reflowed*. If reasonable care is exercised, the dried paste is strong enough to hold components in place. The board is then inverted and solder paste is applied to the underside. Components are again placed and the paste dried. The board is then sent through the reflow oven to form both topside joints and underside joints simultaneously.

The success of this approach depends on the dried flux being able to hold the components in place until the solder reflows. Again, the mass of the component is critical, and the process works best with small chip components. Excessive board vibration during the second placement process can

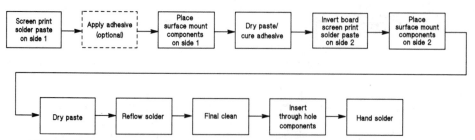

FIG. 8.8   Process flow for double-sided mixed assembly via single-pass reflow.

dislodge even small chip components. Little data on this technique has yet been published. To reduce risk, the components on the underside can be adhesively attached, but this is not possible for devices such as PLCCs, that have large gaps between the component body and board.

Adding through-hole components

There are few easy ways to add through-hole components to a double-sided reflow soldered board. If added immediately after the topside reflow process, the tails of the through-hole component leads interfere with the second-side screen printing operation. If added after the second reflow pass, the underside SMCs prevent the use of a solder wave on the through-hole connections. Ordinarily, through-hole components are inserted after the second pass and hand soldered.

One possible alternative is to dispense solder paste via syringe rather than by screen printing. Through-hole components can then be inserted and wave soldered after the topside reflow process. The syringe process does not require a flat board surface, so the leads do not interfere with paste application on the second side. If an automatic dispenser is used, the speed of the process might not be seriously degraded.

8.4 FACTORY FLOOR LAYOUT

The layout of the factory floor depends on such factors as production volume, number of different board types, batch or continuous manufacturing flow, and overall cost objectives. Factories can be divided into two overall categories based on the extent of automation employed. Fully automated factories are used for high-volume production. Semiautomated factories employ an *islands-of-automation* approach in which individual process steps are automated but links between processes are manual. Within each category lies a wide range of factory configurations and capabilities.

8.4.1 Fully automated factory design

Lowest manufacturing cost is achieved with a totally automated in-line manufacturing operation. Facilities in this category have a maximum capacity in the range of 25–250 million components per year. Except in rare cases where the volume of a single product warrants a dedicated line, the facility must readily accommodate a variety of board types.

A typical fully automated factory is illustrated in Fig. 8.9. The U-shape configuration improves operator accessibility to any point on the line. Production equipment is linked by conveyors to form a complete in-line system.

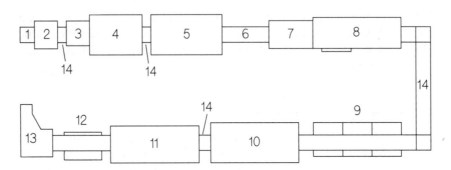

1. Board loader
2. Automatic screen printer
3. Adhesive dispenser
4. High–speed component placement
5. General–purpose component placement
6. Inspection station
7. Adhesive cure oven

8. Infrared reflow oven
9. Manual component insertion
10. Wave soldering station
11. Solvent cleaner
12. Final inspection station
13. In–circuit test station
14. Conveyors

FIG. 8.9 Fully-automated in-line factory.

Factors that must be considered in the design of a fully automated factory include the following:

Flexibility

Unless the line is dedicated to a single board type, low setup time is essential. Time consumed in tearing down one configuration and setting up another is wasted time that increases manufacturing cost and reduces throughput. Low setup time is especially important for factories that act as subcontract manufacturers for a multiplicity of internal or external customers.

Several steps can be taken to reduce setup time. The flexibility of the line is enhanced by selecting production equipment with inherently low setup requirements. Manufacturing can be made easier by designing boards to guidelines that reduce the need for setup. Recommended practices include the following:

1. Standardize subpanel sizes
A major contributor to overall setup time is the time required to readjust conveyor rails. Ideally, all boards should be designed to fit a single subpanel size so that no rail adjustment is required. Locations of tooling holes, fiducial marks, barcode labels, etc., should be standardized on this panel. A representative subpanel design is shown in Fig. 8.10.

Within the panel, boards of any size can be accommodated, but lowest cost is achieved when the board format is optimized for the subpanel. It is

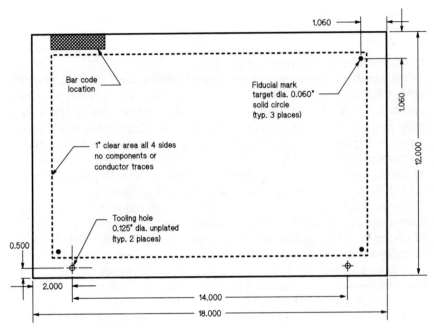

FIG. 8.10 Example of standard subpanel. (Dimensions in inches.)

not essential that a subpanel contain only a single board type as long as production volumes and yields are similar. For example, it might be possible to include all the boards for a single product on one subpanel. (Caution: if production yields for the different boards are grossly different, this approach is not recommended.)

2. Use standard workpiece holders for odd-sized boards

Boards that cannot be laid out on a standard subpanel should be processed on a workpiece holder (refer to Fig. 10.10). The workpiece holder should be designed such that it is interchangeable with standard subpanels. This eliminates the need to readjust conveyor rails when both subpanels and workpiece holders are used on a single line.

The use of a workpiece holder does not entirely eliminate the need for standardization in board layout. Guidelines should be established for board shape, tooling hole location, etc., so that a unique workpiece holder need not be designed for each board type.

Workpiece holders add complexity to the process. Boards must be installed onto the holders at the start of the process and be removed at the conclusion, usually by hand. The thermal mass of the holder may interfere with proper solder reflow, especially in infrared processes. It may therefore be necessary to remove the board from the holder prior to reflow. This adds labor and risks dislodging parts before they are soldered. However, use of a workpiece holder is often preferable to a complete readjustment of all conveyors on a line.

3. Minimize the proliferation of part types

As the number of part types grows, manufacturing costs increase dramatically. Each part number must be tracked separately and requires its own warehouse space. On the production line, an abundance of part types leads to several problems. Once the number exceeds the available space on the component placement machine, setup time must be expended to change component feeders. (This can amount to a minute or more per feeder.) In addition, a separate feeder must be maintained for each part, increasing both the cost of feeders and the space required to store them.

Certain steps can be taken to reduce parts proliferation. Standard components should be selected and publicized in a preferred parts manual. The list should be broad enough to meet most design demands while still keeping the overall parts count manageable. It is not usually necessary, for instance, to include resistor families of 1%, 2%, 5%, and 10% tolerance on a single line. Instead, one or two families should be selected—perhaps the 1% tolerance for precision use and the 5% tolerance for low cost.

The number of different parts within a component family should also be minimized. Resistor values should be limited to the E-12 or E-24 values (see Table 2.1) as opposed to the full E-96 range. Odd values can be obtained by combining standard values in series or parallel. Capacitors can also be restricted to a few standard values. The great majority of capacitors are used in bypass or filter applications; it is often possible to restrict these to just one or two values (for example, $0.01 \mu F$ or $0.1 \mu F$).

4. Invest in tooling to reduce screen printer setup time

Screen printing is inherently a batch-mode process. Few printer manufacturers have adequately addressed the problem of printer setup. In many cases the screens are simply mounted with bolts that do not afford precision adjustment. Alignment must be performed by laboriously adjusting micrometer screws while viewing a sample board through the screen. It can take anywhere from about 5 minutes to align a stencil for a small board to over 30 minutes to align a fine-mesh screen to a large board. Several test prints must usually be run to achieve final alignment.

The alignment process can be considerably accelerated through the use of relatively simple tooling. In one approach, the micrometer adjustments are mounted on the screen frame so that once adjusted, they seldom need readjustment. The extra cost of the screen frame is quickly recovered by the reduction in setup. (Setup times of less than a minute are possible with this approach.)

Where absolute lowest setup time is required, it may be preferable to dispense solder paste via syringe rather than by screen printing. An automatically controlled syringe dispenser requires no setup other than loading of a computer program. It is also less wasteful of solder paste because no paste is left on a screen at the conclusion of the run.

Serial vs. parallel equipment configuration

Highest efficiency is obtained when the throughputs of all individual process steps are closely matched. Unfortunately, real production equipment is seldom overtly designed to achieve this state. An in-line vapor phase reflow system, for example, may have the capacity to process 1000 boards per shift, while a component placement machine may only be able to process 300 boards. Additional placement equipment would be necessary long before reaching the capacity of the reflow system.

Placement equipment can be added either serially or in parallel (Fig. 8.11). In the serial configuration, the two machines are installed in-line. The first machine populates part of the board and the second populates the remainder. Total line capacity is increased over a single machine because while the second machine is finishing one board, the first machine can be starting another.

In the parallel configuration, the two machines operate independently. The first machine populates one board while the second populates another. If separate screen printers are used to feed the two machines, they are completely independent and need not build the same board type simultaneously.

The primary advantage of the serial configuration is a reduction in setup time due to the increased number of components on line. When both machines are identical, component capacity can effectively be doubled.

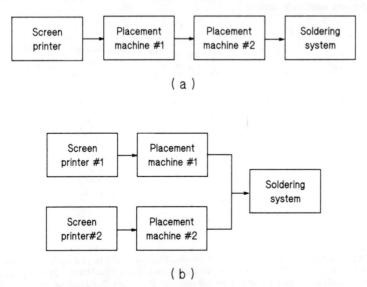

FIG. 8.11   Serial vs. parallel configuration of placement machines: a. Serial, b. Parallel.

Serial configuration is also indicated when the two machines have different capabilities. A serial approach is necessary, for example, when a high-speed machine dedicated to placement of chip components is paired with a precision placement machine for high lead-count ICs.

In general, parallel configuration permits higher throughput than serial configuration of the same machines. Two factors contribute to this effect. First, it is usually impossible to divide the placement program exactly in half. One machine will invariably complete its portion of the program before the other; it must then stand idle until the other is finished. Second, the time required to transport the board between machines degrades total placement rate.

The effect of transporting the board between machines can best be understood from the timing diagram shown in Fig. 8.12a. In the serial case, the time required to populate an entire board consists of:

a. the time to load the board onto the first machine
b. the time for the first machine to populate the board
c. the time to transport the board between machines
d. the time for the second machine to populate the board
e. the time to remove the board from the second machine

The parallel configuration has several advantages. As shown in Fig. 8.12b, all components are placed in a single sequence so a true doubling of capacity can be achieved. It is also possible for the machines to build different boards simultaneously. In addition, a measure of redundancy is provided. Even if one machine fails, the entire line is not shut down. This form of incremental capacity addition is fundamental to current concepts of world-class manufacturing.[2]

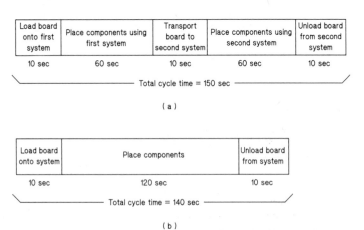

FIG. 8.12 Timing diagrams for serial and parallel configurations of placement machines. In the series configuration shown in (a), the total cycle time is extended by the time required to transport boards between the two placement systems. In the parallel configuration shown in (b), all components are placed on a single machine, eliminating this transport time.

One disadvantage of parallel processing is that the number of parts on line is limited to the capacity of a single machine. More frequent setup changes compared to the serial configuration are generally necessary. This can sometimes be overcome by configuring each machine to build only a subset of the total product range.

8.4.2 Semiautomated factory design

The semiautomated factory is oriented toward lower-volume production or prototyping applications. Typical product volumes range from under 1 million to about 25 million components per year. This volume is often spread across a large number of products, none of which achieves significant production quantities.

At the low end of the spectrum, the primary driving force is the need to acquire basic process capability rather than the need for absolute lowest cost. An entry-level factory with capacity of 1–2 million components per year would use less-sophisticated and less-expensive equipment than that used in a fully automated factory. Higher setup costs can usually be tolerated and it is rarely necessary to match capacity among process steps.

At the high end of the spectrum, the driving force is usually to achieve the lowest cost consistent with quality and capacity requirements. Although volumes of 10–20 million components per year may be realized, the diversity of designs prevent efficient production through a fully automated line. These factories use equipment similar to the fully automated line, but each machine is an island of automation rather than part of a fully integrated line.

A typical semiautomated factory layout capable of producing 10–15 million components per year is shown in Fig. 8.13. This line has high inherent flexibility. Work flow can be rapidly configured to meet the immediate needs of production. Line capacity can be increased by adding only individual pieces of equipment at the critical path points in the process.

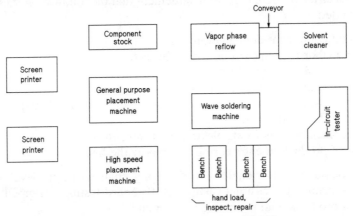

FIG. 8.13 Representative layout for semiautomated SMT factory.

Because of the increased labor content, a semiautomated line does not have as high inherent efficiency as a similar-size fully automated line. However, inherent efficiency is not always realized in production. A fully automated line is difficult to adapt to changing product demands and is less effective at lower product volumes. Unless operated near full capacity, the added cost of automation cannot be recovered through improved efficiencies. A semiautomated line can therefore be a better solution for many low-to-medium-volume applications.

8.5 FACTORY COST ANALYSIS

The most useful measure of manufacturing cost for a surface mount line is *assembly cost per component*. This is simply the cost of operating the assembly line over a given period (excluding the actual purchase costs of the components) divided by the number of components placed during the period. It is usually measured on a monthly basis and is defined as follows:

$$C = \frac{A}{N}$$

where C = assembly cost per component
      A = factory operating cost during the month
      N = total number of surface mount components placed during the month

The number of surface mount components placed during the month is easily determined, but overall factory operating cost is subject to more interpretation. To accurately represent the true factory efficiency, it should include all internally controllable costs while excluding costs controlled by external factors. (Note that this cost may have little bearing on how products are priced, which is often a marketing-driven rather than manufacturing-driven decision.) There is general agreement that the following costs *should* be included:

- capital equipment depreciation cost
- direct labor costs incurred to run the factory
- direct overhead costs for direct labor (e.g., holiday pay, company-paid health insurance, and similar benefits)
- direct cost of supplies (e.g., solder paste, vapor phase fluids)
- cost of direct supervision
- direct facility costs (rent, electricity, water, etc.)
- cost of production engineering to support the line

Other possible costs include manufacturing engineering to develop new process technology, customer liaison staff, board testing, scrapped or reworked products, and procuring components.

The component procurement cost is usually better accommodated as an incremental addition to the component purchase price rather than as a direct manufacturing cost. Scrap or rework due to manufacturing problems should be included but similar charges due to design changes should not.

Because of differences in labor rates, land and building costs, etc., the actual values for the various cost elements will vary widely from one factory to another. However, for a given cost structure, certain general relationships apply. For example, a factory operating near maximum capacity will always be more efficient than one that is only lightly loaded. Also, because overhead costs grow at a slower rate than factory size, a factory with a large maximum capacity is capable of achieving a lower unit cost than a small factory.

Fig. 8.14 shows the approximate cost per component as a function of maximum facility capacity. Since exact costs cannot be calculated, the graph shows relative costs referenced to a high-volume factory operating at full capacity. Three representative factories have been highlighted. These are:

1. Entry-level factory
This is a typical small-volume factory designed for prototyping and small production runs. Factories of this type employ relatively inexpensive batch-mode equipment in an islands-of-automation configuration. They accept boards to about 250 × 330 mm (10 × 13 in) and can place about 1000 components per hour.

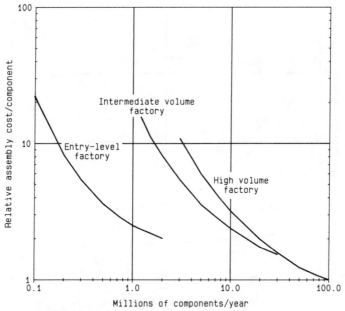

FIG. 8.14 Relative assembly cost per component for three representative surface mount factories.

2. Intermediate-volume factory

This factory employs higher-volume production equipment configured as islands of automation. A typical intermediate-volume factory places components at a rate of 8000 per hour and can accommodate boards to about 300 × 450 mm (12 × 18 in).

3. High-volume factory

This represents a fully automated in-line facility. Typical high-volume factories can place 30,000 components per hour and accept boards to 300 × 450 mm (12 × 18 in).

The high-volume factory, when operating near maximum capacity, achieves lowest production cost. However, the high fixed cost of this factory makes it extremely sensitive to loss of efficiency. The intermediate-volume factory approaches the operating cost of the high-volume factory. For the range between 10 and 30 million components per year it is actually the lowest cost solution.

The entry-level factory cannot compete with the other two in either cost or volume. Labor costs are proportionally higher because the cost of a similar number of operators is distributed across a much lower production volume. The entry-level factory also uses smaller equipment, which is likely to require more setup between runs. For this reason it is much more sensitive to variations in run sizes (Fig. 8.15).

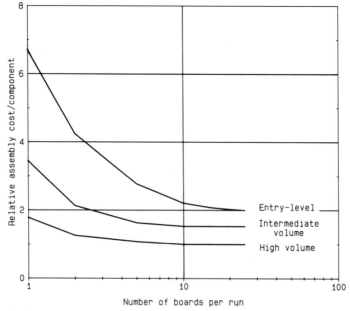

FIG. 8.15   Relative assembly cost per component as a function of run size for three representative surface mount factories.

8.6 FACTORY DESIGN RECOMMENDATIONS

There are no easy answers to the question of how to design a factory for a given set of requirements. Often, success depends more on the commitment of the personnel who design and operate it rather than on the specific technical choices that are made. There are numerous examples of highly successful factories which operate very differently to build similar products.

Certain guidelines can be employed to ease the task of factory layout. While there can be no guarantee that following these recommendations will automatically assure success, the chances are increased.

1. Choose an appropriate process flow

Limit the use of adhesive attach/wave soldering to the attachment of discrete devices. This process is most suitable for attaching chip components and small-outline transistors to analog and high-frequency boards. Small-outline ICs can also be mounted, but solder yields will be degraded.

Reflow soldering is a more versatile process and is recommended for most general-purpose applications. It is preferred for attaching integrated circuits and when complex or thermally sensitive components are used.

2. Design for flexibility

Factories that employ a rigid configuration are difficult to adapt to changing product needs. Even if the line is expected to build only a few product types, increased flexibility is valuable. The market life of a single product rarely exceeds two or three years, while the useful life of the equipment is at least five years. Equipment with high flexibility can easily be reconfigured as needs change. New products can more easily be added to the line, so if market demand for the initial product fails to meet forecast, the entire investment is not wasted.

3. Design for redundancy

A totally serial line is sensitive to the failure of any single machine. A line with parallel machines, on the other hand, can continue to produce (at reduced capacity) even if one machine fails. Surface mount equipment is complex and the potential for downtime is relatively high, so redundant design can make a significant difference in actual operation.

4. Invest engineering to reduce setup times

Many equipment manufacturers have not adequately addressed the issue of low setup time. As more production lines head to continuous flow just-in-time manufacturing, this can present serious problems. A 30-minute setup time is unacceptable when the build time for a whole run may only be 15 minutes.

Setup time can be reduced in several ways. It is frequently possible to modify equipment to eliminate or considerably speed the setup process. Guidelines describing how to design boards for minimum setup should be widely publicized. Larger component placement machines with increased feeder capacity are often a wise investment.

5. Commit full management support

In the final analysis, management commitment is more important than the actual choice of process technology. It is difficult, if not impossible, to identify the absolute optimum technical solution to a given set of requirements. However, there are a broad range of alternatives that can be successful if adequately developed and supported. The extent of management support is often the only real difference between a highly successful factory and a mediocre or unsuccessful factory.

REFERENCES

1. O'Rourke, H., and Sedrick, A. "New Single Pass PWA Soldering Technique for Leaded and Surface Mount (Both Sides) Components," *Proceedings of NEPCON/West '87*, Anaheim, CA, Feb. 1987, pp. 72–86.
2. Schoenberger, R. *World Class Manufacturing*, The Free Press, New York, 1986, pp. 77–100.
3. Markstein, H. "Automation Thrives as Companies Strive for SMT Capability," *Electronic Packaging and Production*, May 1985, pp. 68–74.
4. Tuck, J. "300 Machines Later," *Circuits Manufacturing*, Apr. 1987, pp. 23–37.

9

Solder pastes and application techniques

Solder paste is a basic constituent of the reflow soldering process. It provides both the flux necessary to clean the surfaces and the solder to form the final joint. This chapter discusses the important properties of solder paste and the various methods of applying it to the board. It also briefly reviews solder deposition techniques that do not make use of solder pastes. The chapter begins with a discussion of the important rheological properties of solder pastes.

9.1 RHEOLOGY[1]*

The science of rheology is concerned with the flow of fluids. As far as solder pastes are concerned, there are two important fluid properties that must be considered: viscosity and surface tension. Both properties arise from intermolecular forces within the paste. Viscosity can be defined as the resistance to motion of one layer of fluid past another layer. Surface tension is related to the imbalance of forces that exist at an interface between two fluids, a fluid and a solid, or a fluid and a gas.

9.1.1 Viscosity

Imagine a fluid as being stratified in layers, as shown in Fig. 9.1. The force required to move one layer past another is:

$$F = \frac{\mu A v}{y} \qquad [9.1]$$

where F = force
μ = coefficient of viscosity
A = area of layers
v = relative velocity between layers
y = distance between layers

* This section extracted from *Thick Film Hybrid Microcircuit Technology*, D. Hamer and J. Biggers, authors, published and copyrighted by John Wiley and Sons. Used by permission.

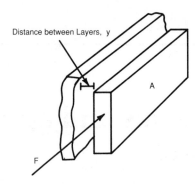

FIG. 9.1   Viscosity relationships. (*Thick Film Microcircuit Technology*, D. W. Hamer. Copyright 1972, Wiley-Interscience. Reprinted by permission of John Wiley & Sons, Inc.)

In many liquids, μ varies only with temperature. These are the so-called *ideal* or *Newtonian* fluids. The temperature variation can be described by the relation:

$$\log \mu = \frac{A}{T} + B$$

where A, B = constants
    T = absolute temperature

In many other liquids, μ is not only a function of temperature, but will also depend on other factors including rate of force application, magnitude of the force, the direction of the force, and the duration of the force. These fluids are called *non-Newtonian*.

Figure 9.2 illustrates the stress–shear rate behavior of four types of fluids.

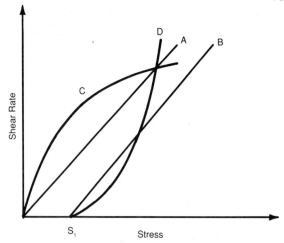

FIG. 9.2   Different rheological behaviors—stress-shear relationships. A = Newtonian; B = Bingham Body (yield point = s_1); C = Dilatent; D = Pseudo plastic. (*Thick Film Microcircuit Technology*, D. W. Hamer. Copyright 1972, Wiley-Interscience. Reprinted by permission of John Wiley & Sons, Inc.)

Curve A shows the behavior of an ideal liquid. The slope of the curve (the viscosity coefficient) is constant for different stress rates.

The other curves represent variations from ideal behavior. Curve B is the stress–shear relation exhibited by a "Bingham Body." This material has a *yield point*—that is, a certain force must be applied before flow will start. In this type of liquid, the viscosity coefficient is constant after flow has started. Curves C and D represent different variations of viscosity coefficient with shear rate. The behavior of these nonideal systems is related to the kinds of chemical bonds between the molecules of the liquid.

The pseudoplastic response of Curve D is of particular importance in screen printing. In this type of material, the shear rate increases more than proportionally to shear stress, particularly at higher rates. This "thinning" action under stress permits the paste to flow easily through the screen during the printing operation while maintaining good print definition afterward. Since pseudoplastic behavior often occurs only after reaching a yield point, it is important that the screen printer be operated at a speed that produces a stress well in excess of this minimum. Pseudoplastic behavior is often confused with *thixotropic* behavior, which describes a fluid whose viscosity decreases with *time*.

9.1.2 Surface tension

Another important property of the paste, which will combine with viscosity to determine its behavior during screen printing, is surface tension. The surface tension is related to the strength of the bond between molecules in the liquid. Most molecules in the bulk of the liquid are surrounded by other similar molecules, and the forces are fairly well balanced. The molecules at the interface between another liquid, solid, or gas phase are in a different environment in that they are not surrounded by similar molecules. The relative strength of bonds formed at this interface determines the behaviour of the liquid at the interface. Consider two hypothetical liquids A and B in contact with the copper conductor of a printed wiring board in a vacuum (Fig. 9.3). Assume that the A–A bonds in liquid A are much stronger than the A–copper bonds and that the B–B bonds are weaker than the B–copper bonds.

If a drop of liquid A is placed on the copper, the surface molecules will experience an inward-directed force that will tend to minimize the area of

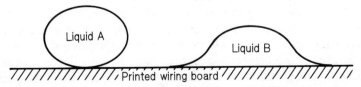

FIG. 9.3 Surface tension: liquid A has high surface tension, liquid B has low surface tension.

liquid A in contact with the copper. Liquid A is said to have a high surface tension.

In the case of liquid B, however, the molecules at the surface of a drop in contact with the copper will experience outward force that will tend to maximize the area of contact. Liquid B is said to have a low surface tension or that it wets the copper.

If liquid A were deposited on the copper through a screen, it would tend to remain on the screen. Liquid B, on the other hand, would tend to adhere to the copper as the screen was lifted away.

9.2 VISCOSITY MEASUREMENT

Since the viscosity of a solder paste changes as a function of such parameters as temperature, humidity, and previous history, characterization of the paste is not a simple matter. Viscosity readings taken by different operators at different times under apparently identical conditions can show wide variations. If meaningful measurements are to be taken, a number of variables must be carefully specified and controlled.

9.2.1 Rotating-spindle viscometer

The most popular method for measuring solder paste uses a rotating-spindle technique. A motorized spindle is immersed in a sample of paste and rotated at a fixed speed. The force necessary to achieve this speed is measured by a gauge on the machine, and viscosity is calculated from this reading.

The Brookfield viscometer (Fig. 9.4) is the predominant machine of this type. Brookfield viscosity measurements are invariably quoted in manufacturers' literature and are the controlling specifications in virtually all commercial and military solder paste documents.

Although widely used, measurements made using this technique are of rather limited engineering value. The spindle does not apply a uniform shear stress across the entire cross-section of paste being tested, so a true stress–shear rate diagram cannot be obtained. Near the center of the spindle, the relative velocity is low, producing low stresses. At the outside tip the velocity is much higher, as is the stress. As a result, two different paste materials with identical readings will not necessarily exhibit similar printing characteristics.

The apparent viscosity reading is highly dependent on the shape of the spindle used in the test. A number of different spindle geometries are available for various applications. For solder pastes, a small "T-shaped" spindle is often used, but there are no absolute standards regarding the spindle shape, speed of rotation, or exact test method that should be used.

Solder pastes are highly viscous materials. If the spindle rotates continuously in one location, it may enter the wake left from the previous revolution. Large errors are introduced in the measurement when this

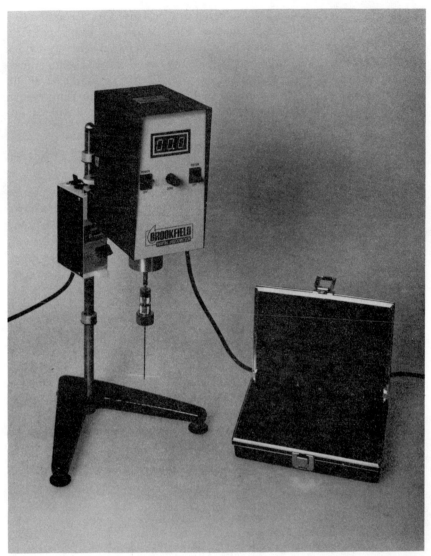

FIG. 9.4 Rotating-spindle viscometer with digital readout. (Used by permission. Brookfield Engineering Laboratories.)

happens. To address this problem, the Brookfield viscometer can be equipped with a motorized "Helipath" stand that slowly elevates the spindle as it rotates. Use of the Helipath stand is always advised when measuring solder pastes.

Several other variables must be carefully controlled when conducting a Brookfield viscosity measurement. Rotational speed, spindle configuration, and ambient temperature are all important parameters. A recommended test procedure is given in the Appendix at the end of the chapter.

Brookfield viscometer measurements are best used as a comparative quality-control tool on the production floor. When the test is properly conducted, new lots of an existing paste can be compared against previous history. Brookfield measurements should not be used as the basis for adjusting the viscosity of a marginal paste, nor should they be used to evaluate alternative paste materials against an existing standard. The machine is not a suitable tool in a laboratory environment where a fundamental understanding of paste properties must be developed.

9.2.2 Cone-plate viscometer

The problems with the Brookfield viscometer can be overcome by using a cone-plate viscometer system. In this approach, a sample of paste is introduced between a rotating cone and fixed plate. Referring to Fig. 9.5, the height and velocity at any distance R from the axis can be found from:

$$y = R \sin \theta$$
$$v = \omega R$$

Inserting these values into eqn. 9.1, it can be seen that:

$$F = \frac{\mu A \omega}{\sin \theta}$$

Force is therefore independent of R.

Using this technique, a rheogram of viscosity over a wide range of shear stresses can easily be obtained. The major limitations of the cone-plate approach are the increased expense of the equipment compared to the Brookfield viscometer and the increased skill level necessary to operate it properly.

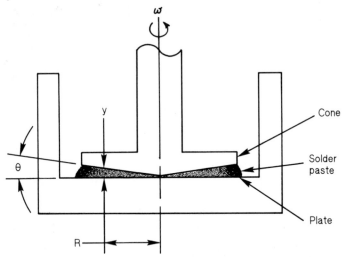

FIG. 9.5 Diagram of cone-plate viscometer system.

Cone-plate viscometers are manufactured by a number of companies, including Ferranti-Shirley, Brabender, and Haake. They are most suitable for laboratory use and are rarely employed on the production floor.

9.3 SOLDER PASTE

Solder paste (also called solder cream) consists of a powdered solder alloy bound in a flux vehicle. In SMT applications, the paste performs three basic functions:

- provides the solder that forms the final joint
- supplies the flux necessary to clean the surfaces and promote wetting
- holds the components in place until the solder is reflowed

For optimum performance, the paste must be formulated for compatibility with the intended deposition technique. A paste designed for syringe dispensing, for instance, might not be suitable for screen printing. Since there are few standards for solder deposition or reflow processes, a great many paste formulations have been devised.

Pastes are comprised of the following constituents:

- solder powder
- flux
- rheological modifiers/viscosity control agents
- solvent system

9.3.1 Solder powder

The solder powder is the heart of the paste. It is produced by atomizing molten solder in an inert environment. The two most popular approaches are gas atomization and centrifugal atomization.[2] In gas atomization, a high-pressure inert gas blows across a stream of molten solder. The gas stream causes the solder to break into tiny spherical droplets that quickly cool and fall into a container. In centrifugal atomization, the molten solder falls onto a rapidly rotating disc. Solder is dispersed into small drops that again cool and are collected in a container. Both methods can be used to produce spherical or nearly spherical powders.

Alloy composition

The various solder alloys and their uses are described in Chapter 5. Those alloys most often used in solder pastes for surface mounting are listed in Table 9.1. Eutectic or near-eutectic tin–lead alloys, because of their low cost, are preferred for general-purpose applications. Tin–lead–silver is sometimes used when soldering to silver-bearing surfaces, and tin–silver or

Composition	Temperature (°C)		Application
	Liquidus	Solidus	
63Sn/37Pb	183	183	General assembly of components
60Sn/40Pb	188	183	to printed wiring boards
62Sn/36Pb/2Ag	179	179	For use with silver-bearing component terminations and thick film conductors
96.5Sn/3.5Ag	221	221	High melting temperature alloy for
95Sn/5Ag	240	221	step-soldering applications
75Pb/25In	264	250	High ductility alloy useful for
50Pb/50In	209	180	soldering to gold surfaces. Also
25Pb/75In	165	156	useful in applications where large CTE differences must be accommodated
10Sn/90Pb + 100Sn	see text		Special formulation designed to eliminate solder wicking

TABLE 9.1   Alloys used in solder pastes

lead–indium are used when the properties of these alloys (as described in Chapter 5) are desired.

The specialty paste at the bottom of Table 9.1 has been formulated to reduce the potential of solder wicking on J-lead devices (Section 5.5.7). Wicking is primarily a problem when using vapor phase reflow and occurs when the component lead reaches reflow temperature before the land. The molten solder is drawn up the lead and away from the joint, leaving an unsoldered connection.

One solution to the wicking problem is to prevent the solder from melting until both lead and land come up to temperature.[3] The paste described in the table achieves this effect in a unique way. It consists of a combination of two separate powders. The first is an alloy of 90% lead and 10% tin, with a melting range of 268–302 °C. The second is 100% tin, with a melting point of 232 °C. The two powders are mixed such that the net tin–lead ratio is 63/37.

Neither individual powder will melt at the vapor phase reflow temperature, 215 °C. However, solid state diffusion at the interfaces between adjacent particles creates nucleation points of eutectic tin–lead alloy, which do melt. Diffusion accelerates as the interfaces liquify, eventually carrying the process to completion. The length of time required for complete liquefaction can be controlled by the diameter of the particles. The larger the particles, the longer the delay.

This time delay allows the circuit land and device lead to reach reflow temperature before the solder melts. The wetting forces which tend to draw the solder up the lead and away from the joint are thus neutralized. The approach is promising in principle, but additional experimental work must be performed to confirm its efficacy in actual production applications.

Oxide content

Electronic-grade solder alloys must be extremely free of any contamination that would degrade performance. Oxidation of the solder is a serious concern that can lead to a number of problems, including reduced solderability, bridging between adjacent lands, and formation of solder balls. To reduce oxide formation, careful control of the powder manufacturing process is essential. Powders must be processed and stored in an inert atmosphere at all times prior to the mixing of the paste.

Oxide levels above 0.5% are generally considered unacceptable.[4] Figure 9.6 shows the result of one study that examined the impact of oxide level on the percentage of solder balls. As can be seen, even 0.5% oxide content produced an appreciable percentage of balls. At least one paste manufacturer claims the ability to produce pastes with oxide levels as low as 0.03%, and recommends a specification limit of 0.15%.[5]

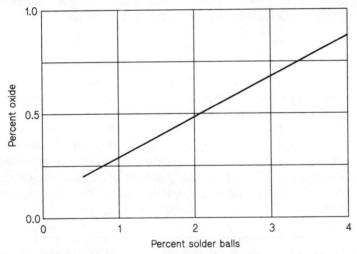

FIG. 9.6   Effect of solder powder oxide level on solder ball formation. (Used by permission. Copyright 1984, International Society for Hybrid Microelectronics.)

Particle shape

When screen printing or dispensing by syringe, spherical or nearly spherical particles, as shown in Fig. 9.7a, are preferred. A spherical shape has the least surface area for a given volume, minimizing the opportunity for oxidation. Spherical shapes are also easiest to dispense. Elongated or irregular particles, such as those pictured in Fig. 9.7b, are more likely to snag in the screen.

The use of a certain percentage of nonspherical particles has been advocated as a way to reduce slump, or bridging across closely spaced pads.[5] The assertion is that these particles tend to interlock, preventing dispersion of

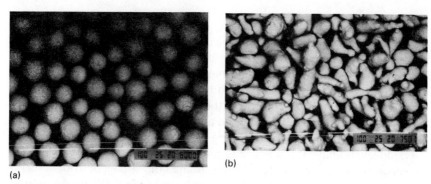

(a)

(b)

FIG. 9.7 Solder powders: a. Spherical particles, b. Irregular particles. (Used by permission. Senju Metal Industry Co., Ltd.)

the powder as the flux melts during reflow. Few commercial pastes take advantage of this concept, and most manufacturers have chosen to reduce slump through judicious selection of rheological modifiers.

Particle size

For best performance, the solder particles in a paste should all be of roughly the same size. Since the raw powder consists of many different size particles, it must be sorted by sifting through a series of metal screens. Powders are classified by defining the mesh size limits used for screening. A powder designated as − 200/+ 325, for instance, will pass through a 200 mesh screen but not through a 325 mesh screen. A powder with only a maximum size designation (e.g., − 325) contains no particles larger than the designated screen size, but sets no limit on the smallest diameters. The approximate mesh dimensions for various screen sizes are presented in Table 9.2.

Mesh count per inch	Wire diameter		Mesh opening	
	in	μm	in	μm
200	0.0016	41	0.0034	86
250	0.0016	41	0.0024	61
270	0.0014	36	0.0023	58
325	0.0011	28	0.0020	51
325	0.0009	23	0.0022	55

Note 1: Swiss fine wire cloth

TABLE 9.2 Screen sizes for sorting solder powders

Particle size must be consistent with the intended application technique. As a general rule, the maximum particle diameter should be three to five times smaller than the opening through which it is to be dispensed. Larger particles tend to clog the screen or syringe nozzle, producing voids in the pattern. When screen printing with an 80 mesh stainless-steel screen (screen opening of 266 μm), for example, the particle diameter should be 50–90 μm. A −200/+325 powder would be acceptable in this application. With a 105 mesh screen (165 μm opening), maximum diameter should be 30–55 μm, requiring a −325 powder. Stencils, because of their larger openings, are less sensitive to particle size.

Particles smaller than about 10–15 μm are generally undesirable. The surface area in relation to volume is greater for these particles, so any surface oxidation becomes proportionally more significant (Fig. 9.8). Since it is impossible to totally eliminate oxidation during the paste manufacturing process, appreciable quantities of small particles in a paste are virtually certain to degrade solderability. Small particles are also more likely to be washed away from the joint as the flux melts, increasing the incidence of solder balls.

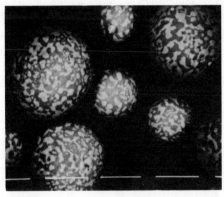

FIG. 9.8 Oxide layer on surface of solder powder. (Used by permission. Senju Metal Industry Co., Ltd.)

9.3.2 Flux

Most solder pastes have historically been formulated with rosin-based fluxes. As described in Chapter 5, rosin fluxes are classified in Federal Specification QQ-S-571 according to activity: nonactivated (R), mildly activated (RMA), and fully activated (RA). The so-called "super-activated" RSA flux and the water-soluble organic acid (OA) fluxes, because of their highly corrosive residues, are not ordinarily used in SMT solder pastes. Pastes based on solvent-soluble synthetic fluxes are now becoming available and may increase in importance in the future.

The choice of activity level is based on the metals to be joined. When soldering tin-lead component terminations to copper or solder-coated conductors, RMA or RA fluxes are used. RMA flux is preferred where possible because of the benign nature of its residues. Soldering defects can some-times be reduced by using an RA flux. Type R flux, because of its relatively low activity level, is rarely used. It is, however, suitable for soldering highly wettable surfaces such as gold-plated chip carrier terminations to gold-bearing thick film conductors.

Regardless of which flux is used, thorough cleaning after reflow is essen-tial. The flux itself is not so much of a problem as are residual solder balls on the assembly. Controlling a production process to the level necessary to completely eliminate solder balls is exceedingly difficult. Cleaning is an effective way to remove the small quantity of isolated balls that can be expected even in a well-controlled process.

9.3.3 Rheological modifiers

The rheological modifier, also called a viscosity control agent, establishes the viscosity and deposition characteristics of the paste. For screen printing applications it must be selected to promote screenability, reduce slumping of the paste, and prevent separation of the solder from the flux after repeated printing cycles. If the paste is to be dispensed by syringe, the rheological modifier must prevent clogging of the syringe and minimize *stringing*—the tendency for the top of a solder dot not to break cleanly away from the nozzle but to carry a small string of paste to the next deposition site.

9.3.4 Solvents

More solvents may be added as a vehicle for the flux activator and to improve the shelf life of the paste. These volatile elements must have low toxicity and a high flash point. They must also totally evaporate without spattering during the paste drying step. Any solvent remaining in the paste at reflow temperature will boil violently, scattering solder particles across the board.

9.4 SOLDER PASTE SPECIFICATIONS AND TESTS

Several paste characteristics must be carefully controlled to achieve opti-mum production results. These include:

- percent metal
- viscosity
- slump
- solder balls
- flux activity
- working life
- shelf life

9.4.1 Percent metal

The percent metal defines the amount of solder that is deposited in a given volume of paste. Percent metal is routinely specified as a *weight* percentage rather than as a *volume* percentage. This is unfortunate since it is the volume that primarily impacts the physical properties of the paste and quality of the finished joint. Too little solder will result in an excessive number of voids and an increase in the amount of slump. The relationship between weight percent and volume percent solder is shown in Fig. 9.9.

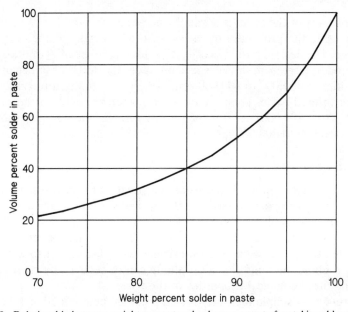

FIG. 9.9 Relationship between weight percent and volume percent of metal in solder paste.

Early pastes contained as little as 70% solder by weight, or less than 25% by volume. It is now felt that a much higher weight percent is necessary to achieve high-quality joints. Pastes with 85–92% metal are recommended by most manufacturers when the paste is to be screen or stencil printed. Stencils are preferred for dispensing pastes with above about 90% metal because they are less likely to clog. For a similar reason, a somewhat lower metal percentage (80–85%) is necessary when dispensing via syringe.

Percent metal can be measured easily by the following procedure:

1. Weigh 10 ± 1 g of solder paste in a ceramic crucible. Record exact weight of the paste to the nearest 0.01 gram.

2. Dry the paste according to the manufacturer's directions. This is necessary to prevent the paste from spattering small balls of solder during reflow.

3. Reflow the paste to produce a single pellet of solder. Elevate the temperature slowly (2–5 °C per second) to avoid spattering.

4. Carefully remove the pellet (and any other isolated spheres of solder) and rinse in a fluorinated or chlorinated hydrocarbon solvent such as Dupont Freon® TMS to removal all traces of organics.

5. Weigh the solder to the nearest 0.01 g.

6. Calculate the percent metal as: (weight solder/weight paste) × 100.

9.4.2 Viscosity

The viscosity of the paste is normally measured with the Brookfield viscometer using the procedure described in the Appendix at the end of this chapter. The desired paste viscosity depends on the specifics of the application process (screen mesh size, speed of squeegee, etc.). For screen printing, viscosities of 400,000 to 600,000 centipoise (cps) are often recommended. Stencil printed pastes should have even higher viscosity, in the range of 800,000 to 1,100,000 cps. If dispensed by syringe, the viscosity should be about 150,000 to 300,000 cps.

9.4.3 Slump

Once the paste is printed, the forces of gravity and surface tension work against it, causing the pattern to collapse and spread out from its original boundaries. This phenomenon, called *slump*, causes the paste to flow out and possibly bridge to adjacent features. The dynamics of reflow may be such that the solder wets to these extraneous surfaces prior to wetting the joint, robbing the joint of solder. Slump can be reduced by carefully controlling the rheological properties of the paste.

A relatively simple measure of slump can be determined as follows:

1. Prepare a test board with a series of 0.010-in (0.25-mm) conductors separated by 0.010-in spaces.

2. Dispense paste onto the conductors using the standard production process. If the normal process uses screens, prepare a suitable screen. If the process uses stencils, prepare a stencil.

3. Immediately examine the width of the printed lines under a measuring microscope. Take several readings along each line and compute an average width.

4. Dry the paste according to the manufacturers' recommendation.

5. Remeasure the width of the lines. Slump is calculated from:

$$\% \text{ slump} = \frac{100 \times (\text{final width}-\text{original width})}{\text{original width}}$$

The desired specification depends on the specific geometries of production boards. For many applications, 10% maximum slump is suggested.

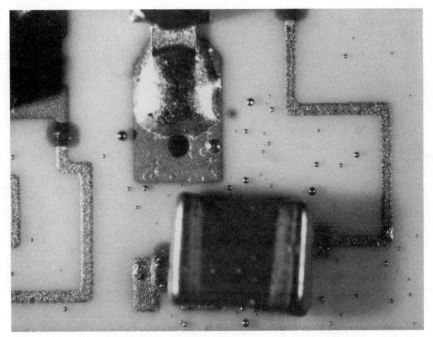

FIG. 9.10   Solder balls on ceramic hybrid circuit. (Photograph by the author.)

9.4.4 Solder balls

This is perhaps the most widely discussed characteristic of solder paste. Isolated balls of solder (Fig. 9.10) can occur across the surface of the board after reflow for any number of reasons. High oxide content in the solder, excessive slump, poor particle shape, and inadequate drying prior to reflow are just some of the contributing factors. Whatever the reasons, these balls can create reliability problems. If not removed in cleaning, they can later short between adjacent conductors. In extreme cases, the volume of solder left at the joint may be insufficient to form a reliable connection.

The propensity of a paste to form solder balls can be determined by reflowing a sample of paste on a non-wettable surface such as a ceramic substrate. A general procedure is as follows:

1. Obtain a clean, non-metallized ceramic substrate of about 1×1 in (25×25 mm) dimensions, 0.025 in (0.63 mm) thick.

2. Use a metal washer as a mask to apply the paste. The washer should have an inner diameter of about 0.20 in (5 mm) and an outer diameter of about 0.5 in (12.5 mm).

3. Secure the substrate in a vise and hold the washer on the substrate with tweezers. Using a spatula, apply enough paste to completely fill the washer.

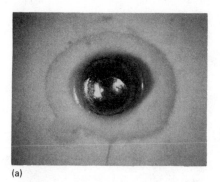 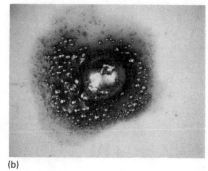

(a) (b)

FIG. 9.11 Results of solder ball test on solder paste: a. Preferred, b. Unacceptable. (Photographs by the author.)

4. Carefully lift the washer off the substrate, leaving a cylindrical column of paste. (If paste smears, clean thoroughly and repeat.)

5. Reflow the paste using the standard reflow process. Optionally, a "worst case" test can be performed by heating the substrate rapidly on a hot plate. (This increases flux spattering and maximizes the tendency to form solder balls.)

6. Visually examine the resultant ball of solder. It should be a single large lump with no extraneous balls larger than 125-μm diameter evident under 10× magnification (see Fig. 9.11). The flux ring should be colorless to pale amber, not dark or greenish. There should be no evidence of a halo of minute solder balls surrounding the main ball.

9.4.5 Flux activity

The activity level of the flux determines its ability to clean the metal surfaces to promote wetting. It can be measured by the Spread Factor Test described in Section 5.7.5. A controlled amount of solder paste is applied to a copper surface with a known oxide thickness. The more active the flux, the greater will be the diameter of the reflowed solder.

To rigorously calculate the spread factor, it is necessary to carefully weigh the copper coupon before applying the paste, before reflowing it, and again after reflow and cleaning. This is a laborious process not well suited for use on the production floor. If paste is applied to a diameter of 0.200 in (5.08 mm) and a thickness of 0.025 in (0.063 mm) (as described in Section 5.7.5), then the graph in Fig. 9.12 can be used to calculate an approximate spread factor by measuring only the diameter of the reflowed solder.

A spread factor of 80 has been experimentally found to remove a layer of oxidized copper about 2000 Angstroms thick.[11] This thickness could be expected to grow over a period of about one year in a normal industrial environment.

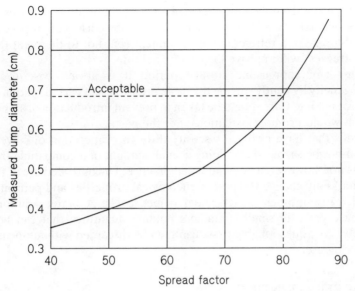

FIG. 9.12 Spread factor vs. diameter of reflowed solder paste. Refer to text for details of this procedure. (From Ref. 11.)

9.4.6 Working life

The working life of the paste determines how long an interval can elapse between paste application and component placement. For screen printed pastes, it also indicates how long the paste can be used before it must be discarded.

A minimum three-day working life is frequently cited so that boards can be screen printed on a Friday and populated with components the following Monday. Although plausible in principle, considerable experimental evidence suggests that lowest defect levels are achieved when only a few hours elapse between paste application and component placement, even for a paste with a long specified working life. Working life is more relevant as a measure of how long the paste can be left on a screen or stencil without degrading.

Working life is easy to specify but difficult to measure. Generally, tests look at the tackiness of the paste at various intervals after screening to verify that it is still adequate to hold components in place. More thorough testing would also examine the change in viscosity and percentage of solder balls that occurs over these intervals.

9.4.7 Shelf life

The shelf life of a solder paste is normally specified by the manufacturer as between 6 and 12 months. Evaporation of solvent, sedimentation of the

solder powder from the flux, chemical reactions between the various constituents, and oxidation of the powder all contribute to a loss of properties over
time. Storage in a refrigerated environment (but not to the point that the
paste freezes) will improve long-term shelf life.

After any appreciable storage period it is always wise to insure
homogeneity by gently stirring the paste prior to use. A small spatula can be
used for mixing. Care should be taken to prevent introduction of air bubbles
(which would promote oxidation) into the paste.

Pastes that have changed viscosity through evaporation of solvent can
sometimes be salvaged by adding a small amount of a compatible thinner.
This is not, however, a recommended practice. Uncontrolled use of thinner
can markedly change the paste's rheological properties and percentage of
metal, causing much higher solder defect levels. A better solution is to
purchase paste in small containers holding quantities that can be used
quickly. Any questionable paste can then be discarded without incurring a
large expense.

9.5 SCREEN PRINTING

Despite concerns that it is a complex process not well suited for today's
just-in-time (JIT) manufacturing concepts, screen printing and its variant,
stencil printing, remain the predominant methods for depositing SMT solder pastes. Although syringe dispensing is a promising alternative, the state
of the technology has not yet reached the point where it can be considered a
serious competitor, especially in high-volume applications.

Screen printing,* when properly controlled, is a fast and reliable method
for applying controlled quantities of solder paste onto a printed wiring
board. The speed of the process is essentially unaffected by the size of the
board or number of solder joints, and complex patterns can be dispensed as
easily as simple ones.

Screen printing, however, does have limitations. One of the most important is that it does not tolerate a casual approach to process control. Every
element of the process must be carefully monitored: solder paste parameters
(e.g. viscosity and metal content); printing parameters (e.g., screen characteristics, printer setup, and squeegee speed); and room ambient conditions
(temperature and humidity). Inadequate attention in any of these areas can
lead to inconsistent results that are difficult to identify and correct.

Even a carefully controlled screen printing process is not optimum for
small-lot production runs. The setup time required for a new production run
can vary anywhere from about 5 minutes to nearly an hour depending on the
equipment and extent of changes necessary. With this amount of setup, it is
desirable to run a large quantity of boards before making a changeover.

---

* In this book, the term *screen printing* is used to describe both stencil printing and true screen
printing unless clearly indicated otherwise.

Small-lot production is not always efficient even when setup time can be eliminated. The amount of solder paste left on the screen after producing only a few boards may be much more than the amount deposited onto the boards. It is not generally considered good manufacturing procedure to recover this paste, so unless the screen will be reused in a few hours, the paste must be washed away. This amount of waste can easily drive manufacturing costs to unacceptable levels.

With these limitations it is not surprising that alternatives to screen printing are continually being investigated. Dramatic changes are unlikely to occur rapidly, however, so a thorough understanding of the process is essential for anyone involved with the manufacture of reflow soldered SMT assemblies.

9.5.1 Screen printing theory

The basic screen printing cycle is illustrated in Fig. 9.13. The key components are: the *screen*, a mask with openings at the locations where paste is to be dispensed; the *solder paste*, which is applied to the top surface of the screen; the *squeegee*, a rubber blade that travels along the screen pushing paste through the openings; and the *board*, which is held securely in place by a suitable fixture.

In operation, the squeegee pushes a bead of paste along the surface of the screen. As the paste reaches an opening in the screen, the downward pressure exerted by the squeegee forces paste through the opening and onto the board. The amount of paste that remains on the board after the screen retracts is a complex function of the paste rheology and its wetting characteristics to both board and screen.

The general process of "screen printing" can actually be divided into two subcategories: screen printing and stencil printing. True screen printing employs a wire mesh screen covered with a photosensitive emulsion. Openings in the emulsion are created by photographic techniques, but the wire mesh remains in place even at the openings (see Fig. 9.14a).

Stencil printing makes use of a solid metal sheet with chemically milled openings. In this approach, there is no wire mesh to partially block the openings, so a greater volume of paste can be dispensed for a given size opening (see Fig. 9.14b).

Screen printing is usually done in an *off-contact* mode. At rest, the screen does not actually touch the board but is separated by a gap of about 1.5–2.5 mm (0.060–0.100 in). During the print cycle the squeegee forces the screen into contact with the board and drives the paste through the openings. As the squeegee continues through the stroke, the screen snaps off the board, leaving a portion of the paste behind. This *snap-off rate* determines the ratio of paste deposited on the board to that which remains on the screen.

Stencil printing can be performed either in the off-contact mode or by

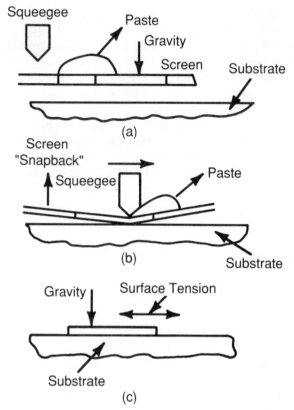

FIG. 9.13 Transfer of solder paste: a. Before printing, paste is on the screen. It will not flow through the open mesh because of rheological properties, b. During printing, the screen openings fill with paste. Paste is transferred to substrate as screen snaps back, c. After printing, gravity and paste rheology control predrying spreading. (*Thick Film Microcircuit Technology*, D. W. Hamer. Copyright 1972, Wiley-Interscience. Reprinted by permission of John Wiley & Sons, Inc.)

contact printing. In contact printing, the stencil is in direct contact with the board during the entire print cycle. After printing, it is "peeled" away from the board by lifting from one end.

9.5.2 Screen printing equipment

A typical screen printer is illustrated in Fig. 9.15. It consists of the following elements:

- screen (or stencil)
- screen holder
- substrate holder
- squeegee
- squeegee holder
- base

(a)

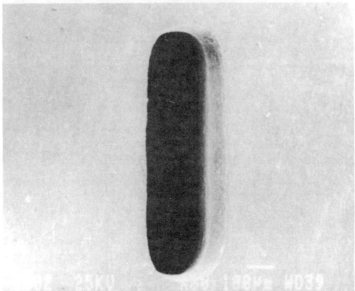

(b)

FIG. 9.14   Scanning electron micrographs of emulsion screen (a), and metal stencil (b). (Reprinted with permission. Copyright 1985, *Circuits Manufacturing*, Miller Freeman Publications.)

FIG. 9.15 Solder paste screen printer employing clamshell design. (Used by permission. Crystal Mark, Inc.)

Screens

The screen is the heart of the printer. It controls the locations where solder will be deposited and the thickness of the wet paste. A typical screen (Fig. 9.16) consists of a mesh woven from fine stainless steel wire. The size of the screen openings is controlled by the diameter of the wire and the *mesh size*, or number of wires per inch. Table 9.3 lists the mesh sizes most commonly used for deposition of SMT solder pastes.

The mesh is coated with a photosensitive emulsion. Areas of the emulsion exposed to light polymerize into a durable coating. Unexposed regions can be dissolved in a suitable developer. By exposing the emulsion to a negative image of the pattern and developing it, a series of openings is created in the emulsion at the locations where paste is to be dispensed.

Some screens use a thin metal foil electroplated onto the screen instead of the organic emulsion. Holes are chemically milled in the foil using standard photolithographic techniques. The advantages of the foil approach are longer screen life and better resistance to solvents.

The screen is held taut in a frame. Although wooden frames have been used, much greater control is afforded through the use of cast aluminium

FIG. 9.16   Overall view of stencil. (Used by permission. Affiliated Manufacturers, Inc.)

Mesh count per inch	Wire diameter		Mesh opening	
	in	μm	in	μm
60	0.0045	114	0.0122	309
80	0.0020	50	0.0105	266
80	0.0037	94	0.0088	224
105	0.0030	76	0.0065	165
120	0.0026	66	0.0057	145

Note 1: Swiss fine wire cloth

TABLE 9.3   Screen sizes for depositing solder pastes

frames. The maximum frame size that can be used is a function of the particular printer and can range from as small as 125 × 125 mm (5 × 5 in) to as large as 915 × 915 mm (36 × 36 in). For printing of large boards, the screen should be at least 150 mm (6 in) larger than the board on all sides so as not to deform the screen wire beyond its elastic limit during printing.

The orientation of the mesh on the frame can be specified by the user. Mesh parallel to the sides of the frame is designated as 90°. An angle of 45° is often selected because it affords better resolution and edge acutance of the printed image. In addition, the stress due to squeegee pressure is distributed over a larger number of wires, resulting in longer screen life.

The approximate wet thickness of the solder paste deposited by a screen can be found from the following formula:

$$T_w = (T_m \times A_o) + T_e$$

where T_w = wet paste thickness
$\quad\quad T_m$ = mesh weave thickness
$\quad\quad A_o$ = decimal fraction of open area
$\quad\quad T_e$ = emulsion thickness

Stencils

Today, much of the so-called screen printing of solder pastes is actually performed with stencils. Although the initial cost of a stencil is somewhat higher than that of an emulsion screen, the usable life is considerably greater—by as much as 25 times. Stencils do not employ a wire mesh and are therefore less sensitive to solder particle size. In addition, they are less likely to deteriorate after long periods of storage or repeated cleaning cycles.

Stencils are chemically milled from solid sheets of brass, beryllium-copper, stainless steel, nickel, or molybdenum. They can be manufactured in a wide range of thicknesses from under 0.025 mm (0.001 in) to over 1.27 mm (0.050 in). The thickness of the deposited paste is precisely controlled by the thickness of the stencil.

Stencils for contact printing are usually glued directly to the frame. For off-contact printing, the stencil is mounted to the frame by way of a polyester or stainless steel mesh. The mesh is epoxied to the stencil and provides the resiliency necessary to insure intimate contact between stencil and board. It does not, however, extend into the printable area of the stencil.

Screen holder

The screen holder holds the screen and frame assembly rigidly in place during the printing operation. It must be capable of accurately registering the screen to the printed wiring board and maintaining this registration throughout the entire production run.

Design of the printer follows one of two general forms. The first is the *clamshell* approach (Fig. 9.15), in which the screen holder is hinged to the machine at the rear, opening and closing in an arc above the substrate holder. (In some equipment, the screen holder is fixed and the substrate holder rotates.) The second is the *vertical post* approach. This design employs a screen holder that is supported by either two or four posts and travels vertically along the posts (Fig. 9.17). Clamshell printers are less expensive but vertical post printers are capable of better registration accuracy.

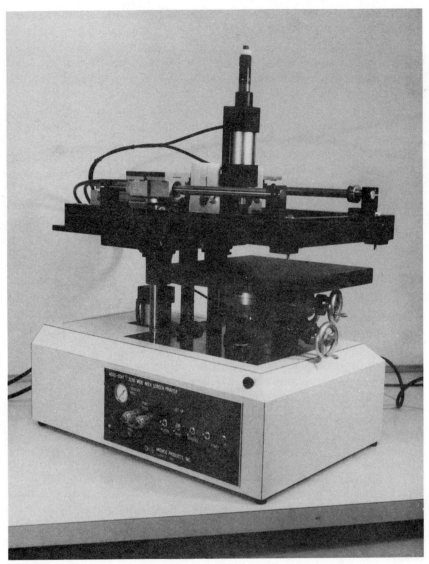

FIG. 9.17   Screen printer employing vertical post construction. (Used by permission. Aremco Products, Inc.)

Substrate holder

The substrate holder must firmly support the printed wiring board during the printing process. It must also be able to repeatedly locate boards with respect to the screen. Lightweight ceramic substrates are normally registered to the press by aligning the edge of the substrate to the edges of a machined pocket in the holder. They are usually held in place by a vacuum fixture.

Larger printed wiring boards must employ alternative techniques. It is not usually feasible to register to the edges of the board because of the loose alignment tolerances between the board edges and the artwork (refer to Section 10.4.3 for a more complete discussion of artwork alignment). Tooling pins are more commonly used as the locating features. Where extreme accuracy is required, a vision system that registers with respect to fiducial marks in the artwork can be employed.

In some cases it is possible to rely only on the tooling pins and gravity to hold the board in place. When this is not practical, mechanical clamps can be employed. To prevent damage to the screen, clamps and tooling pins must not extend above the top surface of the board. Vacuum hold-down is not normally used on large boards because via holes prevent formation of a firm vacuum.

Squeegee

The squeegee is normally constructed of neoprene or polyurethane rubber. Hardnesses range from about 30 to 90 durometer (Shore A), with 60 durometer being most common.

Diamond-shaped or V-shaped blades, as shown in Fig. 9.18, with a 60–80° contact angle are most commonly used. Squeegees wear quickly under continuous use, so it is important that the blade be checked regularly and be sharpened or replaced when the edge becomes dull.

Squeegee holder

The squeegee holder orients the squeegee and moves it through the printing cycle. The velocity of the stroke and pressure exerted by the squeegee on the screen are adjustable. Some equipment also provides for adjustment of *squeegee skew*, an angular variation of the blade from perpendicularity to the direction of travel. Some evidence suggests that skew can be an important parameter in controlling resolution and edge acutance of the printed image.[6]

Print quality is relatively insensitive to squeegee speed for lower velocities, reaching a maximum at an intermediate value. Above this value, quality decreases rapidly.

Another important function of the squeegee holder is to support the *flood bar*, a bar that travels ahead of the squeegee to spread paste uniformly across the screen. Flooding is usually accomplished in a separate stroke prior to the printing stroke.

A separate flood step is not generally used in stencil printing because the paste would flow through the large stencil openings. This would cause the paste to smear on the board. Instead, the squeegee is programmed to print

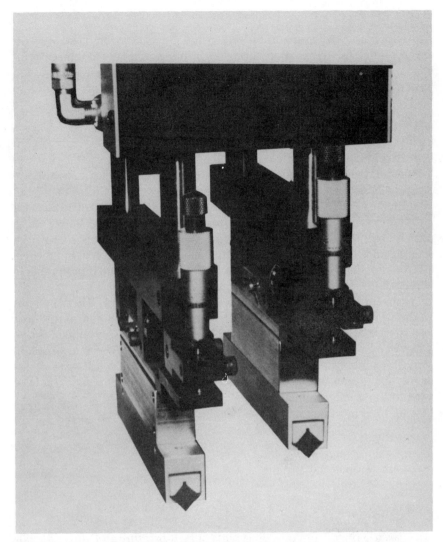

FIG. 9.18 Squeegee head. This dual-head design permits paste to be printed on both the forward and backward stroke, eliminating the need for a separate flooding stroke. (Used by permission. Affiliated Manufacturing, Inc.)

on both forward and reverse strokes. After printing on the forward stroke, the squeegee lifts up off the screen and travels a short distance farther to pass over the bead of paste. It then lowers down onto the screen and is able to print again on the reverse stroke.

Some machines use two separate blades for printing in the forward and reverse directions. The blades are separated by a short distance and the paste is trapped between them. The blades can be lowered independently and, at any one time, only one blade makes contact with the screen.

Base

The base must rigidly support the screen and squeegee assemblies, preventing unwanted relative motion during the printing cycle. On automatic printers, it also contains the board feeding mechanism and, optionally, a vision system to automatically align the screen to the board artwork.

9.6 APPLICATION OF PASTE BY SYRINGE

Screen printing is not efficient for small production lots since setup time can become a significant fraction of the total run time. Small lot sizes also are wasteful of solder paste. The amount of paste necessary to charge the screen may be far in excess of that actually deposited on the boards. The physical properties of the paste can change after being worked by the squeegee, so the paste should not be returned to its original container. If the screen will be used again within a short time the paste can be left on the screen, but the risk of oxidation increases. An alternative deposition technique is preferable in these situations.

Syringe dispensing systems are an attractive alternative. These systems deposit precise dots of paste under the control of a computerized 3-axis transport mechanism. The only setup is the time necessary to load a new program, and the waste of solder paste is eliminated. The rate of solder deposition is considerably lower than screen printing. Typical systems dispense one to four solder dots per second, and components require at least one dot for each termination.

The three most commonly used deposition systems are:

- air-driven syringe
- peristaltic pump
- positive displacement pump

9.6.1 Air-driven syringe

Air-driven syringes employ a short burst of high-pressure air to drive a small volume of paste out the tip of a fine-tip syringe of about 0.6 mm diameter. A typical burst would consist of 50 PSI for up to 3 seconds. Unfortunately, solder paste is not a Newtonian fluid, so the application of pressure at one end of the syringe will not necessarily result in a repeatable volume of paste exiting the tip. The high-pressure air can cause the heavy solder to separate from the lighter flux and binder.

9.6.2 Peristaltic pump[7]

The peristaltic pump avoids many of the difficulties of the air-driven syringe. It does not employ high-pressure air, so separation of paste constituents is

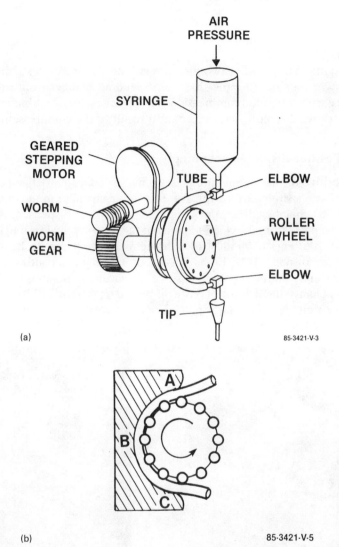

FIG. 9.19 Peristaltic pump system for dispensing solder paste: a. Overall view, b. Detail of pump. (Used by permission. Cahners Exposition Group.)

less of a problem. It also dispenses a fixed quantity of paste that is repeatably determined by the design of the pump.

A typical system is illustrated in Fig. 9.19a. Paste is driven from the syringe by low-pressure air into the pump tubing. The pump moves controlled volumes of the paste to the tip where it is dispensed onto the board. The operation of the pump can be understood from Fig. 9.19b. Rotating rollers compress a flexible silicone tubing. Paste enters the tubing at Point A, where a measured volume of paste is trapped between successive rollers, and exits at Point C. In operation, the rollers are rotated a fixed amount for each dot of paste to be dispensed. The volume of paste is set by the amount of rotation and the diameter of the tubing. Typical volumes range between 0.05 and 0.2 μl.

Peristaltic pumps suffer two limitations. The volume of paste dispensed varies over time because the shape of the tubing changes from circular to elliptical with continued compression. The tubing is also a high-maintenance item because it rapidly deteriorates as a result of the compression forces.

9.6.3 Positive-displacement pump[8]

The positive-displacement pump is similar in concept to the peristaltic pump. Paste is driven by low-pressure air into a chamber in the pump. The size of this chamber determines the volume of paste dispensed. A piston forces the paste from the chamber and out the tip. A typical system is shown in Fig. 9.20a. Fig. 9.20b illustrates the detail of the pump itself. A typical system can dispense 0.1-μl dots at rates of 4 dots per second.

The primary limitation of the positive-displacement pump is the inability to easily change the volume of paste dispensed. It is frequently necessary to dispense multiple dots on large pads. This results in a considerable reduction in effective throughput.

(a)   (b)

FIG. 9.20 Positive displacement pump dispenser for solder paste: a. Overall view, b. Detail of pump. (Used by permission. Creative Automation, Inc.)

9.7 ALTERNATIVE SOLDER APPLICATION PROCESSES

The problems associated with solder pastes have led researchers to explore alternative methods of supplying solder to the joint. These fall into two general categories, depending on whether the solder is applied to the printed wiring board or to the component. Several approaches are described in the following paragraphs. For various reasons, none has gained widespread acceptance within the industry and should be considered only when solder paste cannot be employed effectively.

9.7.1 Deposition on printed wiring board

In this approach, solder is deposited directly onto the component lands as part of the printed wiring board fabrication process. It is popularly known as the *solder bump* process in reference to the appearance of the completed board land patterns. The solder bump process has the following advantages over solder paste deposition:

- Setup time associated with paste deposition can be completely eliminated, making single-unit lot sizes more practical.
- Solder coated boards can be stored for extended periods and used only as needed.
- Solder balls are not a problem as there is no spattering of paste.

Two variations of this process have been used. In the first, a heavy solder plating is applied to the board. In the second, solder paste is applied and immediately reflowed.

Heavy solder plating[9]

An amount of solder sufficient to form a reliable joint can be plated onto the board as an extension of a standard tin–lead plating process. A separate masking step to expose only the component lands is necessary prior to plating, and the final solder thickness should be in the range 0.1–0.2 mm (0.004–0.008 in).

The plating process produces flat-topped bumps of uniform thickness. The shelf-life of the bumped boards can be improved by reflowing the boards to alloy the solder, but this degrades the bump uniformity. The primary disadvantage of this technique is the extended plating time required to build up the necessary bump thickness.

Paste deposition and reflow

An alternative method for applying solder to the lands is to screen print and immediately reflow a standard solder paste. This approach does not eliminate the difficulties associated with the use of solder paste but merely transfers them to an earlier point in the process. One advantage is that defects can be identified and corrective action taken before the board is populated with components. Another advantage is that any solder balls that occur during reflow can easily be removed prior to component assembly.

Reflowed bumps have irregular geometries, which increases the difficulty of obtaining intimate contact between component lead and land. Lead coplanarity thus becomes much more critical. Little data has been published to clarify the problems encountered in this approach.

9.7.2 Pretinned components

Rather than applying the solder to the printed wiring board, it is possible to apply it to the component terminations. In the solder transfer application technique (STAT), solder paste is screen printed onto an unmetallized ceramic substrate.[10] The components are placed into the solder and the assembly is reflowed. Since the solder cannot wet the substrate, it flows entirely onto the leads instead. The tinned components can then be placed onto a fluxed printed wiring board and reflowed.

STAT is an effective method for depositing a controlled amount of solder onto the component terminations. The reflowed solder forms a flat-bottomed surface and can actually improve the coplanarity of leaded devices. However, components with leads pretinned in this manner are not commercially available, so the process must be performed manually at the user's facility. This results in a considerable cost increase and also increases the risk of handling damage.

9.7.3 Fluxing

Regardless of the approach used to apply the solder, flux must be applied to the board immediately prior to component assembly. The flux serves two purposes: it promotes solderability of both components and board and it holds the components in place prior to reflow. Various techniques can be used to apply the flux, which is generally a Type RMA or Type RA rosin flux. Screen printing is often used, but this largely negates the benefits of reduced setup time. More practical approaches include dipping the entire board in flux or painting it on with a brush.

APPENDIX

Brookfield viscometer test procedure. The following standardized test can be used to perform viscosity measurements on solder paste using the Brookfield viscometer.

a. *Equipment/materials*
   Brookfield Model RVTD Viscometer with Model C Helipath Stand
   Model TF Spindle
   Thermometer capable of measuring to $\pm 1\,°C$
   Spatula
   Isopropyl Alcohol

b. Procedure

1. Level the viscometer and turn the power on to stabilize. Install the TF spindle 50–75 mm (2–3 in) above the top of the paste container to avoid spindle damage. Set the bottom stop on the Helipath so that the spindle stops 10 mm (0.4 in) above the bottom of the container of solder paste.

2. Paste temperature should be maintained at $25 \pm 1\,°C$ during the measurement. Measure the temperature of the paste with the thermometer. Use a water bath around the paste container if necessary to stabilize temperature.

3. Use the clean spatula to thoroughly stir the paste, being careful not to entrap air in the paste.

4. Center the paste container under the spindle and carefully lower the spindle into the paste.

5. Reset the top stop on the Helipath stand so that the total vertical travel is 25 mm (1 in) or so that the spindle does not emerge from the paste during the test.

6. Set spindle rotation for 5 RPM.

7. Simultaneously turn on spindle and Helipath motors.

8. After 2 minutes, record the reading. Multiply by a factor of 20,000 (TF spindle at 5 RPM) to obtain the viscosity in centipoise. A recorder connected to the viscometer can provide a record for quality control as well as to show the time dependence of viscosity.

9. After completion of test, thoroughly clean spindle and spatula in isopropyl alcohol.

REFERENCES

1. Hamer, D., and Biggers, J. *Thick Film Hybrid Microcircuit Technology*, John Wiley and Sons, 1972, pp. 95–100.
2. Evans, G. "Specifying Solder Pastes for Surface Mounting," *Connection Technology*, May 1986, pp. 25–29.
3. McLellan, N. "Wicking Free Solder Joint Formation In 'J' Leaded Surface Mount Devices," *Technical Papers on Surface Mount Technology 1984–1986*, Texas Instruments, Houston, TX, 1986.
4. *Federal Specification QQ-S-571E, Solder, Tin Alloy; Tin-lead Alloy; and Lead Alloy*. U.S. Government Printing Office, 1981.
5. Rubin, W. "Smoothing The Way for Solder Creams," *Circuits Manufacturing*, Oct. 1983, pp. 74–80.
6. Frecska, T. "Screen-Printing Press Review," *SITE*, Aug. 1986, pp. 36–43.
7. Peterson, N. "A Solder Paste Dispenser for SMD Assembly," *Proceedings of NEPCON/West '86*, February 1986, pp. 619–621.
8. Engel, J. "Dispensing As An Alternative To Screening Solder Paste," *Assembly Engineering*, July 1986.
9. Hendriks, H., and Inpyn, B. "Fluxless SMD Soldering," *Circuits Manufacturing*, Oct. 1984, pp. 40–44.
10. Kershner, R., Panousis, N., and Jaffe, D. "A New Solder Transfer Application

Technique (STAT) for Coating Leads of Applique Components," *Journal of The International Society for Hybrid Microelectronics*, Oct. 1981.
11. Rice, D., and Wells, B. *Spread Factor of Solder Paste on Oxidized Copper: A Measure of Flux Activity*, Hewlett-Packard Laboratories, Palo Alto, CA, Sept. 1985.
12. Roos-Kozel, B. "Solder Pastes," *Surface Mount Technology*, ISHM Technical Monograph 6984–002, International Society of Hybrid Microelectronics, Silver Spring, MD, 1984, p. 140.

10

Component placement

The component-placement operation, often called "pick and place," consists of all steps necessary to remove a component from its packaging materials and mount it onto the printed wiring board. Because of the extreme accuracy required (± 0.2 mm or less for many component types), automatic equipment is mandatory for all but the smallest production volumes.

The basic placement sequence consists of the following seven steps:

a. Board indexing: the positioning of a new board onto the system;
b. Board registration: alignment of the board to the machine's coordinate system;
c. Component presentation: presentation of components to predetermined locations for pickup by the placement tool;
d. Component pickup: extraction of components from the feeders in preparation for placement;
e. Component centering: alignment of the component to the machine's coordinate system;
f. Component placement: actual placement onto the board;
g. Board indexing: removal of the fully loaded board from the machine.

Two optional steps can be included to provide additional capability:

a. Adhesive dispensing: application of adhesive for devices that are to be wave soldered;
b. On-line electrical verification: electrical testing of components as part of the placement cycle.

10.1 GENERAL MACHINE CONSTRUCTION

A generalized component-placement machine is illustrated in Fig. 10.1. Major machine components are as follows:

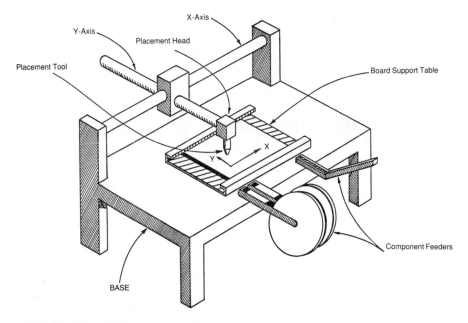

FIG. 10.1   Generalized component placement machine.

Base

This is the structure on which all other parts of the machine are mounted. It must be rigid enough to support the rest of the system without allowing excessive vibration, which would degrade placement accuracy.

Component feeders

Components can be presented to the system from a variety of shipping containers. Commonly available feeders accept components in magazines, tape and reel, waffle trays, or bulk packaging.

Board support table

The board must be rigidly secured during the placement operation. The table prevents board movement without intruding into the useable placement area. On some equipment, it also automatically feeds a new board into the machine and removes the populated board for delivery to the next process step.

Placement head

The head contains everything necessary to pick components from the feeders and accurately place them onto the board. It includes the placement tool, centering jaws (if used), and optional features such as an adhesive dispenser, electrical verification fixturing, and optical board alignment system.

Placement tool

The heart of the placement head is the tool used to pick components from the feeders and hold them securely during transport to the placement site. A single tool can usually only handle a limited range of part sizes. On machines that must place a wide variety of component types, tools must be changed either manually or under program control.

10.2 EQUIPMENT CHARACTERISTICS

The three characteristics of primary importance in component placement equipment are:

- accuracy
- speed
- flexibility

The accuracy of a machine determines the range of component types that it can place. Its speed sets the capacity of the line and determines how many machines are necessary to meet anticipated product volumes. Its degree of flexibility determines whether one type of machine can handle all placement needs or whether several more specialized machines are needed.

10.2.1 Accuracy

Many definitions of machine accuracy have been used by equipment manufacturers. When comparing equipment it is essential that the definition used in the product data sheet be fully understood. Some of the terms in common use are:

- placement accuracy
- resolution
- repeatability

Placement accuracy

The term *placement accuracy* (more properly, placement *in*accuracy) describes how accurately a component can be positioned with respect to its target location on the board. It is defined as the position error of the component termination whose deviation from target position is largest. It consists of the two error components in Fig. 10.2:

- translational error (misalignment of component centroid)
- rotational error (angular displacement of component axes)

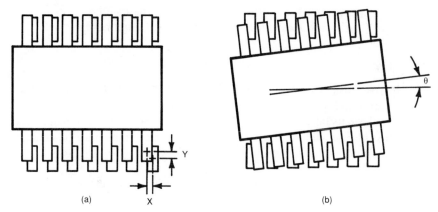

FIG. 10.2   Placement accuracy error components: a. Translational error, b. Rotational error.

Translational error

Translational error primarily results from inaccuracies in the X-Y positioning system and includes offset, scaling, and axis orthogonality errors. The component centering mechanism is also a factor if it does not accurately align the component centroid to the placement tool axis.

Ideally, translational error should be specified as a *true position radius* (TPR) about the design center,[1] as shown in Fig. 10.3a. Many equipment manufacturers specify simple X-Y tolerances. Although this gives the appearance of an improved specification, the greatest deviation from design location can be greater than the implied specification by as much as a factor of 1.4 (Fig. 10.3b). If only X and Y tolerances are specified, TPR error can be found from the equation:

$$T = \sqrt{X_t^2 + Y_t^2}$$ [10.1]

where T = true position radius error due to translational errors
X_t = error component along X-axis
Y_t = error component along Y-axis

where T = true position radius error due to translational errors
X_t = error component along X-axis
Y_t = error component along Y-axis

Rotational error

Rotational error results from inaccuracy in the component centering mechanism and from the rotational precision of the placement tool. It is specified as an angular tolerance about the target placement orientation.

Rotational error is greatest on those terminations farthest from the component centroid. To simplify the analysis, this error is commonly approximated by calculating the displacement of the package corner. Referring to Fig. 10.4, displacement can be found from the equation:

$$R = 2L \sin(\theta/2)$$ [10.2]

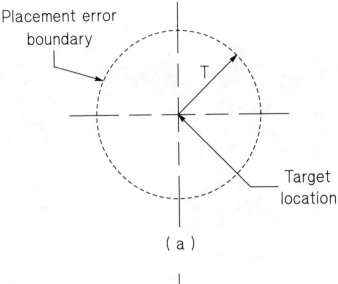

(a)

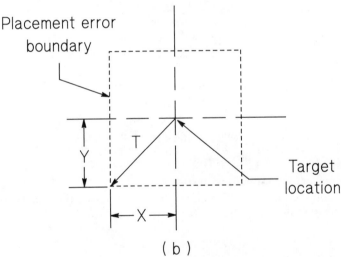

(b)

FIG. 10.3   Definitions of translational placement error: a. True position radius, b. X-Y tolerance.

where R = true position displacement due to rotational error
L = distance from center of component to package corner
θ = maximum angular deviation from target orientation

It is sometimes desirable to calculate the components of rotational error along the X-axis and Y-axis. For the small error angle of a typical component-placement machine, these error components can be found from the equations:

$X_r = 2L \sin (\theta/2) \sin \phi$
$Y_r = 2L \sin (\theta/2) \cos \phi$

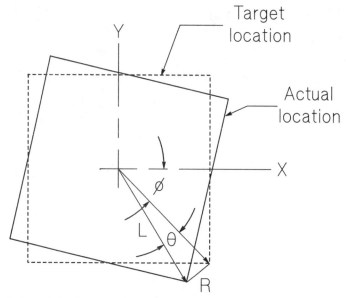

FIG. 10.4 Package corner displacement due to rotational error.

where X_r = X-axis error due to rotational error
$\quad\quad Y_r$ = Y-axis error due to rotational error
$\quad\quad \phi$ = angle from the center of the component to the lead, referenced to the component X-axis per Fig. 10.4.

Total error
Rotational error combines with translational error to produce a cumulative effect. Total TPR error is found by the vector addition of the two components. The X-axis and Y-axis errors are found from:

$$T_x = X_t + X_r \quad\quad\quad\quad [10.3]$$
$$T_y = Y_t + Y_r$$

where T_x = X-axis component of total error
$\quad\quad T_y$ = Y-axis component of total error

Total error is then found from:

$$\text{TPR} = \sqrt{T_x^2 + T_y^2} \quad\quad\quad\quad [10.4]$$

Since the effect of rotational error depends on component size, it is not possible to define a single number to represent overall machine performance. Instead, translational error and rotational error must be specified separately. Knowing the types of components to be placed, overall placement accuracy can be calculated from these two numbers.

Consider the following example. A placement machine has a specified translational error of ±0.02 mm in the X and Y axes and a rotational error of ±0.25 degrees. What is the worst-case displacement of the corner leads of an 84-lead PLCC?

Referring to Fig. 10.5, the first step is to calculate the rotational error from eqn. [10.2]. For an 84-lead PLCC, L = 21 mm. Rotational error is then:

$$R = 2(21) \sin(0.125) = 0.092 \, \text{mm}$$

Next calculate the X-axis and Y-axis components of rotational error:

$$X_r = 0.092 \sin(45°) = .065 \, \text{mm}$$
$$Y_r = 0.092 \cos(45°) = .065 \, \text{mm}$$

Total error along the two axes is then:

$$T_x = 0.02 + 0.065 = 0.085 \, \text{mm}$$
$$T_y = 0.02 + 0.065 = 0.085 \, \text{mm}$$

And,

$$TPR = \sqrt{(0.085)^2 + (0.085)^2} = 0.120 \, \text{mm}$$

Placement accuracy requirements
The accuracy requirement for a component is a function of such factors as component type, design criteria, and reliability requirements. The factors of greatest importance are:

Component types. The effects of rotational errors are seldom significant for small chip components but can become the dominant error source for the

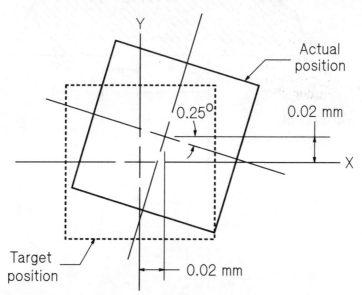

FIG. 10.5   Placement error components for text example.

corner leads of large PLCCs or ceramic chip carriers. As a result, equipment designed to place integrated circuits must be more accurate than equipment that places only chip components.

Acceptable lead-to-land misalignment. The extent to which the component termination is allowed to overhang the edge of the land has a major impact on required equipment accuracy. Some specifications define that a component is acceptably located if no more than one-half of the termination width extends beyond the circuit land (Fig. 10.6). Others restrict this to one-quarter of the width, and still others do not allow any of the termination to extend off the pad. Acceptance criteria are driven exclusively by product requirements—a high-reliability life-support system would permit less deviation than an inexpensive consumer product.

Land pattern design. One way to reduce overhang is to widen the lands so that greater misalignment can occur before exceeding the lead-to-land registration specification. However, this approach can only be a partial solution. Lands that are too wide can cause increased soldering defects due to

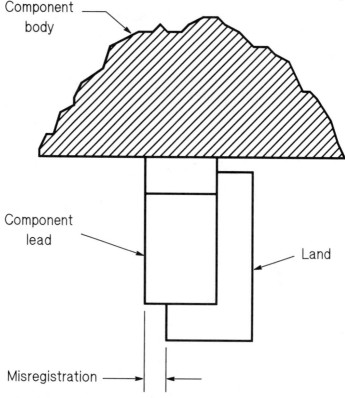

FIG. 10.6   Lead-to-land misregistration.

component skewing and tombstoning. Larger solder fillets also have lower ductility and degrade the reliability of noncompliant joints. Finally, large circuit lands reduce the amount of space available for conductor routing on the board. Generally, lands should be kept small enough to permit at least one trace to be routed between IC leads and under chip components.

Large lead-count integrated circuits demand the highest placement accuracy. Since translational and rotational errors combine to produce the total error, some tradeoff is possible. For a given component type, a machine with small rotational inaccuracy can tolerate greater translational error than one with larger rotational inaccuracy. Approximate requirements for several IC types as a function of translational and rotational accuracy of the equipment are shown in Fig. 10.7.

Resolution

Any real machine has a finite ability to resolve successive points in space. Machine resolution is fixed by the resolution of stepping motors and the rotary or linear encoders on the axis drive mechanisms. When the axes are programmed to travel to a particular point, they will actually go to the nearest point capable of being resolved. This can result in a position error (called *quantization error*) of up to one-half of the machine resolution.

While resolution defines the ultimate precision of the machine, it does not necessarily have a direct relationship to total placement accuracy. Resolu-

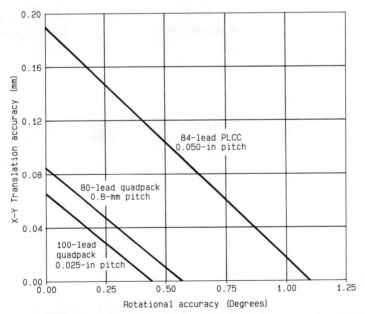

FIG. 10.7 Tradeoff between rotational accuracy and translational accuracy for various IC packages.

tion is simply a measure of the finest increments the machine can move. Accuracy includes all other error contributions, some of which can be far larger than quantization error. In fact, it is possible for one machine with high resolution to have worse total accuracy than a different machine with lower resolution.

Although resolution can be important in certain special cases, it is much less useful as an overall measure of machine performance. It should never be the sole specification for machine accuracy.

Repeatability

This term describes the ability of the placement tool to repeatedly return to a target point. Bidirectional repeatability is defined by the National Machine Tool Builders' Association as the "expected dispersion from the mean resulting when the approach to any given point is programmed from both directions in a series of trials."[2] It is normally specified as a 3-sigma limit, as shown in Fig. 10.8.

The relationship between repeatability, resolution, and placement accuracy should be clearly understood. Standard practice is to include repeatability within the placement accuracy specification, as shown in Fig. 10.9. For example, a machine with an accuracy specification of 0.1 mm true position radius and repeatability of 0.05 mm true position radius can be expected to place the component termination within 0.1 mm of the design location 99.7% of the time (if specified to a 3-sigma limit). Over a large number of placements to the same location, the deviation of any single placement will not exceed 0.05 mm of the center of the distribution. Not

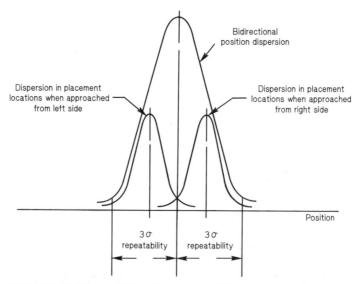

FIG. 10.8 Definition of bidirectional repeatability.

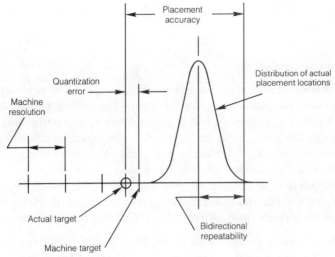

FIG. 10.9 Relationship between various accuracy-related terms.

every machine manufacturer uses this convention, so it is wise to review published specifications carefully.

10.2.2 Speed

In most surface mount factories, the component-placement operation is the slowest element in the process. The speed of the placement machine is thus the limiting factor in overall line capacity. Since faster machines do not incur proportionally higher overhead expenses, they are capable of achieving lower factory operating costs.

Unfortunately, comparing the speed of one machine to that of another similar machine is not an easy task. No standard methods have yet been developed. Data published by equipment manufacturers tends to present their own machines in the most favorable light. Some users have been unpleasantly surprised when they discovered, after purchasing a specific machine, that actual production throughputs were considerably less than projections based on data-sheet information.[3]

The problem arises because actual speeds are heavily dependent on a number of factors outside the control of the equipment manufacturer. Board design, number and location of component feeders, production lot sizes, setup complexity, and the efficiency of the board loading program all heavily influence the volume of product that can be produced in a given day. Equipment specifications can only represent the performance achieved on some "average" board that may have little relation to actual customer designs. Few manufacturers adequately define how published data was taken or how users can extrapolate that information to their own boards.

Several of the more commonly used definitions of machine speed are presented below:

Equipment placement rate

This is the most common data-sheet specification, defined as the speed at which an average placement cycle is completed excluding any external factors. A placement cycle consists of a complete round trip from pickup site to placement site and return, during which a component is actually placed. On machines with multiple heads it is defined as the effective rate of placement when all heads are included in the calculation.

The amount of head travel permitted during the cycle is restricted, either by specifying a maximum distance of travel, a maximum distance between successive feeders, or both. A typical specification reads as follows:

> Placement rate is measured as cycles from pickup point to placement point and return. Feeder travel is not to exceed 12 locations between consecutive 8 mm tape feeders. Under these conditions, placement rate is at least 4500 components per hour.[4]

Cycle rate

This is the most basic measure of machine speed. It is similar to placement rate except that the machine is operated in a *dry cycle* mode in which no parts are actually placed. This number thus excludes the effects of component pickup, centering, and placement, and so is somewhat higher than the equivalent placement rate. Although cycle rate can be useful in comparing machines, it should be used carefully. Unless information is provided describing how to derate this number for actual component placement, it cannot be used to predict production throughput. Some manufacturers use the term *test rate* instead of cycle rate.

Production throughput

This is the most important parameter to the equipment user. It is defined as the number of components placed per hour over an entire production shift, and is found by taking the total number of components placed during the shift and dividing by the length of the shift. For example, if a certain machine places 50,000 components during an 8-hour day, the hourly production throughput is $50,000/8 = 6,250$ components per hour.

Production throughput is derived by applying a number of derating factors to the placement cycle rate. The most significant are:

Board load/unload time
Before the placement sequence can begin, the board must be loaded onto

the machine; upon completion, it must be removed. This loading and unloading period is "dead" time during which the machine cannot place components. Board load/unload time can vary from as little as 5 or 10 seconds for an automated system to a minute or more if boards must be loaded manually.

Production mix
In factories that must handle a large number of board types, the number of different components might exceed the machine's feeder capacity. It is then necessary to periodically stop production to change the feeder setup. For boards of different physical sizes, the board support system must also be readjusted. These factors contribute dead time that is beyond the control of the equipment manufacturer.

Machine configuration
The feeders on sequential placement machines are generally arranged in rows at the sides of the machine. The time required to pick a component depends on the distance the head must travel to access the feeder. It may take twice as long to access feeders near the end of the row compared to those near the center. It is usually possible to optimize feeder placement for any particular board, but if several board types are built with a fixed setup, speed will inevitably be compromised.

Component mix
Machine cycle time is a function of component type. Integrated circuits must be positioned more precisely than small chip components, so a board with large numbers of ICs will generally take longer to populate than a board with a similar number of resistors and capacitors.

Available hours
In most cases, an eight-hour shift does not represent eight full hours of production. Lunch periods, coffee breaks, and miscellaneous other time off can reduce the actual time available for production to as little as six or seven hours. Factories with highly automated equipment that can be left running during these periods are less sensitive than factories that depend on the presence of operators.

Unscheduled downtime
This is potentially the most significant factor but the one least frequently discussed. Unscheduled downtime can result from such varied factors as poorly designed boards, components that do not meet specification, or poor placement-machine design. It is virtually certain to occur at least occasionally, so the machine should be designed to facilitate problem diagnosis and repair.

Because production throughput depends on many factors beyond the

| I. MINIMUM CYCLE TIME | 0.600 sec. (This yields a maximum throughput of 6000 components per hour) |

II. MACHINE CYCLE ADDED FACTORS

a. Component Spacing	Up to 1 in: no increase in run time
	Over 1 in: add 0.056 sec/in
b. Feeder Spacing	Up to 2.5 in: no increase in run time
	Over 2.5 in: add 0.170 sec/in
c. Rotation	Up to 90°: no increase in run time
	Over 90°: add 0.002 sec/degree
d. Tweezering	Normal: no increase in run time
	Alternate: add 0.460 sec

III. COMPLETE RUN ADDED FACTORS

a. Tool change	Add 2.800 sec PLUS:
	Add 0.170 sec/in in excess of 2.5 in of feeder movement
b. Manual Load/Unload	Operator dependent: estimate 40 seconds
c. Automatic Feed	Add 15 seconds

| IV. OVERALL RUN TIME | Calculated by taking minimum cycle time times number of machine cycles PLUS the largest time from Section II for each machine cycle PLUS each addition from Section III. |

TABLE 10.1 Placement cycle derating factors for the Dynapert/Precima MPS-500 sequential placement machine. (Used by permission. Dynapert Precima Ltd.)

control of the equipment manufacturer, it cannot be specified on equipment data sheets. The ideal data sheet would list equipment placement rate and provide derating factors that can be used to estimate production throughput. Although rare, some manufacturers do provide this derating data. Table 10.1 lists the factors that must be considered for one such machine.

10.2.3 Flexibility

Flexibility measures the ability of a machine to accommodate varying placement requirements. The factors that contribute to machine flexibility include:

- *component variety*
- *number of feeders*
- *ease of setup*

Component variety

A machine that can place a wide variety of components is more versatile than one that accepts only small chip devices. Although the fundamental limit on component variety is set by machine placement accuracy, this is not the only influence. The placement tool and centering mechanism must be compatible with the components, and appropriate component feeders must be available.

Most placement tools can accommodate only a limited range of component sizes. Increased flexibility is obtained through the use of two or more interchangeable tools. Ordinarily, both the tool tip and centering jaws (if present) are changed as a unit. To be most effective, the machine should be able to change tools automatically under program control.

The most common component feeders include tape-and-reel, magazine, bulk, and waffle tray. Some equipment, especially high-speed machines, can accept only limited feeder styles. More versatile equipment is able to handle all or most types of feeders, generally at some sacrifice in speed.

Number of feeders

Changing feeders on a placement machine is a slow process that increases cost and reduces production throughput. On small machines with limited feeder capacity, it might be necessary to reconfigure the machine with every change in board type. Larger machines require less setup. When feeder capacity increases to about 120–150 feeders, it might be possible to permanently store all components on line. No time is then consumed in feeder setup when changing from one production run to another.

The feeder capacity of a machine is usually expressed in terms of the maximum number of 8-mm tape feeders that can be mounted onto the machine. Some manufacturers instead specify the number of inches of feeder space. This can be converted to the equivalent number of 8-mm tape feeders by knowing the width of the feeder. This is often 1 in (25 mm) wide, although some machines house two tapes on one feeder.

Not all parts can be packaged in 8-mm tape, so the actual capacity of the machine will always vary from the specification. Feeders for wider tapes consume more space and diminish the total capacity. Magazine feeders consume less space and can result in increased capacity. However, magazine feeders hold far fewer parts than tapes and must be replenished more often. Feeder designs vary by manufacturer, so it is not possible to define space requirements in a general way. Approximate widths of several feeder types are given in Table 10.2.

With some machines, feeders can be positioned only at fixed locations, typically in 1-in increments. In this case, a feeder that is 1.5 in wide will actually consume two full inches of feeder space. Other machines permit *feeder compacting*. This makes it possible to compress all feeders together and increase the effective capacity of the machine. For this feature to be realizable, the equipment firmware must be capable of accessing any point along the feeder axis.

It is important to compare similar numbers when studying the capabilities

Feeder Type	Approximate Width Per Feeder
TAPE FEEDERS	
8 mm	15–25 mm
12 mm	25–30 mm
16 mm	25–30 mm
MAGAZINE FEEDERS	
SOIC—Narrow	10 mm
SOIC—Wide	15 mm
PLCC—20	15 mm
PLCC—44	30 mm
PLCC—84	30 mm
VIBRATORY FEEDERS	
Chip components	30 mm
SOT–89	60 mm

TABLE 10.2   Component feeder widths

of several machines. Some manufacturers have been known to emphasize the absolute maximum feeder capacity in their data sheets. This number, obtainable only when using magazine feeders exclusively, can be triple the 8-mm tape feeder capacity.

Ease of setup

The steps necessary to change from building one type of board to another combine to determine machine setup time. Elements that contribute to setup time can include any or all of the following:

- machine reprogramming
- feeder changeover
- board support system adjustment
- placement head adjustment/changeover

Machine reprogramming
Programming the placement machine to load a new board can be as simple as downloading a file from a computer or as complex as manually teaching the machine by stepping it through the desired placement sequence. Simple machines generally use *teach-mode* programming, while more sophisticated equipment offers several options.

Most production-grade machines now use magnetic floppy disks for program storage and have the ability to receive programs from an external computer system. A few machines still use magnetic tape as the program storage medium, but this is rapidly becoming obsolete. In either case, these machines are generally programmed in an *off-line* mode. Design coordin-ates for each component are entered into a separate computer, from which the actual placement program is generated. This approach is fast and does not take the machine out of production during the programming process. With boards designed on a CAD system, automatic program generation is possible by downloading the CAD data directly to the program-generating computer.

Lower-volume machines for prototyping and small-volume production are usually less flexible. Placement programs often must be generated by manually stepping the machine through the placement sequence. Once programmed, the data can usually be stored electronically for future recall. This *teach-mode* programming is more time-consuming and less precise than off-line programming. However, it has the advantage of inherently compen-sating for any systematic inaccuracy in the placement machine. (The machine accuracy on the least expensive equipment is frequently very poor. Accurate placement cannot be guaranteed if design coordinates are used to determine placement location.)

Feeder changeover
Unless all components can be stored on line, it will be necessary to change at least some of the component feeders when setting up for a new production run. Most equipment manufacturers have given special consideration to this problem and have attempted to reduce the time required for setup.

The most common solution is the "quick-release" feeder, which allows single feeders to be inserted and removed by simply operating a lever. An even faster method involves changing entire banks of feeders in one opera-tion. Using this approach, separate feeder banks can be maintained for each product or group of products to be built on the line. Changeover then becomes a simple task of removing one feeder bank and installing another.

Board support system adjustment
If the new board is smaller or larger than the machine can currently accommodate, the board support system must be adjusted. On automated machines, boards are transported on conveyor rails that contact only the edges of the board. Rail width is adjusted either manually or automatically under program control. Less expensive machines frequently make use of a dedicated tooling plate. In this case, setup consists of removing the old plate and installing a new one.

Setup can be eliminated by using workpiece holders to transport boards of all sizes. Holders such as shown in Fig. 10.10 serve as adapters that allow any board to be carried through the system without adjustment. However, the benefit obtained by this technique must be balanced against the added tooling cost incurred in the holders and the extra labor necessary to install and remove boards from holders.

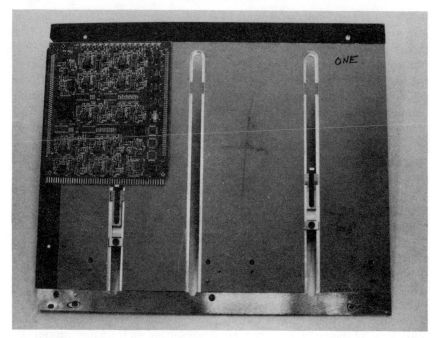

FIG. 10.10   Workpiece holder. (Photograph by the author.)

Placement head adjustment/changeover
The placement head must be changed or adjusted if it is not currently able to handle all components in the new production run. In many machines, this happens automatically under program control, but less expensive machines require manual adjustment.

10.3 EQUIPMENT CLASSIFICATION

Equipment can be designed either to sequentially place individual components or to simultaneously place all components on a board. Simultaneous placement systems offer short cycle times and high throughput, but sequential systems provide higher flexibility.

A variation of sequential placement is known as in-line placement. In this mode, a board progresses through a series of individual placement heads, each of which places only a single component. As with simultaneous placement systems, in-line systems are used when high production volumes must be achieved.

10.3.1 Sequential placement

Most surface mount machines employ a sequential placement technique. Individual components are picked from feeders and placed successively by the placement head. Unlike through-hole technology, sequencing and placement are performed on the same equipment, so no separate component sequencer (or sequenced tape) is required.

Equipment is usually classified into one of four categories, depending on its intended position in the marketplace:

- entry-level
- general-purpose
- high-speed
- precision

Entry-level

This category consists of small, relatively inexpensive equipment with limited capability. Machines in this category are primarily intended for prototype or very low volume production use. They have limited feeder capacities, small maximum board sizes, and relatively low placement rates. They are not usually designed for the heavy, continuous usage as would occur on a volume production floor.

Their primary advantage is low capital cost. To keep cost down, certain tradeoffs are unavoidable. The range of acceptable component types is restricted to devices with 0.050-in lead pitch or greater. Component centering, if performed at all, occurs at a separate centering nest. The feeder capacity rarely exceeds twenty to thirty 8-mm feeders. Average placement rates are 500–1500 components per hour with relatively poor placement accuracy.

Despite the compromises that must be made in design, entry-level machines can be very useful in certain situations. Placement rates, although low, still exceed manual rates by a considerable margin. Such machines are also able to place IC packages that would be difficult to align manually. They are especially suited for experimental use in facilities investigating the benefits of surface mount technology for new products. A typical entry-level machine is shown in Fig. 10.11.

General-purpose

Placement systems suitable for continuous production usage can cost hundreds of thousands of dollars. With such a significant investment, there is strong incentive to purchase a single machine capable of meeting all placement needs. General-purpose machines are targeted for this market. They are highly flexible with moderate production throughput. The majority of all installed systems fall into this classification.

Machines designed for general-purpose applications often employ a single placement tool that accesses a linear row of component feeders. To increase feeder capacity, feeders can be mounted in two rows—one at the front and

FIG. 10.11   Entry-level placement machine. (Used by permission. Manix Division of Henry Mann, Inc., Huntingdon Valley, PA.)

the other at the rear of the machine. Speed can be increased by mounting two tools on the head, one to pick components from the front row and the other to pick from the back row. This allows one tool to be picking a component while the other is placing, cutting cycle time approximately in half.

Typical general-purpose equipment places 3000 to 6000 components per hour. Parts are placed sequentially using a programmable placement head. Feeder capacity is at least one hundred 8-mm tape feeders and exceeds two hundred in some designs. The range of compatible components extends from small chip capacitors to large plastic leaded chip carriers in tape, magazine, or bulk packages. Some machines also accept matrix trays and bare semiconductor die. Accuracy is sufficient to permit placement of 0.050-in lead pitch devices to at least 84 leads, and finer pitch devices can frequently be accommodated. The typical maximum board size exceeds 300 × 450 mm (12 × 18 inches), and some equipment is able to handle 450 × 600-mm (18 × 24-in) boards.

This high flexibility invariably leads to compromises. General-purpose machines are slower than equipment optimized for a more limited range of components. They are also less accurate than machines designed for precision placement. These compromises, however, are what make this class of equipment so useful. Although not providing exceptional performance in any single area, general-purpose machines offer a range of performance that is often sufficient to satisfy the entire demand of a given factory. Representative equipment is illustrated in Figs. 10.12 and 10.13.

FIG. 10.12   General-purpose placement machine. (Used by permission. Photograph courtesy of Universal Instruments Corporation.)

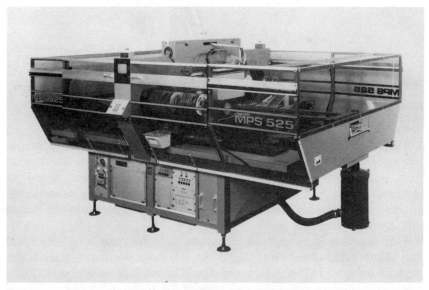

FIG. 10.13   General purpose placement machine. (Used by permission. Dynapert Precima Ltd.)

High-speed

This category consists of machines similar to general-purpose equipment but optimized for rapid placement of fewer component types. Because the earliest machines were only able to place small passive devices fed from 8-mm tape, they have commonly been called "chip shooters." More recent products can also accommodate larger components in wider tape sizes, but still cannot place the full range of components handled by general-purpose equipment.

High-speed machines make use of multiple placement tools mounted in a turret. The number of tools is equal to or greater than the number of steps performed during the placement cycle. A typical turret design is shown in Fig. 10.14. At any given time a tool is at each step in the sequence, permitting the effective cycle time (once all tools have been primed with components) to equal that of the longest individual step.

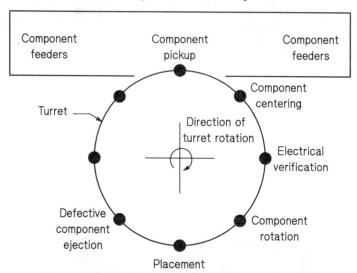

FIG. 10.14   Schematic of turret design for representative high speed placement machine (top view).

Typical high-speed machines are capable of sequentially placing components at rates between 9000 and 24,000 per hour. Feeder capacities extend from under sixty to over one hundred twenty 8-mm tapes. Nearly all machines in this category accept only tape-fed parts. One exception is equipment for placing cylindrical MELF resistors; these parts are loaded onto the machine from bulk.

Most machines in the current generation can place parts from both 8-mm and 12-mm tapes at full rated speed. Several models will also place larger parts up to 24-lead SOICs in 24-mm tape. The machine usually slows down when placing these larger parts to achieve the required accuracy. Typical high-speed machines are shown in Figs. 10.15 and 10.16.

(a)

(b)

(c)

FIG. 10.15 High speed machine for 8-mm taped components only: a. Overall view, b. Tape carousel, c. 4-station placement head. (Used by permission. Photograph courtesy of Universal Instruments Corporation.)

Precision

High lead-count integrated circuits, especially those with lead pitches below 0.050 in, present special challenges during placement. Because of their large bodies and closely spaced leads, they must be placed extremely accurately. Moreover, their fragile leads are easily damaged and are not compatible with mechanical centering tools. General-purpose machines are not usually adequate for these complex parts.

A relatively new class of equipment has emerged to address this more specialized need. Precision placement equipment is designed to place complex parts to accuracies of ±0.05 to ±0.1 mm at rates of 500 to 1000 components per hour. Parts are fed from magazines, waffle packs, or in some instances, tape-and-reel packaging. Several design approaches exist, but certain similarities are usually present. Vision systems are essential, both for board alignment and optical component centering. Robotic arms are frequently used to achieve the required level of accuracy. A typical system is illustrated in Fig. 10.17.

FIG. 10.16 High speed placement machine for components up to 16-mm tape. (Used by permission. Fuji Machine Manufacturing Company, Ltd.)

FIG. 10.17 Robotic placement machine for precision placement requirements. (Photograph by the author.)

10.3.2 Simultaneous placement

For extremely high production volumes it is sometimes cost-effective to perform simultaneous placement. In this approach, a head with multiple placement tools is used to simultaneously pick a number of components and place them on the board. A typical machine is illustrated in Fig. 10.18a. Components are fed from reels and picked by a set of 32 pipettes. The pipettes slide along a machined plate to locations set by hardware stops (Fig. 10.18b). The plate lowers to place all components simultaneously. Up to 12 stations can be connected in series, permitting placement of as many as 384 components per board at rates exceeding 500,000 components per hour.

The complexity of this approach requires that stringent rules be observed in the design of the board. Normally, components must be laid out on a grid format that corresponds to available feeder locations on the machine. The maximum number of components cannot exceed the number of feeder locations, and component types must be compatible with the feeders. Simultaneous placement machines usually accept only passive devices and small discrete semiconductors. Reconfiguring the machine to accept a different board type is usually very time-consuming.

10.3.3 In-line placement

Using this technique, extremely short cycle times can be achieved with fewer restrictions than imposed by simultaneous placement systems. A series of machines is employed, each designed to place only a single component on the board (Fig. 10.19). Boards are loaded sequentially as they progress down the line. Individual machines can be optimized to place a wide variety of component types and components need not be laid out on rigid grids.

Once the line is primed with boards, a new board reaches the end of the line after each placement cycle. The total cycle time is then just the time required to place a single component.

Since a separate machine is required for each component, in-line placement is usually economical only for boards with small numbers of components. Capital equipment costs can become prohibitive for boards with large numbers of components. Reconfiguration of the system is difficult. In-line placement is best justified when the unit volumes of a single product are high enough to keep the equipment in continual operation.

10.4 EQUIPMENT DESIGN CONSIDERATIONS

The mechanical design of a component-placement machine sets its ultimate performance limits. To maximize performance in some areas, compromise is generally necessary in others. For instance, a machine designed for highest placement accuracy must concede a certain amount of speed. Likewise,

(a)

(b)

FIG. 10.18 Mass placement machine: a. Overall view, b. Close-up of underside of head showing mechanical stops for pipettes. (Used by permission. North American Philips SMD Technology, Inc.)

FIG. 10.19   In-line placement machine. (Used by permission. Universal Instruments, Inc.)

equipment designed for high speed might sacrifice accuracy and also restrict the component types and feeding mechanisms it can accommodate.

Factors that determine machine capability include the following:

10.4.1 Overall mechanical structure

Placement speed and accuracy are controlled largely by the approach used to transport and position components. Two general approaches are used:

i. Equipment in which all movement is confined to the placement head. The board remains stationary while components are placed.

ii. Equipment in which both the board and the placement head move during the process. Typically, the head picks components from the feeders and presents them to a fixed location. The table moves the board in both the X and Y axes to position the correct component land pattern under the component.

Highest placement accuracy is generally obtained when all motion is confined to the head because only two transport mechanisms contribute to overall X-Y positional error. When both head and board move, an additional mechanism is necessary. The X and Y axis mechanisms (now located in the table rather than the head) accurately orient the board under the head; the head must also move, transporting components from the feeders to a repeatable location. Errors in both the head and table mechanisms can accumulate, increasing the total error. In both approaches, component rotation is nearly always performed within the head.

Equipment that employs a moving table can experience another potential problem due to the inertia of components once they are placed. To realize high placement rates, the table must move rapidly to orient the board under the head. Table accelerations of 10 to 30 m/sec^2 are not uncommon under these conditions. Such accelerations can cause large components (such as PLCCs) to move after placement. The problem can be avoided by slowing the table down when placing these components.

The tradeoff for accuracy is speed. When both head and table move, parallel motion is possible. The head can pick a component while the table simultaneously positions the board. Machines of this type can achieve cycle times of about 0.2 to 0.7 second per placement. When all movement occurs in the head, each step in the process must be performed sequentially. Placement cycle times from about 1 to 3 seconds are typical.

10.4.2 X-Y transport mechanism design

The basic speed and accuracy of a placement machine is determined by the design of the mechanism used to move the X and Y axes. Transport mechanisms are either open-loop or closed-loop systems (Fig. 10.20). Open-loop systems, which lack any form of feedback to correct axis drive errors, are inexpensive but lacking in accuracy. Closed-loop systems employ rotary or linear shaft encoders to track the position of the mechanism to reduce positional errors. These systems provide highest accuracy but at a considerable increase in equipment cost. Open-loop systems are found only on the least expensive machines designed for small-volume prototyping. Production-quality systems invariably employ some form of closed-loop feedback.

Several types of drive mechanisms can be used. Chains or belts are often employed in inexpensive open-loop equipment. They can also be used in closed-loop systems. More precise movement can be obtained through the use of a *lead screw*, a ground steel shaft in which a precision spiral track has been cut (Fig. 10.21). A ball-bearing sleeve rides in the track, moving linearly in proportion to the rotation of the shaft. When using lead-screw drives in a closed-loop system, a rotary shaft encoder can be used as the feedback sensor. Rotary encoders count the number of rotations of the lead screw to determine head position. They rely on the precision of the screw track to transform rotational motion to linear position.

An alternative to the lead screw is the patented Roh'lix® drive (Fig. 10.22). It is based on the principle that a bearing in contact at an angle with a precision-ground drive shaft will experience a linear component of force as

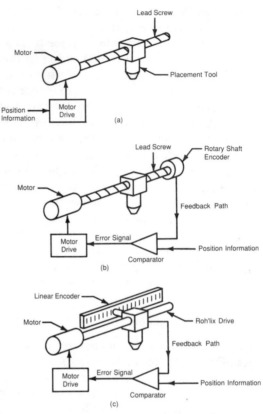

FIG. 10.20 Position control systems: a. Open-loop system, b. Rotary encoder closed-loop system, c. Linear encoder closed-loop system.

FIG. 10.21 Precision ball screw. (Used by permission. IKO International, Inc.)

FIG. 10.22   Roh'lix® drive mechanism. (Used by permission. Zero-Max Company.)

the shaft rotates. This system is said to have less backlash than a lead screw and built-in overload protection. However, the inherent positional accuracy of the mechanism is low, so a separate linear shaft encoder must be used to monitor position.

Linear encoders provide direct feedback on the actual position of the head. A precision-etched metal or glass slide running the full length of the axis is mounted on a stationary portion of the machine. An optical sensor mounted on the moving member reads linear position from the slide. Linear encoders provide true feedback on linear position and so are more accurate than rotary encoders. However, they are more complex and therefore more expensive to employ.

10.4.3 Coordinate registration

Automatic equipment places components at target X-Y locations as defined in the board loading program. To assure that those locations actually correspond to the positions of the board land patterns, both the board and the components must be registered to the machine coordinate system.

Board alignment

Board alignment has never been a serious problem for through-hole assembly. The tooling holes used for alignment are drilled simultaneously with the holes for component leads. Since the critical factor is how accurately the leads are inserted into the holes, misregistration errors are small.

Surface mount technology imposes a new set of constraints. Components must be located with respect to the actual land pattern as opposed to the drilled holes. Tooling holes or other elements used as the reference features must therefore be precisely registered to the board image.

Depending on the accuracy required, several techniques can be used to register the board to the machine coordinate system. Common registration techniques are:

Registration to board edges
In the simplest approach, the board edges serve as the referencing features. The board is forced against mechanical stops that define the origin and orientation of the machine coordinate system.

The accuracy of this approach depends on how precisely the board edges are aligned to the image. Routed edges can typically be located to within about ± 0.25 mm (0.010 in) of the image. Die blanked edges can be located to about ± 0.18 mm (0.007 in), while simple sheared edges may produce tolerances approaching ± 0.5 mm (0.020 in).

Registration to tooling holes
Somewhat more precise registration can be obtained by using tooling holes at the corners of the board. Drilled holes can usually be positioned to within about ± 0.1 mm (0.004 in) of the image, which is sufficient to place components up to about 20-lead SOICs.

When higher accuracy is required, it is possible to precision-punch holes in a secondary operation. Using this technique, hole-to-image alignment of better than ± 0.025 mm (± 0.001 in) can be achieved.[5]

Several additional factors come into play when using tooling holes as alignment features. These factors, listed in Table 10.3, result in an overall alignment accuracy of about 0.17 mm (0.007 in).

Factor	Typical Tolerance
Tooling hole location	
Drilled	± 0.1 mm
Precision Punched	± 0.025 mm
Tooling hole diameter	± 0.05 mm
Tooling pin location	± 0.01 mm
Tooling pin diameter	± 0.01 mm

TABLE 10.3   Tooling hole accuracy factors

Board-level vision alignment
When placing higher lead-count ICs of between 28 and 84 leads, mechanical reference features are usually inadequate. Instead, alignment to features on the actual board image is necessary. (Tooling holes or board edges may still be used for rough alignment.)

With 0.050-in (1.27-mm) lead pitch devices, board-level alignment is satisfactory. In this mode, two or three features designed into the artwork (called *fiducial* marks) near the corners of the board are viewed by an optical system. Placement correction factors are calculated from the difference between target fiducial locations and the actual locations. The entire process is performed within the machine firmware without need for human intervention.

With three fiducials, compensation can be made for linear translation, rotation, orthogonality, and scaling errors in the X and Y axes.[1] If the vision system is located on the machine's placement head, errors due to inaccuracies in the head movement mechanism, as well as inaccuracies in the board image, will be eliminated. If mounted off-line, only board registration errors will be corrected out. Typical board-level vision systems reduce alignment errors to approximately ± 0.025 mm (0.001 in).

Component-level vision alignment
The most precise means of aligning the component to the corresponding land pattern is to optically identify the location of the land pattern immediately prior to component placement. Nearly all linear and nonlinear errors can be eliminated. Such an approach is normally necessary only when placing extremely high lead-count fine-pitch chip carriers. The complexity, expense, and placement rate degradation associated with this technique have discouraged its use in more general applications.

The capability of the various registration techniques is summarized in Table 10.4.

Component centering

The rough orientation provided by component feeders is not usually sufficient for precise positioning. Components must therefore be centered after

Registration Feature	Alignment Accuracy
Board edge	
Sheared	± 0.25 mm
Routed	± 0.18 mm
Tooling holes	
Drilled	± 0.17 mm
Precision punched	± 0.10 mm
Board-level vision	± 0.025 mm
Component-level vision	± 0.01 mm

TABLE 10.4 Approximate accuracies of various alignment techniques

pickup. Centering can be performed with mechanical centering jaws, centering nests, or optical alignment systems.

Centering jaws

This approach uses tweezer-type mechanical centering jaws mounted coaxially with the vacuum tool. As shown in Fig. 10.23, two sets of opposing jaws are normally used, one for each axis. The jaws close around the part after pickup and release just prior to placement.

FIG. 10.23 Tweezer-type centering jaws. (Used by permission. Photograph courtesy of Universal Instruments Corporation.)

Two jaw-centering modes have been devised. Most common is simultaneous centering, in which both sets of jaws close on the part simultaneously. This approach produces the highest accuracy, but any jaw set can be used only for a limited range of part sizes.

Sequential centering, in which one set of jaws is first actuated, followed by the second set, avoids this problem; a single set of jaws can be used for both large and small components. The disadvantage of sequential centering is that since both jaw sets do not close around the part simultaneously, any lateral movement of the part introduced by the second jaw set cannot be eliminated.

Inexpensive machines sometimes use only a single set of jaws. The component is first centered in one axis and then rotated 90° to center on the other axis. This approach, although the least expensive alternative, is also the least accurate. In addition to the problems with sequential centering, it is sensitive to the rotational accuracy of the head.

It is not necessary that centering jaws be mounted on the placement tool. Off-line centering jaws can be mounted at a fixed location adjacent to the feeders. In this mode, a part is first picked from the feeder and delivered to the jaws for centering. After centering, the part is picked out of the jaws and placed on the board.

The advantage of off-line centering is that the placement head can be much simpler and less expensive. The primary disadvantage is the reduced placement rate due to the additional steps in the placement cycle.

Mechanical centering is a relatively inexpensive addition to a placement machine. When coaxial centering is employed, the part can be centered while the head is in motion, so machine throughput is not degraded.

Best accuracy is achieved when the jaws align on the component leads. Less accurate alignment is achieved when the jaws must center on the component body because the body is not usually accurately registered to the leads. In this event, the body may be aligned with the target centroid of the land pattern but the leads will not be aligned with their individual lands.

Centering jaws apply mechanical force to the component body. In some cases this force can be enough to damage delicate parts. Small ceramic components and packages with gull-wing leads are particularly susceptible to centering-jaw damage.

Centering nests

Many of the problems with mechanical jaws can be overcome through the use of centering nests. As illustrated in Fig. 10.24, a nest consists of a set of combs designed to fit the component lead. It is mounted off-line from the placement head in a manner similar to the off-line centering jaws.

In operation, the placement tool picks the component from the feeder and carries it to the nest. The part is dropped into the nest and gravity draws the leads into the V-shaped combs to align them with the center of the nest. The component is then picked from the nest and placed onto the board.

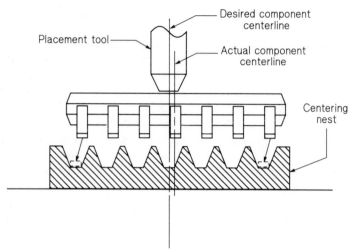

FIG. 10.24   Operation of component centering nest.

Centering nests accurately align the placement tool to the component leads. No force is exerted on the leads, so the technique is suitable for delicate components, such as fine-pitch chip carriers. Although most useful for leaded packages, nests can also be used to center leadless components, such as capacitors and resistors.

The primary disadvantage of centering nests is the reduction in placement rate due to the extra process steps. In addition, a separate nest is required for each different component outline.

Optical centering

This relatively new approach offers the highest degree of accuracy. Rather than mechanically centering the part on the tool tip, its location is determined by a video camera system. The difference between the position of the actual component and its target location determines the placement correction factors to be applied to the programmed coordinates.

The video camera is fixed to the frame, looking vertically upward from under the component. The component is first picked from its feeder and positioned over the camera. The resulting video image is digitized and processed in a computer system to determine the precise locations of all components leads. This information is used to calculate the component rotation and centroid location, from which correction factors are determined.

Because of the large number of calculations required, optical centering is generally slower than mechanical centering methods. It is most effective for placing high lead-count ICs or delicate components that could be damaged by mechanical centering jaws.

10.4.4 Component feeders

Although often overlooked, component feeders are critical to machine performance. Components that are not fed properly cannot be picked reliably by the vacuum tool. The complexities associated with feeder design make this the largest single contributor to defects during the placement process. Because of its particular importance, feeder design is discussed separately in Section 10.5.

10.4.5 Computer control

Component-placement machines are driven from a computer controller either built into the machine or in a separate console. The basic machine controller contains all the preprogrammed software (called *firmware*) necessary to convert the component placement coordinates into actual machine movement. The current board-loading program and perhaps several others are also stored in the machine controller.

More sophisticated machines can interface to an optional process control computer known as a *local host*. The local host coordinates all operations of an entire line. It stores all loading programs used in the factory, keeps track of production schedules, and transmits the appropriate board-loading program to the machine. Additional layers of control can be added to interface with other factory functions, as shown in Fig. 10.25.

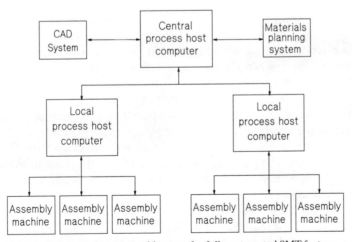

FIG. 10.25 Control system architecture for fully-automated SMT factory.

Machine controller hardware

The machine controller is the "brain" of the placement machine. Most controllers consist of dedicated microprocessors running custom-designed firmware to direct such operations as head movement, pickup sequence, and optical alignment routines. A terminal or hand-held keypad provides the basic operator interface to the machine.

Although the machine interface can be used to control any machine function, it is generally easier to control operations from a local host. Many different computers have been used as local hosts and there is no single best solution. Commercially available personal computers are a popular choice because of their wide availability, low cost, and general familiarity. More powerful technical microcomputers are preferred in highly automated factories. The increased computational power of a technical computer is particularly suited for multitasking environments where large volumes of data are passed between various production machines and a central process controller.

Programming mode

Low-cost placement machines are often programmed using a teach-mode approach. The operator manually steps the machine through the complete placement sequence for a new board, and the machine stores the taught locations in memory. Programs can usually be transferred to tapes or disks for future recall.

Teach-mode programming is the least expensive approach because a separate computer for program generation is unnecessary. Also, the operator can compensate for errors between the actual location of the board artwork and its design location. This can be important when the board artwork has been manually taped and no design data is readily available.

Teach-mode programming has several disadvantages. Since it depends entirely on the operator's skill at positioning the placement tool, it is inherently low in accuracy. It is also a slow method that takes the machine out of production during the programming operation.

For these reasons, most production operations use machines that can be programmed off line. In this mode, the placement program is generated at a computer console entirely separate from the placement machine. The operator enters design data and the computer generates the placement program. This program is then stored on disk and can be loaded into the machine whenever necessary.

Off-line programming avoids the problems with teach-mode programming. Since it uses design data directly, much higher accuracy can be obtained. It also does not interfere with production. Finally, it is possible to send CAD data to the computer electronically, avoiding the human interface entirely and reducing the chance for error.

Off-line programming requires an additional capital investment and is less intuitive than teach-mode programming. Programmers must undergo an intensive initial training program to learn how to write efficient loading programs.

Data storage medium

The punched paper tape used on early numerically controlled machines has now been entirely supplanted by electronic methods of data storage. Magnetic disks are most popular today, although magnetic tape continues to be used primarily in older equipment. Most equipment now comes standard with 5¼-in flexible disk drives (known as *floppy disk* drives). The relatively new 3½-in flexible disk format promises to be increasingly important in the future.

The removable disks in these systems can store up to several megabytes of data. It is convenient to store each board-loading program on a separate disk even though the data capacity of a single disk is sufficient to store several independent programs.

Hard disk drives, also known as *Winchester* drives, are preferred in highly automated facilities. Each hard disk can store 20–80 megabytes of data. Storage can be further increased by linking several independent drives. Besides the higher storage capacity, hard disks offer faster access times and better reliability than floppy disks. They are, however, considerably more expensive.

Communications protocol

If a local process host is used, it must be connected to the placement machine by way of a communications port from the machine controller. As a minimum, this interface should allow direct control of all machine features and permit programs to be downloaded to the machine from the local host. More sophisticated interfaces also are able to send process monitoring and control information back to the local host to track machine errors or for statistical analysis.

Few standards exist to define the communications link between the local host and placement machine. The mechanical link normally conforms to the EIA RS-232 specification, but this standard does not address the software format. Most manufacturers have developed unique protocols, making direct transfer of data between different machines impossible. Recent efforts have been undertaken to promote the SECS-II communications protocol standard developed by the Semiconductor Equipment and Materials Institute (SEMI),[6] but few manufacturers are yet able to offer this option.

10.4.6 Component verification

The component-placement machine rapidly mounts large numbers of SMCs in a highly automated fashion. Unless potential defects are automatically detected and corrected during placement, the number of defective assemblies will quickly rise to intolerable levels.

There are three basic methods for component verification:

- part presence/absence
- mechanical verification
- electrical verification

As an absolute minimum, the machine should detect whether a part has been successfully picked from its feeder. However, this alone is not always sufficient. Is the part properly oriented? Is it the correct part or has an incorrect feeder been mounted onto the machine? If it is the correct part, does it meet its electrical specifications? These additional questions require more sophisticated detection systems for answers.

Once an error is detected, the machine must take suitable corrective action. On general-purpose machines, this normally consists of immediately discarding the defective component and picking another. On high-speed machines with multiple placement tools, it might not be possible to immediately pick a replacement. Instead, the new part is picked at the first opportunity in the sequence. Alternatively, the defect can be stored in machine memory and the new part placed after all other components have been mounted.

Part presence/absence

This is the simplest form of component verification and is found on nearly all placement machines. In most cases, sensing is done with a vacuum detector. A part picked up by the placement tool will block the flow of air through the tool and create a vacuum within the head. The detector senses this vacuum and indicates that the part has been successfully acquired.

Vacuum sensing is only able to detect the presence or absence of a part. It is not able to check for proper orientation, value, or electrical functionality. Nevertheless, it provides valuable feedback and is generally considered a necessary machine feature.

Vacuum systems tend to pull small bits of foreign matter into the vacuum lines, which over a period of time can block air flow. Not only can this prevent a part from being picked up, it can also falsely indicate that a part is present. Adequate periodic maintenance can prevent errors due to clogged vacuum lines.

Mechanical verification

Some machines perform a more comprehensive mechanical inspection of the part by measuring the travel of the centering jaws. If the jaws close too far, the part is either missing or too small. If they do not close far enough, the part is incorrectly oriented or is the wrong size.

Mechanical verification can also be performed using a video camera. This approach is most common on machines that use an optical part-centering technique.

Electrical verification

The most comprehensive method of component verification is to perform an electrical test as part of the placement cycle. Two-lead devices, such as resistors and capacitors, are tested via electrical contacts built into the mechanical centering jaws. The test then becomes an integral part of the centering process. The contacts are connected to an external meter that performs a comprehensive check of each device.

More complicated components must be tested in a dedicated test nest. The head picks up the component and transports it to the test nest, where its electrical performance is verified. Afterward, the part is again picked up by the head, centered, and mounted onto the board. The extra steps can cause a significant degradation of placement rate.

Reliable on-line electrical verification is exceedingly difficult. Contact must be made, readings taken, and results calculated, all in only a few hundred milliseconds. Even the best systems will occasionally fail to detect a defective component or will reject a good one. With the very high incoming quality levels now available from many component manufacturers, this form of testing might not provide a measurable contribution. In fact, if the defect rate of the test is higher than the defect level of the parts, it will actually degrade the efficiency of the line.

One area where electrical verification provides a significant benefit is in confirming proper machine setup. In this mode, electrical testing is performed only while the first board in a production run is being populated. Any improperly loaded feeders or reverse-oriented polarized devices can be quickly detected and corrected before building the entire run.

10.5 COMPONENT FEEDING SYSTEMS

The success of the component-placement operation depends in part on reliable presentation of components. Components that are skewed, inverted, or otherwise misoriented cannot readily be picked from their feeders. Operator intervention may be necessary to clear the resulting feeder jams. In some cases, the machine will not detect the error and will attempt to complete the placement. Such defects may not be found until the end of the manufacturing process, when repair is much more difficult and costly.

Component feeding must be viewed as a system consisting of the component shipping container as well as the actual mechanical feeder. While good feeder design is important, the component manufacturer must also provide properly packaged parts. If the component cannot easily be extracted from the shipping container, or if it moves so freely as to become misoriented, the placement machine will not be able to compensate. Many apparent machine malfunctions can in fact be traced to shipping containers that do not meet the required specifications.

A variety of component shipping containers has been developed. Those most commonly used in SMT are:

- tape and reel
- magazine (stick)
- bulk
- matrix tray

10.5.1 Tape-and-reel feeding

For most component types, tape-and-reel containers are preferred. Tape feeders are extremely reliable, and large quantities of components can be held in a single reel. Tape packaging also provides individual protection for each component. The main drawback is the somewhat higher packaging cost over other formats. This is usually more than offset by the improved feeder reliability during placement.

Tape-and-reel specifications

Typical component tapes are shown in Fig. 10.26. They consist of two parts: a carrier tape that holds the components and a cover tape that prevents them from falling out of the carrier. The carrier tape can be made from any of several materials. Embossed tapes made from plastic or aluminium are most common. Punched paper or plastic is also used, principally in the smaller tape widths. The cover tape is usually a transparent polyester that has been glued or seam welded to the carrier tape. Opaque covers are sometimes used, but this makes visual inspection of the parts more difficult. Antistatic or electrically conductive materials to prevent electrostatic damage are gaining popularity for both carrier and cover tapes.

Both EIA and IEC have prepared standards for component tapes and reels. In most areas, these documents are in agreement, but a few specifications are different. Most notable is the range of allowable variations in cover tape peel strength. The EIA specification permits peel strength to vary from 0.1 to 0.7 Newtons (10 to 70 grams). The IEC document permits an even greater variation, from 0.2 to 1.3 Newtons (20 to 130 grams). The wide lattitude allowed by either standard has made feeder design extremely difficult for equipment manufacturers.

A summary of tape widths and pitches defined in the two standards is presented in Table 10.5. Major dimensions for tapes from 8 mm to 24 mm in width are shown in Table 10.6.

Tape feeders

Typical tape feeders are illustrated in Figs. 10.27 and 10.28. The feeder must accurately index the part for pickup while simultaneously removing the

FIG. 10.26   Components in tape. (Photograph by the author.)

cover tape. It must operate smoothly at all times so that parts are not jarred out of their pockets prior to being picked by the placement tool.

No feeder is totally immune to vibration, and the longer the part is exposed, the more chance that it will vibrate out of position. Therefore, feeders that do not remove the cover tape until the final indexing step are preferred over those that expose several components at a time. Some feeders even employ a shutter that further covers the exposed part, retracting only after the indexing step is complete and the tool is ready to pick the part.

Tape Type	EIA-481A[1]		IEC-286-3[2]	
	Width	Pitch	Width	Pitch
Punched	8 mm	4 mm	8 mm	See note 3
	12 mm	4 mm	—	—
	12 mm	8 mm	—	—
Embossed	8 mm	4 mm	8 mm	See note 3
	12 mm	4 mm	12 mm	See note 3
	12 mm	8 mm		
	16 mm	4 mm	16 mm	See note 3
	16 mm	8 mm		
	16 mm	12 mm		
	24 mm	12 mm	24 mm	See note 3
	24 mm	16 mm		
	24 mm	20 mm		
	24 mm	24 mm		
	32 mm	16 mm	—	
	32 mm	20 mm		
	32 mm	24 mm		
	32 mm	28 mm		
	32 mm	32 mm		
	44 mm	24 mm	—	
	44 mm	28 mm		
	44 mm	32 mm		
	44 mm	36 mm		
	44 mm	40 mm		
	44 mm	44 mm		
	56 mm	40 mm	—	
	56 mm	44 mm		
	56 mm	48 mm		
	56 mm	52 mm		
	56 mm	56 mm		

Notes:
1. Electronic Industries Association, 2001 Eye St. N.W., Washington, DC 20006.
2. International Electrotechnical Commission, 3 rue de Varembe, Geneva, Switzerland.
3. Acceptable pitches are any multiple of 4 mm.

TABLE 10.5   Standard tape sizes

10.5.2 Magazine feeding

Magazines, also called sticks or tubes, are frequently used for integrated circuits and other large parts (Fig. 10.29). Typical magazines consist of a semitransparent polyvinyl chloride (PVC) extrusion that has been treated with an antistatic coating.

Magazines are less expensive than tape-and-reel packaging but hold far fewer parts. For larger components where tape-and-reel packaging is not

Dimension	EIA-481A	IEC 286-3
Tape width tolerance	± 0.3 mm	± 0.3 mm
Carrier tape thickness	0.400 mm max	0.3 mm max
Overall thickness		
8 mm tape	2.4 mm	2.5 mm
12 mm tape	4.5 mm	4.5 mm
16, 24 mm tape	6.5 mm	under consideration
Sprocket hole pitch	4.0 ± 0.1 mm	4.0 ± 0.1 mm
Cover tape peel force	0.1–0.7 newtons	0.2–1.3 newtons
Minimum bending radius		
8 mm tape	25 mm	30 mm
12 mm tape	30 mm	30 mm
16 mm tape	40 mm	30 mm
24 mm tape	50 mm	30 mm
Maximum number of consecutive missing components	1	3
Total missing components	not specified	0.5%

TABLE 10.6   Standard tape dimensions (8 mm–24 mm embossed tape)

readily available, they are a popular substitute. They are also preferred for lesser-used parts where the tape-and-reel format would represent a sizeable inventory. Perhaps their most important advantage is the reduction in feeder space they afford when compared to tape feeders. This allows a significant increase in the maximum feeder capacity of the placement

FIG. 10.27   Tape feeder. (Used by permission. Dynapert Precima Ltd.)

FIG. 10.28   Dual tape feeder. This design incorporates two feeders on a common frame to reduce feeder setup time. (Used by permission. Siemens AG.)

machine. This benefit, however, must be weighed against the disadvantage of having to replace empty feeders much more often.

Magazine specifications

Both EIA and IEC are considering proposed standards for magazine packages, but few actual standards currently exist. A sampling of magazine outlines is presented in Fig. 10.30.

Wide variations exist in magazines from different manufacturers. This has made feeder design extremely difficult. A specific feeder may work well with magazines from one manufacturer and not at all with those from a second manufacturer. This situation is unlikely to change until widely disseminated international standards can be developed and implemented.

Magazine feeders

Typical magazine feeders are shown in Figs. 10.31 and 10.32. They can hold several independent magazines in separate parallel tracks. Although the

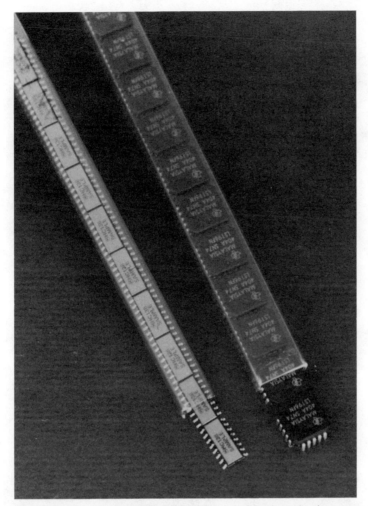

FIG. 10.29 Components in magazines. (Photograph by the author.)

magazines are usually held at an angle to take advantage of gravity, feeders do not generally rely strictly on gravity to feed the parts. Most designs incorporate a mechanical vibratory action to insure reliable component movement. The amplitude of this vibration must be adjusted to match the weight of the parts being delivered. If insufficient, the part may not move into position by the time the head is ready to pick. If excessive, the part may vibrate all the way out of the track, causing a feeder jam.

In some designs, the vibratory action operates continuously. In others, it is turned on only long enough to position a new part. The best approach incorporates several features to insure reliable delivery of parts without allowing them to vibrate out of the track. The feeder track should be

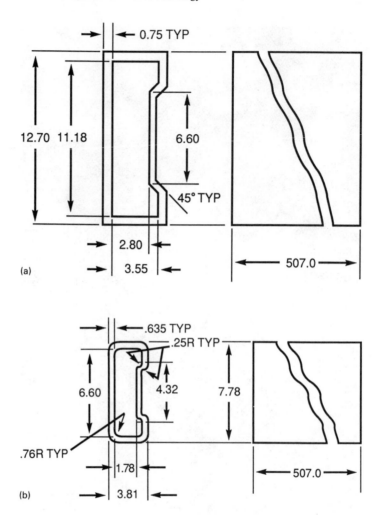

FIG. 10.30 Outline drawings for representative magazines: a. Wide body SOIC, b. Narrow body SOIC.

designed to totally capture all components except the one being picked. A shutter should be employed over this part so that it cannot be accidentally dislodged. Finally, the vibratory action should operate intermittently and be turned off when the shutter is opened for part pickup.

Certain newly introduced magazine feeders employ a conveyor system to move parts into location for pickup. Feeder reliability should be improved because of the more positive action this approach provides. Additional experience is necessary to uncover any potential problems.

Not every component type is entirely suited to magazine feeding. Molded plastic parts whose bodies touch in the magazine (such as SOICs) can be

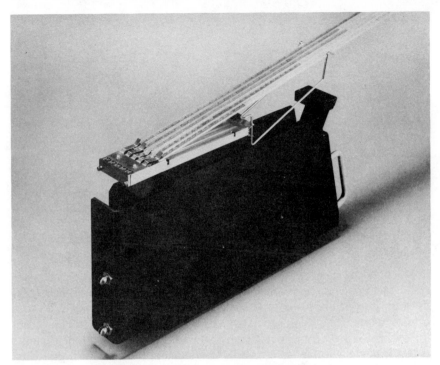

FIG. 10.31 Non-vibratory "ski-slope" gravity feeder for SOIC magazines. (Used by permission. Photograph courtesy of Universal Instruments Corporation.)

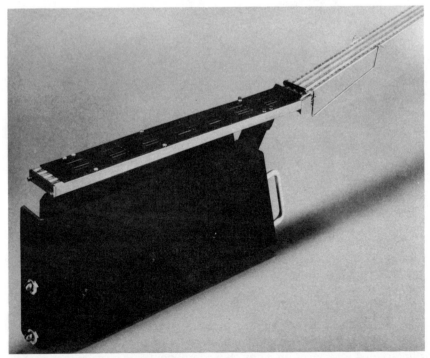

FIG. 10.32 Vibratory magazine feeder for SOIC packages. The extended front portion allows magazines to be replaced without interrupting the supply of components to the placement head. (Used by permission. Photograph courtesy of Universal Instruments Corporation.)

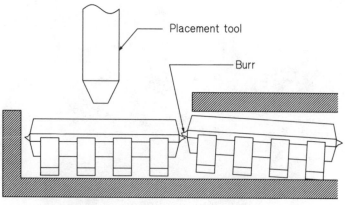

FIG. 10.33   "Shingling" of ICs in magazine feeder.

subject to a phenomenon called *shingling*. Small plastic burrs or flash from the mold parting line can extend up to 0.1 mm or more away from the bodies of these parts. If burrs on successive parts overlap, as shown in Fig. 10.33, the part being picked may become dislodged as the placement tool attempts to lift it out of the feeder. A similar phenomenon occurs with gull-wing quadpacks when the leads of the trailing component ride up over those of the component being picked.

10.5.3 Bulk feeding

The packaging cost of bulk parts is lower than that of any other format, so there has been considerable interest in this type of feeder. Unfortunately, the low reliability of bulk feeders usually increases assembly costs far beyond the savings realized in packaging.

The typical bulk feeder (Fig. 10.34) consists of a linear vibratory track that includes a series of baffles to prevent any part not correctly oriented from reaching the front of the feeder. Rejected parts are automatically dropped back into the parts reservoir and sent through the sequence repeatedly until they finally achieve the correct orientation. Bulk feeders can accommodate rectangular and cylindrical chip devices, as well as various small outline semiconductors. They cannot be used with polarized devices unless the part includes a distinct mechanical feature indicating polarity.

Bulk feeders suffer from problems similar to those of magazine feeders. Vibration amplitude is extremely critical and must be matched to the mass of the part. The optimum setting becomes a compromise between insuring reliable feeding and preventing parts from jumping out of the track. In addition, bulk feeders are sensitive to exact part mechanical dimensions. The baffles must be adjusted to permit correctly oriented parts to pass without accepting those that are incorrectly oriented. Unfortunately, the dimensional tolerances on many chip components are so wide that a single

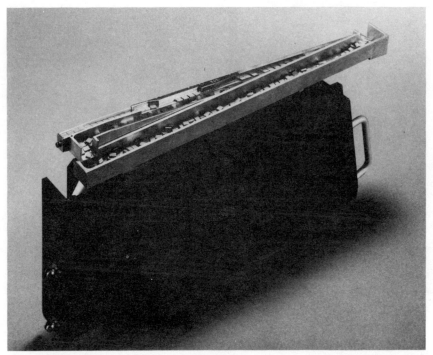

FIG. 10.34 Bulk feeder. (Used by permission. Photograph courtesy of Universal Instruments Corporation.)

baffle setting will not work across the entire range of the specification. It may therefore be necessary to readjust the baffles for each new lot of parts. Even then the feeder reliability depends on a certain amount of similarity within the lot.

10.5.4 Matrix tray feeding

Matrix trays have traditionally been employed to hold bare semiconductor die for hybrid assembly. They have also been adapted for use with large quadpacks that are not compatible with other feeding methods. They have not been widely utilized in surface mount assembly but are useful in certain situations.

Unlike all the previous feeders, the matrix tray feeder (Fig. 10.35) does not deliver all parts to the same location for pickup. Instead, a grid of indented pockets in the tray holds the parts to be placed, and the placement head must be able to access each pocket. Parts are accessed in a regular pattern, left to right, front to rear. The placement machine firmware keeps track of which part to pick next and when the tray must be replenished with parts.

Matrix trays are usually custom-designed for the particular components to

FIG. 10.35   Matrix tray feeders. (Used by permission. Photograph courtesy of Universal Instruments Corporation.)

be accommodated. Parts must be individually loaded into the tray by hand, making this approach slow and prone to error. Matrix tray feeding should be avoided when possible, but it is preferred over totally manual parts placement.

REFERENCES

1. Amick, C. "Close Doesn't Count", *Circuits Manufacturing*, Sept. 1986, pp. 35–43.
2. *NMTBA Definition and Evaluation of Accuracy and Repeatability for Numerically Controlled Machine Tools*. National Machine Tool Builders' Association, McLean, VA, Second Edition, Aug. 1972.
3. Francis, D. *Surface Mount Technology Today*, Micro Process Technology, San Jose, CA, May 1986.
4. MCT6000 equipment specification, Micro Component Technology, Inc., St. Paul, MN.
5. Cooper, R. *Precision Registration for Surface Mounted Devices/Components, IPC-TP-589*, Institute for Interconnecting and Packaging Electronic Circuits, Lincolnwood, IL, 1986.
6. *Book of SEMI Standards, Volume 2 Equipment Division*, Semiconductor Equipment and Materials Institute, Inc., Mountain View, CA, 1986, pp. E4.1–E5.69.

11

Reflow soldering

Although reflow soldering processes have existed for many years, they have never received widespread consideration. Most attention has been focused on wave soldering, the dominant technique for through-hole printed wiring assembly. Reflow soldering has remained the relatively obscure province of the hybrid circuit engineer. However, the benefits that have made reflow technology popular for hybrid circuit assembly are equally advantageous in SMT. With the rise of SMT, reflow soldering has grown in importance.

Unlike wave soldering, the reflow process deposits measured quantities of solder directly on the joint. After components are placed, the final interconnection is formed by fusing, or *reflowing*, this solder. Problems of thermal shock and solder shadowing, which are serious concerns in the wave soldering operation, are virtually eliminated in the reflow process.

For engineers familiar with wave soldering, reflow technology presents an entirely new set of challenges. Besides the obvious differences in technique, the situation is complicated by the fact that several different reflow heating methods are in common use. No single method has become dominant, and much has been written to extol the virtues of competing processes. Unfortunately, some of these claims have been oriented more toward selling a particular manufacturer's reflow system than toward furthering the state of the technology. As a result, a body of unsubstantiated folklore has grown around the reflow process. The manufacturing engineer chartered with setting up a production line must sift through and interpret volumes of conflicting information.

This chapter provides a comprehensive review of reflow soldering processes and equipment. Rather than advocating any single approach, the advantages and disadvantages of each alternative are described in detail. The chapter concludes with a summary of the important factors to be considered during the equipment selection process.

11.1 REFLOW THEORY

The term *reflow* soldering is somewhat misleading, as it implies the fusing of previously flowed solder. In most cases the so-called reflow step actually consists of the initial fusing of tin-lead solder paste. A more proper description would be *flow* soldering, but this term has historically been synonymous with wave soldering.

The principles behind reflow soldering are simple. The two parts to be joined are brought into intimate contact and a quantity of solder is placed in contact with them. The temperature is elevated above the melting point of the solder, at which time it wets to the metallic surfaces. When the temperature is lowered, the solder solidifies, completing the joint.

Reflow soldering offers several benefits. A primary advantage over wave soldering is the fact that solder is applied only where it is needed. This is especially important for components that would be damaged if immersed in molten solder. Another benefit is that the temperature profile seen by the assembly can be more precisely controlled. Surface mount components sensitive to thermal shock are more compatible with a reflow process than a wave process.

11.1.1 Temperature profile

To prevent component damage during exposure to high temperatures, the temperature profile during reflow must be carefully controlled. An ideal profile is shown in Fig. 11.1. It consists of a slow rise to an intermediate temperature (the *preheat* zone), a relatively quick excursion above the

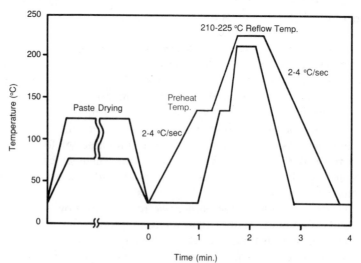

FIG. 11.1   Idealized reflow temperature profile.

liquidus temperature (just long enough to ensure complete melting of all solder), and a gradual cooling back to ambient.

The specific nature of the temperature profile can vary depending on how it is measured. The profile recorded by a bare thermocouple may be vastly different from that recorded by a similar thermocouple affixed to a printed wiring board. In the case of a nonequalibrium process such as infrared reflow, the profile depends entirely on the thermal mass of the assembly. Temperature profiles should always be measured by thermocouples attached directly to the printed wiring board, preferably at several locations.

An often overlooked fact is that the shape of the reflow temperature profile is more important than the method used to achieve this profile. Vapor phase, infrared, thermal conduction, and thermal convection have all been successfully used to solder surface mount assemblies. Most problems attributed to particular processes are a result of large deviations from the ideal profile rather than an inherent defect in the technique.

Preheating

Adequate preheating is important for several reasons. Components such as ceramic capacitors are sensitive to thermal shock and can be damaged by too rapid a temperature rise (refer to Section 2.4.1). Rapidly increasing temperatures also disturb the thermal equilibrium of the assembly and cause small components to reach the liquidus temperature more quickly than the larger printed wiring board. When this occurs, the molten solder will preferentially wet the component lead and may flow along the lead and away from the joint. This "wicking" phenomenon is observed primarily on J-lead components, such as PLCCs (see Section 5.5.7). Finally, preheating is necessary to achieve proper flux activation. Inadequate preheat time and temperature will prevent the flux from removing surface oxides at the joint prior to reflow.

It has been suggested that excessive preheating is detrimental because the flux loses activity well before reflow occurs. The surfaces are then free to reoxidize before the solder wets. While this is technically accurate, the author's experience indicates that it is not a problem under normal conditions; preheating for as long as 15 minutes at 160 °C does not degrade solderability. Apparently the rosin residues seal the surface and prevent oxide growth even after the activators have been consumed. Readers should be cautioned, however, that not all solder pastes may behave in a similar manner. If degradation of flux activity is of concern, an inert atmosphere, such as nitrogen or argon, can be employed in the preheater.

For maximum benefit, preheating should be performed as an integral part of the reflow process. To maintain the gradual temperature rise, boards should not be allowed to cool between the outlet of the preheater and inlet of the reflow zone. This suggests that preheating should be incorporated in the reflow system rather than performed on a separate machine.

Paste drying

Solder paste contains volatile solvents that improve screenability and extend the working life of the paste. If these solvents remain in the paste during reflow, they will boil violently and spatter solder balls across the surface of the board. To prevent spattering, the paste must be thoroughly dried.

The optimum drying profile depends on the nature of the volatile elements contained in the paste. These are in turn determined by the desired screening properties and working life of the paste. Pastes with low boiling-point solvents may require only 5–10 minutes of drying time at 60–80 °C. Higher boiling-point solvents may need to be dried for as long as an hour at temperatures as high as 125–150 °C. Consult the paste manufacturer for specific recommendations.

Some manufacturers now offer pastes that they claim do not require drying. Such claims should be considered cautiously. Although satisfactory results may be obtained in the absence of a drying step, highest yields are still likely to be achieved when the paste is dried prior to reflow.

The effectiveness of a drying profile can be determined by measuring the weight loss of a sample of the paste as a function of drying time and temperature. One proposed definition of an optimum profile is to require that 95% of the most volatile solvent in the paste be driven off.[1] Unfortunately, most pastes contain multiple solvents, making this calculation rather difficult. The weight loss of a representative solder paste as a function of drying time at three temperatures is presented in Fig. 11.2.

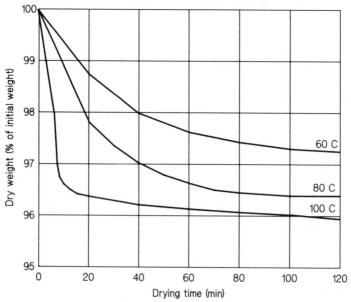

FIG. 11.2   Effect of drying time and temperature on Kester R-226 solder paste. (Hewlett-Packard Co.)

The drying process should always be distinguished from the preheat portion of the reflow process. Drying time and temperature must be selected on the basis of the composition of the solder paste. The preheat profile is governed by the need to minimize thermal shock and maintain thermal equilibrium at all points on the assembly. It is rare that a single process profile can be employed to simultaneously achieve both results.

11.2 REFLOW-RELATED PARTS MOVEMENT

In most reflow processes, the SMCs are held on the board only by the solder paste. As the solder liquifies at elevated temperature, it attempts to minimize free surface energy by reducing the area of exposed solder. In so doing, it may pull the component into a position other than that in which it was placed. Normally, the wetting forces are symmetrically distributed on all leads and there is very little actual part movement. If all leads do not wet simultaneously, an imbalance in forces can cause considerable movement. The three primary movement modes are:

- self-alignment
- skewing
- tombstoning

11.2.1 Self-alignment

A component placed off-center on the land pattern may tend to self-align when the solder melts. This occurs because the surface area of the molten solder is smallest when the component is completely on the land. As long as all terminations wet simultaneously, the component will be pulled approximately into the correct position (Figs. 11.3a and 11.3b). The effect is most pronounced on small chip components but is also frequently seen on SOICs and PLCCs.

The degree to which self-alignment occurs depends on a number of factors, including termination solderability, reflow profile, and component mass. Variability in any of these factors can reduce or eliminate the phenomena so it should never be relied on to correct known process problems.

11.2.2 Skewing

The beneficial effect of self-alignment depends on all component terminations wetting nearly simultaneously. If this is not the case, the same surface energy phenomenon can become detrimental. When only a single termination wets, the solder will attempt to minimize the surface energy at that land. This can pull the component into one of several orientations. Frequently, the end of the termination will align with the diagonal of the land (Fig. 11.3c) or will pull back toward the rear of the pad (Fig. 11.3d). This skewing effect can be minimized by judicious land pattern design, such as described in Chapter 7.

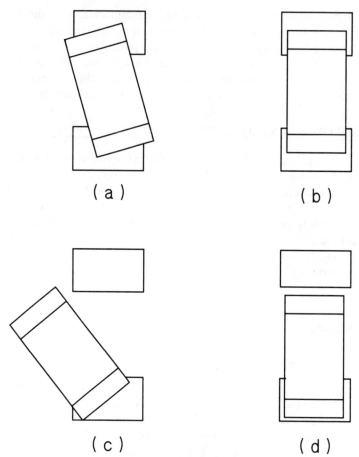

FIG. 11.3 Possible effects of solder surface tension on component movement:
a. Component as originally placed, b. Self-alignment. Both sides wet simultaneously, pulling the component to the center of the pattern, c. Skewing. One side wets before the other, aligning the termination with the diagonal of the land, d. Shifting. One side wets before the other, pulling the component toward the rear of the pad.

11.2.3 Tombstoning

Tombstoning is a variation of skewing that occurs on two-terminal passive devices. The phenomenon goes by a variety of names, including *drawbridging*, the *Manhattan effect*, and the *Stonehenge effect*. (The term "tombstone" seem to best express the value of the end result.) Tombstoning results from an imbalance of forces that pulls the component into a vertical or near-vertical position (Fig. 11.4).

Tombstoning has been extensively studied by a number of researchers. A definitive theoretical analysis has recently been performed.[2] In this study, three forces were determined to act on the chip:

FIG. 11.4 Tombstoned chip resistors. (Used by permission. Wela Publications Ltd.)

1. gravity acting on the mass of the chip
2. the surface tension of the molten solder underneath the chip
3. the surface tension of the molten solder in the meniscus of the solder fillet at the outside of the chip.

The situation is modeled in Fig. 11.5. The important parameters are:

α = the angle of tilt of the chip component

β = the angle between the center of gravity with respect to the underside of the component, equal to arctan (H/L)

H   = the height of the component

L   = the length of the component

M   = the mass of the component per mm width

g   = acceleration of gravity

d   = the distance between center of gravity and the cantilever point, equal to $\frac{1}{2}\sqrt{(L^2 + H^2)}$

W   = the width of the underside metallization of the component

S   = the protruding length of the solder land

γ = the surface tension of liquid solder

δ = the angle under which the surface tension of liquid solder in the fillet acts on the chip

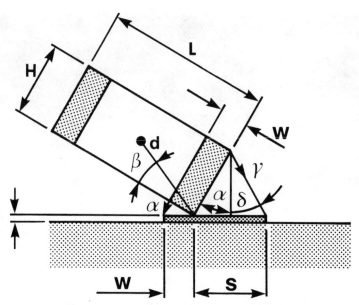

FIG. 11.5 Model of tombstoned chip component. Refer to text for explanation of symbols. (Used by permission. Wela Publications Ltd.)

$$\delta = \arctan \frac{S\text{-}H\sin\alpha}{H\cos\alpha}$$

In terms of these parameters, the moments acting on the chip component are:

Downward:
Gravity:

$$T_1 = Mgd\cos(\alpha + \beta)$$

Surface tension of the solder underneath the chip:

$$T_2 = \gamma W\cos\frac{\alpha}{2}$$

Upward:
Surface tension of the solder in the fillet:

$$T_3 = \gamma H\sin(\alpha + \delta)$$

Plots of the moments $T_1 + T_2$ and T_3 as a function of the tilting angle for 0805 and 1206 chips are shown in Figs. 11.6a and 11.6b. The relevant parameters for these components are also given. It can be seen that a delicate balance exists between the upward and downward moments, being approximately of equal size. Any disturbance of the configuration can result in either moment predominating.

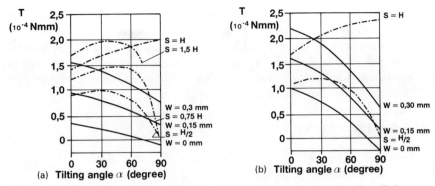

FIG. 11.6   Moments acting on chip components. Solid lines are the moments $T_1 + T_2$ for three values of W. Dashed lines show the upward moment T_3 for values of S. Values of T are specified per millimeter width. a. 0805 resistor, b. 1206 resistor. (Used by permission. Wela Publications Ltd.)

As a countermeasure, the upward moment must be decreased and the downward moments must be increased. One of the downward moments (gravity) cannot be influenced because it is determined by the dimensions and material of the component (and the mass of the earth). The second downward moment can be increased by increasing the length of the metallization on the underside (the solder land on the printed wiring board must be also be matched!). The upward moment of surface tension along the solder fillet can be decreased by decreasing the length of the protruding solder land, thus decreasing the effective arm along which the surface tension acts.

The calculation implies that once a component starts lifting it will always end as a tombstone. Many components, however, lift only part of the way up, presumably because the component body could not displace enough molten solder to cause a complete vertical rise.

Tombstoning can be virtually eliminated through proper land pattern design. Some general guidelines are as follows:

- Use components with a large underside metallization (dimension W in Fig. 11.5). An overlap between the component and its associated land should be at least 0.3 mm (0.012 in).
- Keep the extension of the land (dimension S in Fig. 11.5) to a minimum, preferably just large enough to form a reliable fillet. An extension of about 0.5 mm (0.020 in) or less beyond nominal component dimensions is recommended.
- Select the land width to be equal to or slightly wider than the nominal component width. The land should be no wider than the maximum component width plus 0.25 mm (0.010 in).
- Consider using components with metallization only on the underside. As can be seen from Fig. 11.5, tombstoning can not occur if there is no

metallization on the end of the component because there is no upward acting moment. This must be considered as a last resort because most manufacturers do not offer such components as a standard catalog item. Chip resistors with terminations only on the resistor side are sometimes mounted face down, but this may be inadvisable because of possible problems with flux entrapment under the device.

11.3 REFLOW ALTERNATIVES

Several techniques for reflow soldering are in common use. Those most frequently employed in production SMT applications are:

- thermal conduction
- vapor phase
- infrared
- laser
- thermal convection

One of the oldest reflow techniques is the application of heat via thermal conduction. In its simplest form this consists of nothing more than a hot soldering iron applied to previously deposited solder. Slightly more sophisticated is the temperature-controlled hot plate: the circuit to be soldered is manually positioned on the hot plate until the solder is observed to melt; it is then manually removed and allowed to cool. The most elaborate equipment of this type employs conveyors to automatically transport the circuit across the plate and a cooling section to allow the solder to solidify.

Reflow by thermal convection is another approach with a long-established history. In this method, heated air serves as the thermal transfer medium. An ordinary resistance-heated oven is the simplest example of a convection reflow system. Boards must be manually loaded into the oven and manually withdrawn. Conveyorized ovens can be purchased when high throughput is required.

Condensation soldering, commonly termed *vapor phase* reflow, was developed in the early 1970s by Western Electric Co. Boards are immersed in the saturated vapor of an inert liquid whose boiling point is higher than the melting temperature of the solder. Heat is transferred from the vapor to the board, causing the solder to melt. Since the entire process occurs in an inert environment, there is little potential for oxidation of the molten solder.

Solder reflow by direct infrared (IR) radiation is a more recent development. The first IR soldering ovens were adapted from ovens used to fire thick film pastes. For these ovens, 90% or more of the heat is transferred through direct radiation of near-visible IR energy. Newer systems attempt to improve soldering yields by optimizing the thermal profile specifically for solder reflow. This generally involves changing the peak IR wavelength, which increases the percentage of energy transferred via thermal convection and decreases color selectivity (see Section 11.6).

A special form of direct radiation is laser soldering. In this approach, the energy from a high-power laser is directed onto the joint. Reflow can occur in a fraction of a second, but the process is relatively slow because each joint must be soldered individualy.

11.4 REFLOW BY THERMAL CONDUCTION

Reflow soldering by thermal conduction has historically been used on ceramic hybrid circuits. Equipment for volume production is designed to automatically transport an assembly over preheat and reflow stages and through a subsequent cooling zone. For prototyping or repair operations, simple modified soldering irons are prevalent.

11.4.1 Conveyorized production systems

Conveyorized systems for production use are conceptually simple (see Fig. 11.7). Commercial machines include at least two heating zones, one for preheating and the second for reflow. Additional preheat zones are sometimes included to permit custom tailoring of the reflow profile. The cooling zone normally consists of a metal heat sink over which cool air is blown. A typical temperature profile for a two-stage system is illustrated in Fig. 11.8.

Two types of conveyors can be used. One type is a solid belt made of Teflon-coated fiberglass. The assembly rides on top of the belt while progressing through the heating zones. The other type of conveyor does not use a belt but instead employs a series of *sweeper bars* attached to a drive chain. The assembly is positioned so that a sweeper bar pushes it from behind. Improved heat transfer can be achieved with this technique because the substrate is in direct contact with the hot plates. However, interfacing the system to a component placement machine is more difficult; assemblies

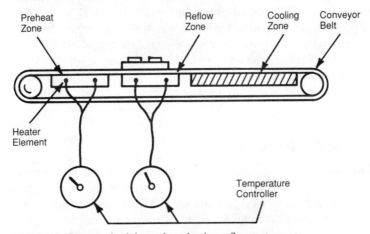

FIG. 11.7 Conveyorized thermal conduction reflow system.

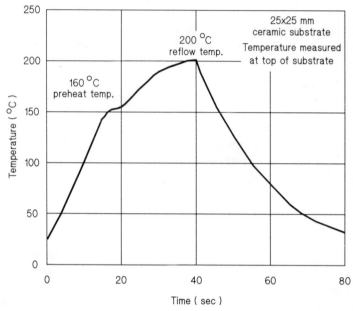

FIG. 11.8 Typical temperature profile for ceramic substrate on conveyorized two-stage hot plate system of Fig. 11.7.

must be sequenced to enter the system between successive bars. Sequencing is not necessary when using a solid belt. The solid belt is also better suited for transporting odd-shaped assemblies.

Because heat must be transferred through the substrate, conveyorized systems are best suited for flat substrates with high thermal conductivity. Ceramic or porcelain-enamel steel substrates are ideal materials. Glass-epoxy printed wiring boards are less compatible because of their relatively low thermal conductivity. To elevate the top of the board to reflow tempera-ture, the hot-plate temperature must be increased above 250 °C. At such high temperatures, a certain amount of board charring and delamination is inevitable, and the flame retardancy properties of the board can be de-graded.

11.4.2 Modified soldering irons

Modified soldering irons are commonly employed in the repair process but are seldom used as production tools. Control of the heating process is difficult and depends largely on the skill of the operator. Soldering defect levels are invariably much higher than with other reflow processes. Refer to Chapter 15 for a discussion of the use of soldering irons in the repair process.

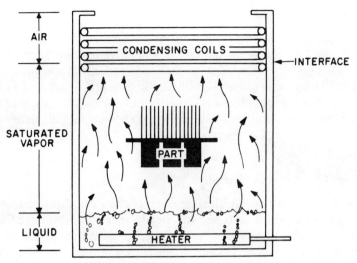

FIG. 11.9 Basic vapor phase reflow system. (Used by permission. American Society for Metals.)

11.5 VAPOR PHASE REFLOW

11.5.1 Vapor phase theory

A basic vapor phase system is illustrated in Fig. 11.9. It consists of a container that holds a quantity of fluid. The fluid temperature is raised to its boiling point by a suitable heater. Above the boiling fluid is a saturated vapor zone that provides the heat for soldering. At the top of the container is a set of condensing coils. The coils reduce vapor loss due to evaporation into the environment.

In operation, the assembly to be soldered is lowered into the saturated vapor zone. The vapors condense on the relatively cool assembly, transferring the latent heat of vaporization to the part. Heat continues to be transferred until the assembly reaches thermal equilibrium with the vapor. By employing a fluid that boils at a temperature above the melting point of the solder, reflow can be achieved.

The vapor phase process has several advantages over other reflow methods. These include:

- well-controlled maximum temperature
- excellent temperature uniformity across the assembly
- soldering occurs in a virtually oxygen-free environment
- heating is relatively independent of the geometry of the assembly.

Well-controlled temperature

The maximum temperature of the assembly is set by the boiling temperature of the fluid. Because of the narrow boiling range of a typical vapor phase fluid, this temperature is very precisely controlled. This is advantageous when soldering temperature-sensitive components. It also makes step-soldering processes practical. Fluids can be obtained with a variety of boiling temperatures, so a progression of solders with lower melting temperatures can be used in complex assemblies.

Excellent temperature uniformity

Vapor phase fluids have high heat-transfer coefficients. Since condensation occurs on all exposed surfaces, the steady-state temperature uniformity across the board is excellent. (However, as described below, different portions of the assembly, because of variations in thermal mass, can have nonuniform dynamic heating characteristics.)

Inert atmosphere

The density of the primary vapor is approximately 20 times that of air, so oxygen is effectively excluded from the system. Once the flux cleans the surfaces, they are unlikely to reoxidize prior to reflow.

In reality, a slight amount of oxygen is always present within the vapor. This is probably due to a combination of the inherent solubility of oxygen in the vapor plus oxygen pulled into the vapor by the conveyor. The total quantity is usually assumed negligible but can have a minor effect in certain cases.

Geometry independence

Because condensation occurs on all surfaces, the geometry of the part has little impact on the process. The vapor will even penetrate underneath devices to solder connections that are not externally visible.

Vapor phase reflow has several potential concerns. These can generally be minimized by proper equipment and product design. The most significant concerns are as follows:

- large temperature gradient if assembly is taken directly from room temperature to reflow temperature
- parts with low thermal mass reach reflow temperature before larger parts; this can lead to preferential wetting of some surfaces (solder wicking)
- vapor phase fluids are extremely expensive
- overheated fluids decompose into toxic compounds.

Large temperature gradient

The inherent design of the vapor phase system causes the assembly to make the transition from room temperature to reflow temperature at a rate limited only by its thermal mass. Typical temperature gradients of 15–20 °C/sec can damage certain types of components.

Thermal shock can be reduced by including a separate preheat stage in the process. Some in-line equipment can be purchased with an integral preheater at the inlet to the system. When this is not available, a separate IR preheater can be installed in line with the vapor phase system. When using a separate preheater, care must be taken to minimize the temperature drop between the outlet of the preheater and the inlet of the vapor phase system.

Preferential wetting

Thermal mass also governs the speed at which individual elements of the assembly come up to temperature. Component leads may reach liquidus temperature well before the corresponding board land patterns. When this happens, solder will preferentially wet to the lead. In extreme cases, enough solder will flow up the lead to cause an open circuit at the joint.

Preheating is effective in improving heating dynamics. By reducing the temperature differential between the board and the vapor to about 60–90 °C, wicking can largely be eliminated.

Fluid loss

Vapor phase fluids are exotic materials that cost in excess of $130/liter ($500/gallon). Excessive losses due to evaporation can rapidly drive up manufacturing costs.

Fluid loss is minimized by careful attention to equipment design. Several methods for reducing this loss are described in subsequent sections.

Thermal decomposition

Thermal decomposition of the fluid produces the highly toxic compound perfluoroisobutylene (PFIB). This is a colorless, odorless vapor that is difficult to detect. An acceptable time-weighted average exposure to this compound over an eight-hour day has been set at 0.010 parts per million (ppm).[3]

In normal operation only trace amounts of PFIB are generated, but when superheated, the rate of generation increases markedly. This can be a concern when using immersion-type heaters if the liquid level drops so low as to expose a portion of the heater element. The local temperature at the liquid-vapor interface can quickly rise high enough to cause decomposition. Early models of vapor phase equipment were not able to detect this potentially hazardous situation. All currently manufactured machines employ safeguards to prevent this occurrence.

Local hot spots can also be created by flux residues that accumulate on immersion heaters. For this reason, heater elements should always be kept clean and free of contamination.

Improved safety can be achieved through the use of ventilation. An airflow of 25 cm/sec (50 ft/min) is now recommended by 3M Corp.[4] (Previously, an airflow of 50 cm/sec (100 ft/min) was recomended.) Studies are underway to determine if this rate of airflow can safely be further reduced. Consult the fluid manufacturer for the latest recommendations.

Another product of thermal decomposition is hydrogen fluoride (HF). In combination with atmospheric moisture, HF can cause severe corrosion of the equipment. This is not a problem when the equipment is operating properly, but a related problem can be of concern in dual-vapor systems (described in Sect. 11.5.3). The temperature of the secondary vapor at the primary-secondary interface can be high enough to cause localized decomposition of the secondary vapor. This results in the generation of hydrochloric acid, which causes similar corrosion. Production systems invariably include an acid stripper to remove any acid generated by this process.

11.5.2 Vapor phase fluids

The fluid used to produce the saturated vapor (called the *primary* fluid) is a long-chain perfluorocarbon blend that consists only of carbon and fluorine atoms. A typical structure is:

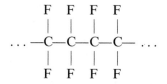

Because of slight variations in the fluid manufacturing process, not all molecules will be exactly the same molecular weight. The fluid therefore does not have a single boiling point, but rather a range over which all the components in the liquid will boil (see Fig. 11.10). Depending on the exact composition of the fluid, the nominal boiling point may vary slightly from batch to batch.

Boiling temperature varies with altitude. A fluid with a specified boiling temperature of 215 °C at sea level may boil at only 205 °C at an altitude of 1500 m (5000 ft). This effect must be considered when developing process parameters for the vapor phase process.

Vapor phase fluids can be obtained in a variety of boiling temperatures for different soldering applications. Key properties of several commercial fluids are summarized in Table 11.1. More detailed properties of a representative fluid are given in Table 11.2.

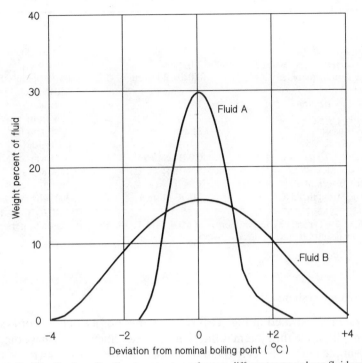

FIG. 11.10 Distribution of boiling temperatures for two different vapor phase fluids with the same nominal boiling temperature. Fluid A exhibits a tight distribution while fluid B has a much wider variation in boiling range. (Used by permission. Air Products and Chemicals, Inc.)

Boiling temperature		Density	Mfgr's	
°C	°F	g/ml	designation	Manufacturer
174	345	1.88	FC-43	3M
215	419	2.03	FC-5311	3M
215	419	2.01	APF-215	Air Products
230	446	1.82	LS/230	Galden
253	487	1.90	FC-71	3M
260	500	1.84	HS/260	Galden

TABLE 11.1 Key properties of commercial vapor phase fluids. (Used by permission. Copyright 1986, Van Nostrand Reinhold.)

11.5.3 Vapor phase equipment design

Vapor phase equipment falls into two general classes: *single-vapor* and *dual-vapor* systems. In addition, equipment can be designed for either low-volume *batch-mode* processing or production volume *in-line* processing.

Boiling Point	215 °C	419 °F
Pour Point	−48 °C	−54 °F
Heat Capacity, 25 °C	0.17 Cal/g · °C	0.17 Btu/lb · °F
Density, 25 °C	2.01 g/ml	125.4 lbs/ft³
Thermal Conductivity, 25 °C	0.040 cal/hr · cm² · °C	0.032 Btu/hr · °F · ft²
Ag. Mol. Wt.	630 g/mole	630 lbs/mole
Heat of Vaporization	16.1 Cal/g	29 Btu/lb.
Kinematic Viscosity, 25 °C	7.4 cs	0.29 ft²/hr
Surface Tension	21 dynes/cm	0.0014 lbs/ft
Vapor Pressure, 25 °C	0.10 torr	0.002 psia
Coefficient of Expansion	0.0014 cm³/cm³ · °C	0.0008 in³/in³ · °F
Refractive Index, 25 °C	1.3338	1.3338
Dielectric Constant, 25 °C (1 KHz)	1.94	1.94
Dielectric Strength, 25 °C	118 Kvolts/cm	300 volts/mil

TABLE 11.2   Typical physical properties of MULTIFLUOR APF-215. (Used by permission. Air Products and Chemicals, Inc.)

Single-vapor systems

The system illustrated in Fig. 11.9 is an example of a single-vapor system. The only liquid in the system is the primary fluid. Such a system is comparatively simple but is subject to relatively high fluid losses due both to evaporation into the atmosphere and *dragout* of vapor as the assembly is withdrawn from the system. For this reason, single-vapor systems are rarely used in batch-mode equipment. On in-line systems where fluid losses can be more easily controlled, single-vapor systems are common.

Dual-vapor system

To reduce the evaporative loss of the primary fluid, a second fluid with a lower boiling point can be introduced into the system. The vapors of this *secondary* fluid form a blanket over the primary vapors and act to minimize loss of the primary. The dual-vapor system is illustrated schematically in Fig. 11.11.

Although the dual vapor concept can significantly reduce losses, it will not totally eliminate them. This is due both to diffusion of the primary vapor through the secondary blanket and to dragout as the assembly exits the system. With in-line systems, a certain amount of dragout is unavoidable whenever the belt is operating.

A common liquid used as the secondary fluid is the refrigerant trichlorotrifluoroethane (R-113), produced under the trade name Freon® TF by E.I. Dupont de Nemours Co., Inc. It has a boiling temperature of 48 °C (117 °F). Because of its lower molecular weight, its vapors float on top of the heavier primary vapors.

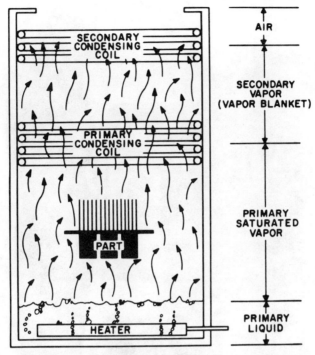

FIG. 11.11   Dual-vapor reflow system. (Used by permission. American Society for Metals.)

Molecular diffusion causes the secondary blanket to contain a slight amount of primary vapor. The vapor temperature is therefore significantly higher than the boiling temperature of the pure secondary fluid. Under normal operating conditions, the temperature of the secondary vapor ranges between 70–90 °C (158–195 °F). To minimize loss of the primary fluid it is desirable to keep the temperature of the secondary vapor as low as possible.

Batch-mode equipment

A typical batch-mode system is pictured in Fig. 11.12. It includes a dual-vapor tank, a programmatically controlled elevator, an acid stripper, and automatic flux filtration system. In operation, the assembly is manually placed on the elevator. When the sequence is initiated, the elevator automatically lowers the assembly into the secondary vapor zone where it dwells long enough to reach equilibrium. It is then lowered into the primary zone where reflow occurs. Upon withdrawal, the elevator again pauses in the secondary zone to allow the product to cool. Any primary fluid remaining on the part condenses back into the tank at this point. Finally the elevator rises

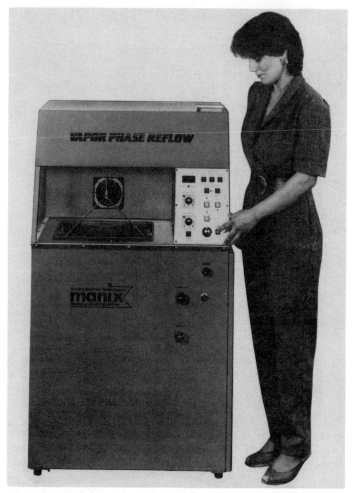

FIG. 11.12   Batch vapor phase reflow system. (Used by permission. Manix Division of Henry Mann, Inc., Huntingdon Valley, PA.)

up to the load/unload position to allow the soldered assembly to be removed.

The throughput of a batch system is limited by the amount of product that can be placed horizontally on the elevator. While this may not be a problem for small ceramic hybrids or printed wiring boards, it can be a serious concern for larger boards that must be soldered one at a time.

In-line equipment

Higher throughput is obtained by using in-line construction as illustrated in Fig. 11.13. With this design, a new board can be loaded as soon as the

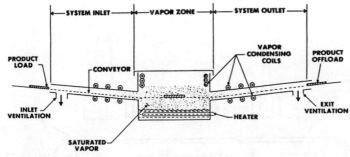

FIG. 11.13 In-line single-vapor soldering system. (Used by permission. American Society for Metals.)

previous board has been carried into the system. An additional advantage is the inherently lower fluid loss that can be attained because of the smaller air-vapor interface. With the in-line design, this interface is reduced to a small opening at the inlet and outlet of the system. The slightly inclined conveyors (approximately 7° slope) further reduce vapor loss.

In-line equipment is produced in both single-vapor and dual-vapor versions. Single-vapor systems are less likely to generate corrosive acids because there is no secondary vapor to decompose at the primary-secondary interface. Dual-vapor systems offer the potential for lower fluid losses, although the author's experience indicates that losses are similar for both types of systems. A well-designed and well-operated in-line system with a 457-mm (12-in) wide belt loses fluid at a rate of about 40–43 ml/hr (0.011–0.012 gal/hr).[5] At a cost of $0.17/ml ($640/gal), this amounts to an operating cost of around $7.00 per hour. A typical in-line system is illustrated in Fig. 11.14.

FIG. 11.14 In-line vapor phase reflow soldering system. (Used by permission. Centech Corporation.)

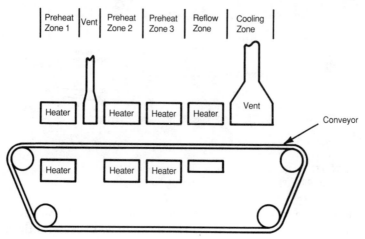

FIG. 11.15   Construction of IR reflow system.

11.6 INFRARED REFLOW

Solder reflow by application of direct infrared energy ("IR reflow") has recently gained widespread popularity. A typical system is illustrated schematically in Fig. 11.15. It is comprised of a conveyor belt that carries the assembly through a series of heating zones. Each zone consists of a set of infrared emitters positioned above and below the belt. The temperature profile seen by the board is controlled by adjusting the emitter temperatures, the distances between the emitters and conveyor, and the speed of the belt.

The advantages of IR reflow are:

- The temperature profile seen by the board can be precisely controlled.
- Energy transfer by direct radiation is faster than by thermal conduction or convection.
- Radiated energy penetrates inside the joint, whereas conducted or convected energy heats only the surface of the joint.

Temperature control

Precise temperature control is achieved by employing several heating zones. Each zone can be individually adjusted to tailor the temperature gradient seen by the board. Commercial systems employ as few as 3 or as many as 20 zones to control the profile. (The exact interpretation of what constitutes a "zone" varies by manufacturer. Some manufacturers count both top and bottom elements as a single zone, while others consider them as separate zones.)

Heat transfer rate

Heat transfer by direct radiation follows the Stefan-Boltzman law:

$$E = K\,(T_1^4 - T_2^4)$$

where E = amount of energy transferred
    T_1 = temperature of emitter
    T_2 = temperture of assembly
    K = a constant

As can be seen, energy is transferred at a rate proportional to the fourth power of the temperature difference between emitter and assembly. This is a much higher rate than transfer by conduction or convection, which is proportional to the simple difference in temperture.

Heat penetration

While convective and conductive reflow approaches are surface-heating phenomena, direct radiation penetrates more deeply into the joint.[6] This has several potential benefits. Solvents in the solder paste are more easily driven off without spattering, so a separate preheat step is not necessary. In addition, the entire joint heats up as a unit, reducing the possibility of preferential solder wicking up the leads of PLCC devices. The combination of gradual temperature rise and penetrating heat virtually eliminates the possibility of chip component tombstoning.

Infrared reflow has several potential disadvantages. These include:

- For any given equipment setting, the actual temperature profile seen by a board is highly dependent on its thermal mass.
- Energy absorption is sensitive to the absorptivity (color) of the components and printed wiring board.
- Direct infrared energy is blocked by tail components.

Thermal mass sensitivity

Infrared reflow is a non-equilibrium process. Because the emitters do not operate efficiently at the relatively low reflow temperature, they must be operated at much higher temperatures. The actual temperature of the board as it passes through any zone is a function of the board thermal mass and the speed of the belt. Fig. 11.16 shows the relationship between the emitter temperatures and the board surface temperature for a board of given thermal mass.

When the machine settings are not optimized for the particular board being reflowed, several things can happen. If the board has a low thermal mass, it will become overheated, causing discoloration or charring. Overheated components can be irreparably damaged. In extreme cases, the

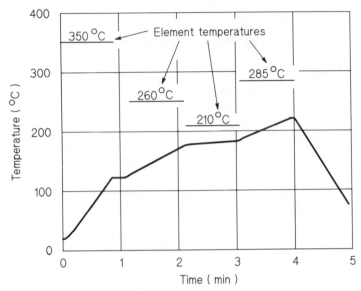

FIG. 11.16   Typical temperature profile for area-source infrared reflow system.

board material can even catch fire. On the other hand, if the board has a high thermal mass, it may not reach reflow temperature. Even if the temperature does reach the reflow point, it may not remain there long enough for all joints to fully form.

Color selectivity

The difference in absorption of IR energy as a function of the color of an object is termed *color selectivity*. Color selectivity is most pronounced when the majority of the radiation is transmitted in the *near-infrared* region of the spectrum (0.72–2 μm wavelength). The so-called *far-infrared* emitters with peak wavelengths in the range 3–5 μm wavelength exhibit much lower color selectivity.

Shadowing

Infrared energy, like visible light, is blocked by opaque objects. This effect, called *shadowing*, is of particular concern for devices such as PLCCs whose joints are hidden underneath the device body. It can also be significant for assemblies with very closely spaced components.

These problems can be reduced by careful system design. One approach, described below, is to reduce the amount of energy transmitted by direct IR and increase the percentage transmitted by thermal convection. Other possibilities include the use of diffusing elements to reduce shadowing effects and the use of active feedback to adjust emitter temperature based on measured board temperature. In spite of these improvements, all presently available IR systems require at least minor adjustments for boards of significantly different thermal mass.

11.6.1 IR sources

The two most commonly used IR sources are the T-3 tungsten lamp and the area-source panel emitter. Systems that use T-3 lamps are commonly called *lamp IR* systems, while those that use area-source emitters are called *panel IR* systems. Each has advantages and disadvantages, and either can be used successfully in SMT applications.

T-3 tungsten lamp

The construction of this lamp is illustrated in Fig. 11.17. It consists of a helically-wound tungsten filament inside a quartz tube. At rated voltage, the

QUARTZ T3 LAMP

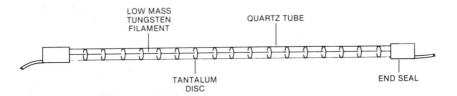

LOW MASS
TUNGSTEN
FILAMENT

QUARTZ TUBE

TANTALUM
DISC

END SEAL

FIGURE II

FIG. 11.17   Construction of quartz T-3 tungsten lamp. (Used by permission. Norman R. Cox, Research, Inc.)

peak wavelength is about $1.15\,\mu m$, corresponding to a temperature of 4225 °C. The amount of energy emitted at this operating voltage is about 100 W/in. An approximate spectrum for the T-3 lamp operating both at full rated voltage and at half voltage is illustrated in Fig. 11.18. As can be seen, a reduction in operating voltage markedly reduces the total power and increases the peak wavelength.

The emission spectrum can be modified by mounting the lamp adjacent to a high-temperature ceramic material, as shown in Fig. 11.19. Energy is absorbed in the backplane and reradiated in the $3{-}5\,\mu m$ wavelength range. The net result of this *dual-emitter* system is a flatter spectrum with increased energy at longer wavelengths (Fig. 11.20).

Area-source panel emitter

A typical panel emitter is shown in Fig. 11.21. It is similar in principle to the dual-emitter T-3 lamp system just described, but with an even higher per-

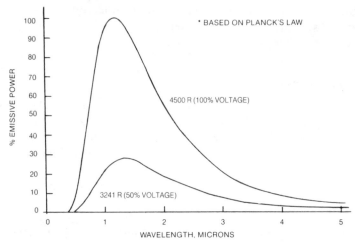

FIG. 11.18 Spectrum of T-3 quartz lamp at full and half rated power. (Used by permission. Norman R. Cox, Research, Inc.)

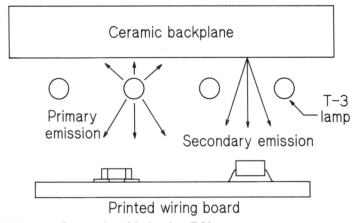

FIG. 11.19 Construction of dual-emitter T-3 lamp system.

centage of energy radiated by secondary emission. The resistive element is backed with a refractory material that absorbs the primary radiation and reradiates it at a longer wavelength. A thin layer of high-emissivity material is mounted over the top of the assembly for protection.

Emitters of this type operate at lower temperatures than the T-3 lamp. The peak temperature is rated at about 800 °C, but for solder reflow the emitters are operated in the range 190–450 °C.[7] At these temperatures, a panel IR system can heat air very efficiently. As a result, as much as 50% of the energy is transmitted via thermal convection rather than direct radiation. In this sense, a panel IR system operates more as an IR-heated convection oven rather than as a direct IR oven.

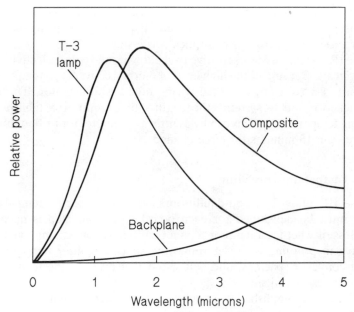

FIG. 11.20   Emission spectra of dual-emitter T-3 lamp system.

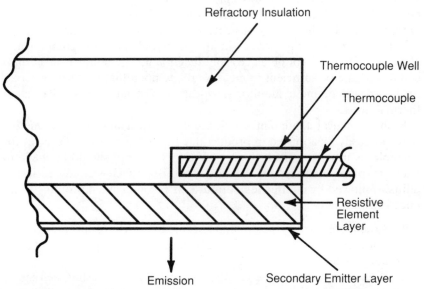

FIG. 11.21   Construction of panel IR emitter. (Reprinted with permission of *Solid State Technology*.)

Comparison of emitter types

Lamp IR systems operate at higher temperatures than panel systems, so the rate of heat transfer is higher. Since as much as 90% of the energy is transmitted via primary emission from the lamp, system temperatures can be adjusted very rapidly. This is sometimes important in a facility that must build a variety of board types in quick succession.

Panel IR systems are less sensitive to shadowing and color selectivity than lamp systems. Because of the high level of thermal convection, temperature uniformity across a large printed wiring board is also better. The main drawback to a panel IR system is the length of time required to stabilize after changing temperatures. This can be as little as 5 minutes for a minor change to more than 15 minutes for large changes.

11.6.2 Temperature profiling

Because IR reflow is a non-equilibrium process, a specific temperature profile must be developed for each board type. This step is necessary regardless of whether a lamp or a panel emitter system is employed. The objective in profiling is to determine the specific emitter temperatures, emitter-conveyor spacings, and belt speed that produce the temperature profile nearest the ideal.

Profiling is accomplished by attaching a set of thermocouples to a representative sample board and monitoring board temperature as it progresses through the oven. The thermocouples are attached to long lengths of heat-resistant wire. Since a number of runs may be needed to determine the optimum profile, the test is considered destructive to the sample board.

For best results, the board should be populated with components, although they need not be electrically functional. The number of thermocouples should be sufficient to measure the temperature uniformity across the board surface and to monitor any local areas of unusually small or large thermal mass.

From a practical standpoint, it is desirable to adjust only those parameters that can easily be adjusted in production. Emitter–conveyor distance, for example, is usually difficult to change. Every attempt should be made to leave this parameter fixed for all board types. Belt speed is usually easiest to adjust, followed by emitter temperature. A recommended profiling sequence is as follows:

1. Attempt to identify the optimum profile by adjusting only the speed of the conveyor belt. Maintain the emitter heights and temperatures at some nominal value.
2. If an acceptable profile cannot be achieved by adjusting belt speed alone, adjust emitter temperatures as necessary. Keep the temperature changes as small as possible and use belt speed to make gross adjustments.
3. If the profile cannot be optimized through use of emitter temperature and belt speed adjustments, adjust emitter heights as necessary.

In the interest of maintaining a just-in-time manufacturing capability, consider using a single setting for a number of different boards. Although for some boards this compromise profile may deviate from ideal, the difference may not have a practical impact on product quality. All board types should still be profiled per the above procedure to assure compatibility with the standard settings.

11.6.3 Reflow atmosphere

The least expensive atmosphere for IR reflow is air, and this is most commonly used. It is not, however, the most chemically desirable atmosphere. The high oxygen content promotes degradation of the flux and joint surfaces. It can also contribute to an increased incidence of solder balling.

Oxygen-free environments have been promoted as a way to improve soldering yields. Pure nitrogen is most common, but other gasses, such as argon or forming gas, are sometimes used. With suitably designed equipment, oxygen levels can be maintained at 5–10 ppm or less. There is some evidence that this improves the range of acceptable process settings.[6]

By adding a small amount of hydrogen (approximately 5%) to the nitrogen, a slight reducing atmosphere (forming gas) is produced. Although not enough to remove all oxide on previously tarnished surfaces, it can have a beneficial effect. One reported benefit is a reduction in the amount of flux spreading during reflow.[8] Care should always be exercised when using hydrogen because of its potentially explosive character. Concentrations above about 5–8% in nitrogen should be avoided.

At present, there is little hard evidence to show that inert environments provide a measurable improvement over ordinary air. Given that they add significantly to operating costs (nitrogen costs approximately $5/hour), routine use in the absence of an identified need is questionable.

11.7 LASER REFLOW

All the reflow methods described thus far subject the entire assembly to the reflow temperature for as long as 30–60 seconds. Some types of components are damaged by exposure to these temperature extremes. Many hybrid circuits, for example, employ components that have themselves been soldered with eutectic tin–lead solder. The lid seal on some hermetic devices is also made with eutectic tin–lead. Obviously, subjecting these devices to a second reflow operation is detrimental.

Laser reflow soldering was developed to address this concern. Unlike the previous methods, heat energy is directed only onto the joints being soldered and each joint must be formed individually. Temperature sensitive components can more readily be soldered without fear of damage.

A typical system utilizes a CO_2 or Nd:YAG laser, a mechanical X–Y positioning stage, and a computer controller. The controller moves the board under the laser as necessary to reflow all the joints sequentially.

The benefits of laser soldering include:

- Heating is highly localized, reducing the potential for damage to thermally sensitive devices.
- Joints are formed very rapidly, reducing the potential for intermetallic growth.
- Stresses in the joint are reduced compared to mass reflow methods.

Localized heating

A typical laser spot size is 0.025–0.1 mm (0.001–0.004 in). The applied heat is thus concentrated into a small area, and reflow can be accomplished extremely rapidly. Heat is not applied in any one area long enough to cause a significant temperature rise outside the immediate area of the spot.

Rapid joint formation

One problem with typical mass-soldering processes is that significant amounts of copper–tin intermetallic can grow during the time the solder is molten. Although a small amount of growth is unavoidable, large amounts can lead to brittleness and dewetting of the joints. In laser reflow, each joint is formed in 0.05–0.30 second, significantly reducing the length of time during which intermetallics can grow.

Reduced joint stress

In a mass-soldering operation, the zero-stress condition exists at the temperature at which the solder solidifies. As the assembly cools further, the components and board contract at different rates, depending on their exact CTEs. While leaded joints are usually compliant enough that this is not a concern, leadless chip carriers can have serious problems. With laser soldering, both the component and board remain at room temperature during soldering, significantly reducing this effect.

Laser soldering has two primary drawbacks:

- The speed of soldering is slow because each joint must be formed individually.
- Equipment cost for a given throughput is much higher than with mass reflow methods.

Slow soldering speed

The effective rate at which joints can be formed includes both the actual soldering time and the time required to position the laser beam. Measured throughputs range from 4–10 joints per second or about 15,000–35,000 joints per hour. Depending on the nature of the board, this can be an order of magnitude less than the capacity of a vapor phase system.

High equipment cost

Commercial laser systems for SMT soldering can cost anywhere from $100,000 to $250,000 each. Although this is roughly comparable to a production-grade in-line vapor phase system, the effective throughput is much lower. As a result, laser systems are considered specialty items that are employed only when their specific advantages are of benefit.

11.7.1 Laser sources

The two types of lasers commonly used for SMT soldering are CO_2 and Nd:YAG. Both types can be obtained in either continuous-wave (CW) or pulsed versions. Better soldering results are generally obtained with CW systems.[9,10]

The CO_2 laser emits energy in the far-IR region at 10.6 μm wavelength. The emission is strongly absorbed by epoxy–glass or ceramic substrates but is reflected by metals (Fig. 11.22a). The situation is nearly reversed with the Nd:YAG laser, which emits energy in the near-IR region at 1.06 μm wavelength (Fig. 11.22b). Since CO_2 laser energy is more likely to damage printed wiring boards, the Nd:YAG laser is now usually recommended for reflow soldering. However, both systems have been used successfully.

Most laser systems are *open-loop* systems: a fixed amount of energy is directed to each joint and no attempt is made to control actual joint temperature. A relatively new concept is the *closed-loop* system, illustrated in Fig. 11.23. This system employs an infrared sensor to dynamically sense the

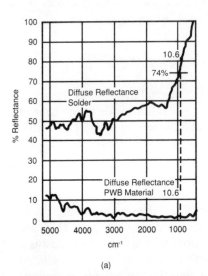

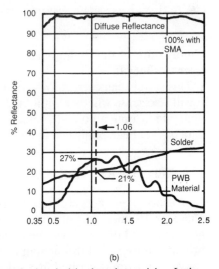

(a)   (b)

FIG. 11.22 Absorption characteristics of solder and printed wiring board material: a. In the region around 10.6 μm wavelength, b. In the region around 1.06 μm wavelength. (Used by permission. Copyright 1985, Martin Marietta Corp.)

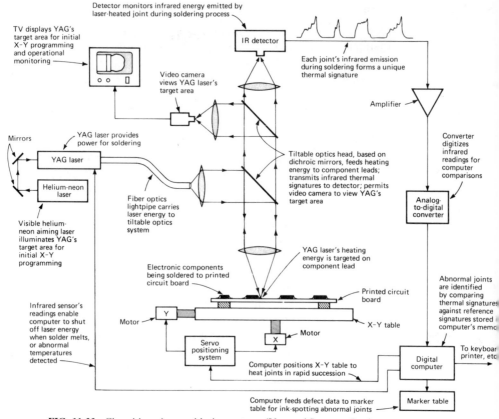

FIG. 11.23   Closed-loop laser soldering system. (Vanzetti Systems, Inc.)

temperature of the joint. When reflow is achieved, the sensor causes the laser to shut off.

This system can correct for variations in individual joint thermal masses. It will also sense whether a joint thermal profile falls outside preset control limits, indicating a possible defect. Although promising in principle, little data has yet been published to indicate the practical benefits of this system.

11.8 REFLOW BY THERMAL CONVECTION

Convection ovens are rarely used to reflow solder paste. Compared to vapor phase or IR methods, the rate of heat transfer is much less. They are normally used only in low-volume applications where equipment cost is a primary concern and throughput is not. Two exceptions are the IR-heated convection oven described in Section 11.6 and the hot gas repair stations described in Chapter 15.

A recent entry in this area is the hot-air knife in combination with a quartz heater (Section 8.3.1). The IR heater elevates the solder temperature almost to the reflow point. Forced hot air from the air knives completes the process.

As with IR reflow, the atmosphere used can have an impact. Ordinary air is inexpensive but can promote oxidation. Nitrogen or forming gas can be used when necessary, but at considerable additional operating expense.

11.9 COMPARISON OF REFLOW TECHNIQUES

Table 11.3 compares the attributes of the various reflow processes. Most mass soldering is performed either with a vapor phase or an infrared reflow system. General recommendations for process selection can be summarized as follows:

1. Reflow by thermal conduction is recommended for small ceramic circuits with components mounted only on one side. It is the lowest cost

Reflow method	Advantages	Disadvantages
Vapor phase	• Insensitive to variations in board thermal mass • Uniform temperature across entire board • Well-controlled maximum temperature • Insensitive to variations in board geometry	• High capital equipment cost • High operating cost due to expense of vapor phase fluid • Fluid decomposition generates toxic by-products • Little control over temperature profile
Infrared	• Precise control of reflow temperature profile • Moderate capital equipment cost • Moderate operating cost • Improved heating dynamics compared to vapor phase	• Equipment parameters must be readjusted for boards of different thermal mass • Possible to overheat board if equipment is misadjusted • Heating rate depends on color of surface • IR energy is blocked by tall components
Laser	• Heat is confined to joint region • Compatible with temperature-sensitive components	• Low throughput because each joint must be reflowed individually • Very high equipment cost
Conductive belt	• Low equipment cost • Simple operation • Moderate control over temperature profile	• Incompatible with organic printed wiring boards • Small maximum board size

TABLE 11.3 Comparison of in-line reflow methods

process for these assemblies. Because it depends on intimate contact between substrate and heating element, it cannot be used for double-sided assemblies. It is not recommended for use with organic printed wiring boards.

2. Vapor phase reflow is suggested for facilities that must produce many different board types. This process has a very uniform heating profile that is largely independent of board thermal mass. For highest soldering yields, an adequate preheat step should be included.

3. Infrared reflow can be used on lines that produce only a few board types. It works best when a single reflow profile can be developed for all boards.

4. Laser reflow should be used for temperature-sensitive components. It is also useful for soldering only a few surface mount components (such as high pin-count quadpacks) on a through-hole board.

REFERENCES

1. Robrish, P., and Wells, E. *Solder Paste Drying*, Hewlett-Packard Laboratories, Manufacturing Research Center, Apr. 16, 1986.
2. Klein Wassink, R., and Verguld, M. "Drawbridging of Leadless Components", *Hybrid Circuits*, No. 9, Jan. 1986, pp. 18–24.
3. Wright, A., and Mahajan, R. "An Overview of Condensation Reflow Soldering Technology," *Proceedings of ASM's 2nd Electronic Packaging: Materials and Processes Conference*, Bloomington, MN, Oct. 1985, pp. 63–68.
4. "Ventilation Rates Can Safely Be Lowered To Cut Down On Fluorinert™ Liquids Losses," *Global Service Bulletin Number 29*, 3M Corp, Industrial Chemical Products Division, St. Paul, MN, Mar. 1987.
5. Ellison, T., and Fine, M. "Fluid Consumption Considerations for In-Line Vapor Phase Soldering," *Proceedings of NEPCON/West '86*, Anaheim, CA, Feb. 1986.
6. Arslancan, A., and Flattery, D. "Infrared Reflow For SMT: Thermal and Yield Considerations," Presented at *EXPO SMT '86*, Las Vegas, NV, Sept. 1986.
7. Dow, S. "Use of Radiant Infrared in Soldering Surface Mounted Devices to Printed Circuit Boards," *Solid State Technology*, Nov. 1984, pp. 191–195.
8. Cox, N. "Infrared Solder Reflow of Surface Mounted Devices," *Hybrid Circuit Technology*, March 1985, pp. 37–41.
9. Stow, J. R. "Laser Reflow Soldering," *Proceedings of ASM's 2nd Electronic Packaging: Materials and Processes Conference*, Bloomington, MN, Oct. 1985, pp. 9–14.
10. Lish, E. "Application of Laser Microsoldering to SMDs," *Proceedings of the 1985 International Symposium on Microelectronics*, Anaheim, CA, Nov. 1985, pp. 1–10.

12

Wave soldering

Wave soldering has been the dominant method for mass-soldering through-hole printed wiring assemblies for over 20 years. The accumulated experience with the process is immense, and virtually every company that produces any appreciable volume of printed circuit assemblies has at least one wave soldering machine. Given its established position in through-hole technology, extending the process to encompass surface mount technology has been a natural evolutionary step.

The first products to use wave soldered surface mount components came from the Japanese consumer electronics industry in the mid-1970s. These early products were relatively simple designs using only surface mount passive devices that could easily be soldered with existing machines. As the complexity of the products increased, serious quality problems, primarily solder bridges and unsoldered joints, were found to occur. To correct these defects, it was necessary to develop improved machines with more complex wave dynamics. The current generation of wave soldering equipment has been expressly designed to solder both through-hole and surface mount components with equal ease. However, basic physical limitations with the wave soldering process make it inherently less flexible than reflow soldering.

The general principles of wave soldering have been thoroughly described in various reference works (see, for example, Refs. 1 and 2). This chapter is not meant to be a definitive treatment of the process but focuses explicitly on those issues of greatest importance in surface mounting.

12.1 WAVE SOLDERING OVERVIEW

In the wave soldering process, the printed wiring board is transported over a fountain of continuously flowing molten solder, as shown in Fig. 12.1. The height of the conveyor is adjusted so that as the board passes over the wave,

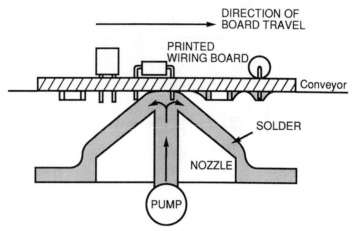

FIG. 12.1   Principle of wave soldering.

its entire underside is washed by the solder. In the case of through-hole components, the solder wets the protruding component leads and is drawn up into the plated through-holes. Surface mount components are soldered by adhesively attaching them to the underside of the board and immersing them directly in the solder wave.

The complete wave soldering process consists of three steps, which are normally performed within a single machine, as illustrated in Fig. 12.2. The steps are:

- flux application
- board preheat
- wave soldering

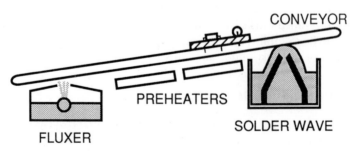

FIG. 12.2   Schematic of complete wave soldering system.

12.2 FLUX APPLICATION

The application of flux is a prerequisite for successful soldering. Either solvent-soluble or water-soluble fluxes can be used. In recent years, water-soluble fluxes have gained popularity for through-hole soldering because of their aggressive nature. Components with widely varying inherent solderability are easily soldered using water-soluble organic acid fluxes. Such fluxes are so active that it is even possible to wet normally unsolderable materials, such as stainless steel. Another advantage of organic acid fluxes is that they can be removed by washing in a relatively simple aqueous cleaning system.

This high activity level makes water-soluble fluxes less suitable for surface mount technology. As described in Chapter 13, flux residues can become trapped under surface mount components where they are not easily removed. Because of water's high surface tension, it cannot penetrate into the narrow clearances between components and board. The remaining residues can cause rapid corrosion of the assembly.

Solvent-soluble fluxes are more popular for soldering complex surface mount assemblies. Both fluorinated and chlorinated hydrocarbon solvents have much lower surface tension than water and are better able to clean flux residues from under components. Rosin-based fluxes are most commonly used, but the more controlled synthetic activated fluxes (Section 5.4.1) show great promise for the future. Both types are readily soluble in fluorocarbon-based solvents.

Regardless of the type of flux used, it must be applied in a uniform layer prior to soldering. For wave soldering, liquid flux is normally used. The most common application methods are foam fluxing, wave fluxing, and spray fluxing.

12.2.1 Foam fluxing

In this approach, illustrated in Fig. 12.3, air is pumped through a porous stone. The resulting stream of air bubbles is directed by a nozzle onto the underside of the board. As the bubbles burst, they deposit a thin, uniform layer of flux on the board. Any excess flux drips back into the flux sump. As long as the exposure time is sufficient to coat the entire board, the thickness of the layer is relatively insensitive to conveyor speed, depending primarily on flux viscosity.

Viscosity control is therefore critical. Normally this is regulated by monitoring the specific gravity of the flux. When necessary, additional solvent is added to maintain viscosity within specified control limits. Because of the importance of viscosity, not all fluxes are suitable for application by foaming.

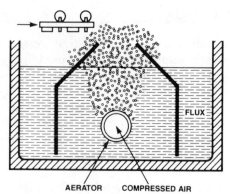

FIG. 12.3 Principle of operation of foam
fluxer. (Used by permission. Signetics
Corporation.)

12.2.2 Wave fluxing

The principles of wave soldering can also be used to apply flux (Fig. 12.4).
An advantage over foam fluxing is that the wave height can be adjusted
much higher. Wave heights as much as 50 mm (2 in) are possible, compared
to 15 mm (0.6 in) for foam fluxing. This can be important for through-hole
components with long wires but is rarely a factor for surface mount components.

The height of the wave is rather critical. It must be adjusted to insure
adequate coverage of the entire board (including an allowance for possible
board warpage) but not so high as to cover the top side of the board.

12.2.3 Spray fluxing

Spray fluxing has been used on single-sided boards without plated through-
holes. A screen is mounted around the periphery of a drum and rotated

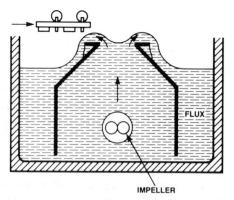

FIG. 12.4 Principle of operation of wave fluxer.
(Used by permission. Signetics Corporation.)

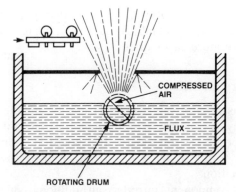

FIG. 12.5 Principle of operation of spray fluxer.
(Used by permission. Signetics Corporation.)

through the flux reservoir, as shown in Fig. 12.5. Air pumped into the drum creates a fine spray of flux. A baffle must be employed to direct the flux onto the board.

This approach is simple but not well-controllable. It can be used with virtually any liquid flux, but is more wasteful than other methods. Flux that sprays out of the baffle cannot be recovered, and the system must be cleaned frequently. The air pressure is not sufficient to force flux into small holes, so the process is not recommended for boards with plated through-holes. On the other hand, large openings can be a problem because they serve as paths for the flux to coat the top surface of the board.

12.3 BOARD PREHEATING

Similar to the preheat step in reflow soldering (Section 11.1.1), preheating prior to wave soldering accomplishes several purposes. The three primary reasons for preheating are:

- solvent evaporation
- reduction of thermal shock
- activation of rosin fluxes

Solvent evaporation (flux drying)

Solvent that remains in the flux at the soldering step will boil violently, spattering solder balls across the board. It also consumes heat from the wave, altering the heating dynamics and possibly delaying the onset of wetting.

Rosin fluxes use solvents with low vapor pressures and are easily dried. Fluxes containing water require longer drying times. It is virtually impossible to completely evaporate all moisture, and the small amount that remains causes a certain amount of spattering during soldering. For this reason, most water-soluble fluxes do not actually contain water but instead use alcohols or glycols, which are more easily dried.

Reduction of thermal shock

Molten solder has an extremely high heat capacity, and thermal shock of the assembly is always a concern. With through-hole technology, the primary concern is the printed wiring board. If a board at room temperature is exposed directly to the solder wave, it can suffer excessive warpage and possible delamination.

Surface mount components introduce an additional concern because they are immersed directly in the wave. Excessive temperature gradients can damage chip components or plastic-encapsulated semiconductors. Preheating reduces this risk by lowering the temperature difference between the solder and the assembly.

The preheat temperature is defined as being measured on the top side of the board. It can be measured with either a thermocouple or temperature-sensitive paint. Preheat temperatures for through-hole boards range between about 80 °C for simple single-sided boards to as high as 125 °C for thick multilayer boards. As described in Section 12.4.5, the preheat profile for surface mount boards must be more tightly controlled than has been necessary for through-hole boards: besides controlling the maximum temperature, the rate of temperature increase must also be controlled.

Activation of rosin fluxes

Rosin fluxes do not become fully active until they reach temperatures of about 80 °C. Preheating assures that they remain at this temperature long enough to remove surface oxides and other contaminants. Organic acid fluxes are less dependent on heat for activation; they begin working as soon as they are applied.

12.4 WAVE SOLDERING

The actual dynamics of the solder wave have a large influence on soldering yields. The two primary equipment classes are *single-wave* and *dual-wave* systems. Single-wave systems have classically been used to solder through-hole assemblies. Dual-wave systems are a relatively recent innovation developed expressly for surface mount soldering.

12.4.1 Single-wave systems

A typical single-wave system is pictured in Fig. 12.6, and its conceptual operation is illustrated in Fig. 12.7. Molten solder is pumped through a

FIG. 12.6 Single wave soldering system. Many machines of this type can be adapted for dual-wave operation by purchasing a modification kit from the manufacturer. (Used by permission. Universal Instruments Corporation.)

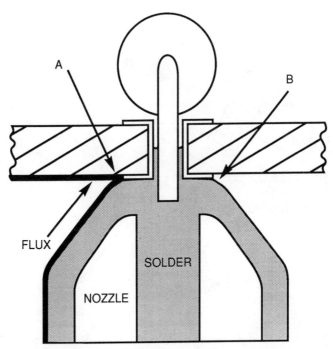

FIG. 12.7 Close-up of single-wave soldering system showing the three distinct regions of the wave. The point of entry is labeled A and the point of exit is labeled B. Soldering occurs in the region between A and B.

channel and spills over an extension plate, returning to the solder reservoir. This results in a smooth flow of solder called a *laminar* wave. A thin, stable oxide layer resides on the surface of the wave.

Three distinct regions of the wave have been described by Manko and are shown in Fig. 12.7.[2] The first is the point of entry, labeled A in the drawing. As a board enters the wave, it pushes aside the oxide layer and makes contact with fresh solder. The large differential velocity between the solder and the board creates a washing action that removes all flux and contaminants.

The region between A and B is where soldering occurs. During this time, the board warms to soldering temperature, at which point the solder wets the metallic surfaces. The length of time between the two points must be adequate to permit the solder to rise and fill all plated through-holes.

At Point B, the board exits the wave. The dynamics in this region are critical to the formation of acceptable joints. The two main concerns are *bridging* and *icicling*. A bridge is an extraneous web of solder that shorts between adjacent conductors. An icicle is a similar finger of solder that does not contact another conductor. Both phenomena are a result of the same influences.

Bridges result from an interaction between the surface energy of molten solder and the dynamics of the wave. The situation is illustrated in Fig. 12.8.

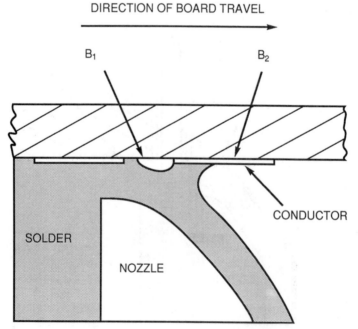

FIG. 12.8 Diagram showing how bridging occurs. Solder in contact with the bare laminate does not wet the board and peels back at point B_1 in the drawing. Solder which wets a metal conductor peels back at point B_2. Bridging can occur between successive conductors.

As the board exits, the solder is in contact with either the nonmetallic board surface or the metal conductors. Solder contacting the board material cannot wet the surface and breaks away from the board at Point B_1 of Fig. 12.8. (This phenomenon is called *peel back*.) Solder that has wetted to a conductor is carried by surface tension to Point B_2. If this extended web begins to solidify before peel back occurs, it will cause a bridge or an icicle.

Various techniques have been employed to reduce the possibility of bridging. Several of the more common methods are described in the following paragraphs:

Inclined conveyor

If the board is conveyed through the wave at a slight angle, the solder will peel back more rapidly. At angles above about 3°, the force of gravity is enough to overcome surface tension, and the solder will spontaneously roll off the board.[3] To take advantage of this effect, the angle of inclination is usually set at about 4–5° in a dry wave and 7–9° when oil is intermixed with the solder, as described in Section 12.5.

Extended wave

In this approach, the extension plates are lengthened to create a wide wave. In combination with an inclined conveyor, this permits the board to exit at a point of zero relative velocity to the solder. Surface tension forces then have sufficient time to pull the excess solder back into the wave. Several variations on this design have been developed. The system illustrated in Fig. 12.9 is known as the "Lambda" wave.

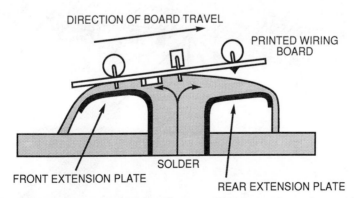

FIG. 12.9   The Lambda-wave patented by Electrovert Corp. is one of several approaches developed to reduce the possibility of solder bridging. In this design the shape of the wave is such that the board exits at a point of zero relative velocity to the solder.

Oil intermixing

Although primarily used to reduce dross formation, oil intermixed with the solder also reduces the solder surface tension. This enhances wetting characteristics and reduces the possibility of bridging. The merits of oil intermixing are discussed in more detail in Section 12.5.

Hot air knife

Rather than preventing bridges from forming, it is possible to remove them after formation. This is done with the patented hot air knife, shown conceptually in Fig. 12.10. It consists of a jet of hot air directed onto the board after it exits the wave. The air, which is heated above the solder melting temperature, blows away all excess solder, leaving clean, bridge-free joints.

The force of the air is not sufficient to blow solder out of properly filled via holes. It will, however, remove solder that has not wetted the joint. The air knife thus provides an additional advantage of exposing latent joint defects.

Most of the solder in a through-hole joint is contained within the plated through-hole, so the small amount removed by the air knife does not impact reliability. On surface mount components the entire joint is exposed to the air knife, and the amount of solder removed by the knife is a much greater proportion of the total available. If too much solder is removed, the amount remaining may not be sufficient to form a reliable joint. Unfortunately, few published studies have examined the impact of solder volume on solder joint reliability. Although a joint may appear solid when initially produced, once it is subjected to mechanical and thermal stresses in the field, it may rapidly fail. In the absence of statistically valid data, caution is advised in employing an air knife in surface mount assembly.

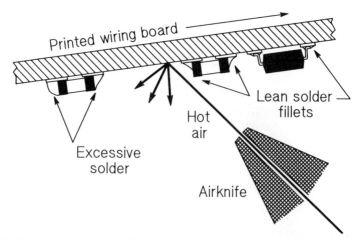

FIG. 12.10   Principle of hot air knife. A jet of heated air blows excess solder off the board to remove bridges. The jet is not strong enough to remove solder from properly wetted joints.

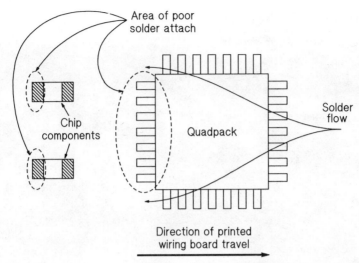

FIG. 12.11   Solder shadowing. The component bodies block the flow of solder, causing incomplete wetting of the trailing leads. (Electronic Packaging and Production Magazine.)

12.4.2 Solder shadowing

Single-wave systems are not entirely successful in soldering surface mount components. The major problem is *solder shadowing*, illustrated in Fig. 12.11. As the components enter the wave, they push the solder aside, forming a wake that prevents solder from flowing properly onto the trailing surfaces of the component. With closely spaced components, the wake may extend far enough to prevent solder from wetting any of the terminations on components near the center of a cluster. Fig. 12.12 shows the appearance of actual components that have not wetted due to solder shadowing.

12.4.3 Dual-wave systems

The dual-wave concept was developed expressly for the soldering of surface mount components. A typical commercial system is pictured in Fig. 12.13. There are several variations in actual equipment design, but the basic concept is to first wet all terminations with a turbulent solder wave, then follow with a laminar wave to remove bridges and icicles.

One implementation of the dual-wave approach is illustrated in Fig. 12.14. Solder is pumped from a common reservoir into both the turbulent and laminar waves. A single pump can be used for both waves, but more control is afforded by using separate pumps. The actual appearance of such a system is shown in Fig. 12.15.

The dual-wave effect can be achieved without actually separating the two waves. Fig. 12.16 shows the principle of the *Omega wave* developed by Electrovert Corp. A vibrating plate in the path of solder flow creates

FIG. 12.12   Solder shadowing. (Photograph by the author.)

FIG. 12.13   Typical dual-wave soldering system. (Used by permission of Sensbey Co.)

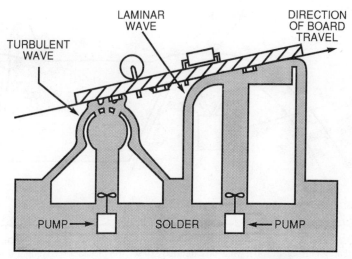

FIG. 12.14   Principle of operation of dual-wave soldering system.

FIG. 12.15   Dual-wave system in operation. (Used by permission. Sensbey Co.)

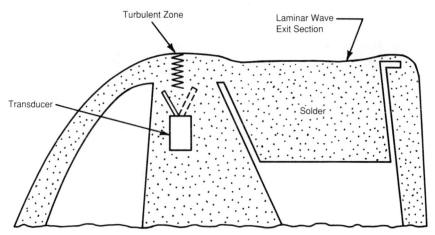

FIG. 12.16   Principle of the Omega-wave soldering system. A transducer at the front of the wave creates a turbulent zone, while an extended exit section provides the laminar flow necessary to remove solder bridges.

turbulence at the front of the wave, while the rear remains laminar. Full solder coverage is assured by the turbulence, while bridges are removed in the laminar portion.

12.4.4 Drag soldering

This approach is relatively common in Europe for through-hole technology but has not gained widespread popularity in the United States. It involves dragging the underside of the board along the surface of a pot of molten solder for a predetermined time. The board is lowered and raised by tilting it at an angle, so the conditions over which the joints are formed vary as a function of location on the board.

When applied to surface mounting, drag soldering suffers from several limitations. As with single-wave soldering, shadowing is a serious problem. Unlike with the wave process, however, there is no easy way to add turbulence to improve the solder coverage. Ultrasonic agitation of the solder pot has been suggested, but this approach has not yet been commercially demonstrated.

Another problem is that gas bubbles from the flux cannot easily escape from under the board. Proper solder drainage is also difficult to achieve because the angle at which the board exits the solder bath varies as a function of distance along the board. When the board is first lifted from the bath, the angle is exceedingly shallow, so gravitational pull is not able to assist in promoting solder peel-back. At the back of the board, the exit angle can be as much as 15°, allowing gravity to be of considerable assistance.

Because of these limitations, drag soldering has not been widely used in surface mounting. It continues, however, to maintain a presence in through-hole technology. For a more detailed description of the drag soldering process, refer to Ref. 1.

12.4.5 Soldering temperature profile

The temperature of the solder wave is a tradeoff between two competing factors. On the one hand, it should be much higher than the solder melting temperature to reduce the potential for bridging. On the other hand, it should be as low as possible to minimize the potential of thermal damage to the components and board.

Solder wave temperatures for through-hole technology commonly range between 245–280 °C. At lower temperatures, an increase in bridging is often noted. This can be understood by reviewing the phenomenon of peel-back described in Section 12.4.1. As the differential between the actual solder temperature and the melting temperature decreases, the solder is more likely to solidify before it can peel cleanly away from the board. In fact, a common solution to the problem of excess bridging is to increase the temperature of the solder wave.

The temperature sensitivity of surface mount components sets a practical limit for the overall wave soldering thermal profile. For most applications, wave temperatures should be in the range 235–250 °C. At temperatures near the low end of this range, it may be necessary to use a supplementary technique, such as a hot air knife, to remove solder bridges.

Preheating is essential for minimizing thermal shock. In many applications, ceramic capacitors are the most thermally sensitive parts. Because the barium–titanate dielectric used in these capacitors undergoes a change in crystal structure at the Curie point temperature of about 120 °C (Section 2.4.1), the temperature gradient through this region must be carefully controlled. The board temperature should be gradually elevated to a point well above the Curie temperature, generally to within 100–125 °C of the soldering temperature. As with reflow soldering, the speed of this ramp should be 2–4 °C/sec. A suggested temperature profile for the total wave soldering process is shown in Fig. 12.17.

The actual temperature profile for a dual-wave system is slightly more complicated than the ideal profile. As the board makes the transition between the first and second waves, it cools slightly, causing a characteristic "double peak" profile (Fig. 12.18). It has been suggested that this rapid temperature fluctuation increases the risk of cracking ceramic capacitors. In this regard, a system such as the Omega wave that combines both turbulent and laminar waves into a single wave may have an advantage over a system in which the two waves are physically separated. Much more experimental work needs to be performed to confirm this hypothesis.

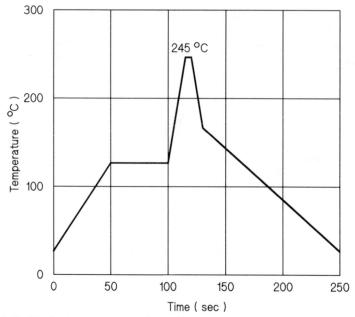

FIG. 12.17   Idealized temperature profile for single-wave soldering system. Temperature is measured at top surface of board.

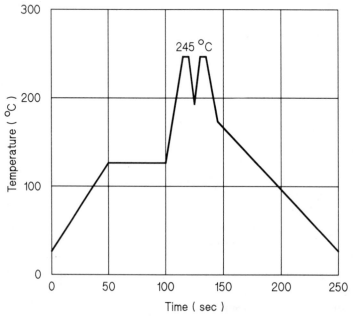

FIG. 12.18   Idealized temperature profile for dual-wave soldering system showing characteristic double-peak profile. Temperature measured at top surface of board.

12.5 WAVE SOLDERING WITH OIL INTERMIX

The surface of a molten solder wave is in contact with ordinary air. As a result, it quickly forms an oxide layer consisting primarily of tin and lead oxides. This layer, called *dross*, floats on the surface of the solder and is detrimental to the soldering process. Besides the obvious impact on wetting and solderability, airborne dross can be a health problem. If inhaled, lead in the dross can lead to lead poisoning over a period of time.

One way to reduce the formation of dross is to mix a tinning oil in the solder. The relatively light oil quickly floats to the surface of the wave and forms a blanket over the solder. It also lowers the apparent surface tension of the solder, minimizing the potential for bridging.

Oil can be introduced either by pumping it into the body of the wave or by dripping it onto the surface. Dripping is simpler, but injection provides a more controlled rate of use.

Oil should not be left on the assembly, so when using oil intermix, a final cleaning step is essential. It is also important to remove oil buildup within the machine by cleaning it frequently. For these reasons, the use of oil is a subject of controversy within the industry.

12.6 ADHESIVES

Prior to wave soldering, the SMCs must be adhesively attached to the board. This adhesive must hold the components securely even while immersed in molten solder. After soldering, the solder fillets provide the mechanical strength and the adhesive is no longer needed. Since removal is impractical, it must remain inert on the board for the entire life of the assembly.

The physical characteristics of the adhesive are important. Desirable properties include:

Adequate post-cure strength

Strength must be sufficient to hold the components securely in place during the soldering process but low enough to permit removal and replacement of defective devices.

High viscosity in uncured state

Once deposited on the board, the adhesive must resist the tendency to sag or bleed out across the board. The drops should retain a high profile so as to fill any gap between component bodies and the board. The viscosity should be high enough to prevent parts from moving prior to cure.

Easy to dispense in high-volume applications

The ideal adhesive should be compatible with any of the common dispensing methods, including syringe, pin transfer, and screen printing. It should have a long working life to minimize the need for frequent cleaning of the dispensing equipment. Shelf life of the unopened container should also be long.

Mechanical stability during curing

The adhesive should cure without moving parts from their as-placed locations. It should not shrink or shift during the cure cycle.

Rapid cure cycle

The adhesive should cure quickly using commonly available processes. Curing times on the order of 3–5 minutes are suggested for compatibility with the remainder of the process.[4] The curing environment should be as mild as possible, with temperatures not exceeding 120–150 °C.

Chemical stability

Since the adhesive remains on the assembly permanently, it must be extremely stable. It must not react with materials such as moisture in the environment to generate corrosive or electrically conductive residues. In both the cured and uncured state it must be nonflammable and nontoxic. It must not react with processing chemicals such as fluxes or solvents.

12.6.1 Adhesive choices

Many different types of adhesives have been advocated for surface mount assembly. They fall into two general categories:

Thermoset adhesives

These materials undergo a chemical change upon curing. They gain their strength by forming cross-linked polymers in a reaction initiated by heat or catalytic action. The process is not reversible.

Thermoplastic adhesives

These materials melt upon application of heat but do not experience any chemical change. The process is totally reversible: bonds can be broken by simply heating the adhesive above its melting point; they are formed again by cooling.

Characteristic	Epoxy	Acrylic
Chip shear strength	4.5–7 kg	2.5–5 kg
Cure schedule	5–30 min at 125–175 °C	30–90 sec exposure to UV followed by 3–5 min at 100–120 °C
Volume resistivity (ohm–cm)	10^{13}–10^{16}	10^{11}–10^{14}
Solvent resistance	excellent	good
Shelf life	6–12 mo	12 mo
Storage requirements	refrigerated (1-part) room temp (2-part)	room temp
Ease of application	good (1-part) poor (2-part)	good

TABLE 12.1 Typical characteristics of adhesives for surface mount applications

Nearly all adhesives presently used are of the thermoset variety. The two most commonly used classes are epoxies and acrylics. Neither type perfectly satisfies all requirements, but both have been used successfully. Typical characteristics are described in the following paragraphs and summarized in Table 12.1.

12.6.2 Epoxies

Epoxy resins offer high mechanical strength, high stability, and good viscosity characteristics. They are normally applied by syringe and are cured through a catalytic reaction accelerated by application of heat.

Both two-part and one-part systems are available. With two-part systems, the resin and hardener are packaged separately and must be mixed prior to use. One-part systems are premixed and must be kept frozen to prevent premature curing. One-part systems do not require any complicated mixing and are generally easier to use. However, they have a rather limited shelf life of about 6–12 months when stored at -40 °C.

The primary disadvantage of epoxies is their high strength once cured. This makes it extremely difficult to remove defective components. Epoxies can cause an allergic reaction in some individuals and so should always be handled with care.

Most epoxies require a relatively long cure cycle. Exact times depend on the specific nature of the material involved and can range from 5 minutes at 125 °C to over 30 minutes at 175 °C.

12.6.3 Acrylics

This class of adhesives can be produced form a wide range of monomeric acrylate or methacrylate species. They are cured by a polymerization reaction brought on by application of heat, ultraviolet (UV) energy, or a com-

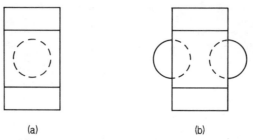

(a)   (b)

FIG. 12.19   Two approaches for dispensing adhesive under chip components. In (a), a single dot is dispensed under the center of the chip. This is suitable for heat-cured adhesives. In (b), two dots are dispensed at the sides of the chip. This is recommended for UV-cured adhesives and for MELF components.

bination of both. By controlling the internal chemical structure of the resin, the cured adhesive can be made to be either rigid or flexible.

Often, the cure cycle can be considerably accelerated by exposing the adhesive to UV energy. A typical system may cure in 30–45 seconds when exposed to high-intensity UV light ($80 \, \text{mW/cm}^2$). When exposed only to heat, this same system may require as long as 5 minutes at 150 °C to effect a similar cure.

A disadvantage of UV curing is that the adhesive must be directly irradiated by the UV source. The most important portion of the adhesive, that directly under the component, is thus least likely to be cured. To avoid this problem, a combination of both UV and heat can be used. The exact cure cycle is dependent on the specific nature of the adhesive, but a typical system would require simultaneous exposure to low-intensity UV energy ($20–30 \, \text{mW/cm}^2$) and 120 °C heat for 3 minutes.

To further promote the UV cure, it is desirable to expose as much of the adhesive as possible. One technique for doing this, shown in Fig. 12.19, is to dispense two adhesive dots at the sides of the component rather than a single dot under its center.

12.6.4 Dispensing methods

The three most common methods for dispensing adhesives are syringe, screen printing, and pin transfer. Both screen printing and pin transfer are mass-dispensing techniques applicable for extremely high throughputs of up to 500,000 components per hour. Syringe dispensing is a somewhat lower-volume technique limited to about 20,000 components per hour. Advantages and disadvantages of the various techniques are described in Table 12.2.

Screen printing

This technique is essentially identical to the screen printing of solder paste described in Chapter 9. To date it has not been widely used because of the

Application Method	Advantages	Disadvantages
Screen printing	• Rapid coverage of entire board • Can apply complex patterns	• Requires flat board surface • Screens must be frequently cleaned • Inflexible process flow • High setup time
Syringe dispensing	• Not limited to flat board surfaces • Variable dot size capability • No setup time	• Relative slow • High maintenance requirements
Pin transfer	• Rapid coverage of entire board • Little maintenance necessary	• Extremely sensitive to adhesive viscosity • High setup time • Sensitive to board warpage • Little control over dot geometry

TABLE 12.2   Advantages of adhesive application methods

relatively rigid process flow and high maintenance requirements. Since screen printing demands a perfectly flat substrate, it cannot be used once through-hole components have been loaded. Therefore, SMCs must be loaded *before* the through-hole components, in reverse of the normal sequence. The risk of dislodging SMCs is greater because they must withstand the rigors of board flexure and mechanical shock during the automatic insertion process. The board must also be carefully laid out to prevent the SMCs from interfering with proper operation of the cut-and-clinch tool on the automatic insertion machine.

Syringe dispensing

This technique is ideally suited for use with a sequential component placement machine. Although similar to syringe dispensing of solder paste (Section 9.6), the requirements are considerably relaxed. Whereas solder paste must be sequentially dispensed onto each component land, adhesive need only be dispensed in a single dot at the component center. Some placement machines even take advantage of this fact by mechanically coupling an adhesive dispenser to the placement head. While the head places a component on one board, the adhesive dispenser deposits adhesive at the corresponding location of a second board. (This technique severely limits the flexibility in locating the adhesive, so most machines allow some amount of independent movement.)

FIG. 12.20   Syringe dispenser for adhesive application. The adhesive head on this machine moves in tandem with the placement head at far left. (Photograph by the author.)

The viscosity characteristics of adhesives are less complex than solder pastes and the dispensed quantity need not be as repeatable, so complex positive-displacement pumps are unnecessary. Dispensing is usually performed with a simple air-pressure-operated syringe such as shown in Fig. 12.20.

Pin transfer

In this approach, illustrated in Fig. 12.21, a steel pin is dipped into a reservoir of adhesive. When the pin is withdrawn, surface tension causes some of the adhesive to cling to the pin. The pin is then positioned over the printed wiring board and lowered until the adhesive touches the board. A portion of the adhesive remains on the board when the pin is withdrawn.

Although in principle a single pin could be used to apply adhesive in sequential fashion, practical systems use a matrix of pins, as shown in Fig. 12.22, to deposit all dots simultaneously. Pin transfer systems are often used in conjunction with high-speed mass-placement systems, which place many hundreds of thousands of components per hour.

To prevent distortion of the adhesive dot, the metal pin must not touch the printed wiring board during the placement process. Since organic printed wiring boards can have a considerable amount of warp (a typical industry specification is 1% of board length), some means must be taken to accommodate this deviation. One approach is shown in Fig. 12.23. A small protrusion is milled on the tip to prevent the main body of the pin from

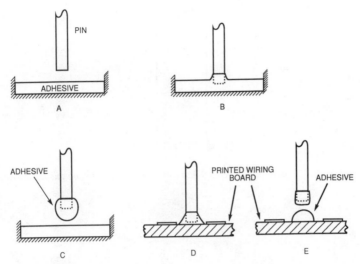

FIG. 12.21 Steps in the pin-transfer process for adhesive application: a. Pin is positioned over adhesive reservoir; b. pin is immersed into adhesive; c. pin is withdrawn, causing an amount of adhesive to remain on the pin; d. pin is lowered over the printed wiring board, causing adhesive to contact board; e. upon withdrawal of pin, a portion of the adhesive remains on the board.

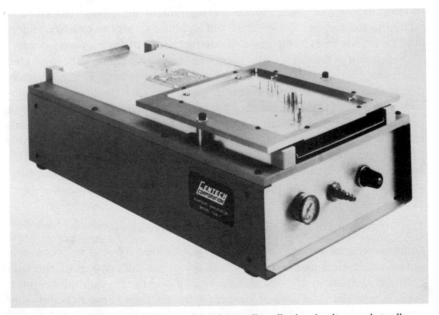

FIG. 12.22 Standalone pin-transfer machine that applies adhesive simultaneously to all locations on a board. (Used by permission. Centech Corporation.)

FIG. 12.23   Modified tip to provide controlled contact distance between pin and board.

making contact with the board. The protrusion is small enough that it has no significant impact on the shape of the dot.

The success of the pin transfer technique depends on several factors. Most important is adhesive viscosity, which controls the ultimate amount of adhesive transferred. Some users control the temperature and humidity of the environment in order to minimize variation. Board warpage is also important. Although the modified tip described above can compensate for a board that warps above the ideal plane, it cannot readily compensate for warpage below the plane. Since the amount of adhesive transferred is related to the distance between the pin and board, this can cause considerable variation. In extreme cases, a complete lack of transfer may occur.

A variation of the pin transfer approach involves applying adhesive to the underside of the component rather than onto the board. This is typically done on the component-placement machine immediately after the component is extracted from the feeder. Adhesive is dispensed from a wheel or a pin onto the component. The advantage of this approach is that no specialized tooling is required for each board, but since adhesive is dispensed onto a single component at a time, it is slower than using a matrix array. This approach has been used on certain high-speed sequential placement machines that place up to about 20,000 components per hour.

12.6.5   Component compatibility with adhesive

Adhesive cannot be used to attach all component types. The problem is purely mechanical and involves the ability of the adhesive to fill the void between component and board. One rule of thumb says that the height of the adhesive dot should be at least twice the distance between component and board (see Fig. 12.24). Depending on the specific adhesive properties, this limits the component standoff height to about 0.1 mm (0.004 in) for

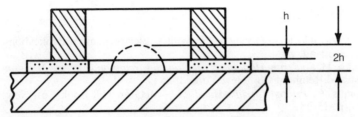

FIG. 12.24 Relationship between adhesive height and component clearance. For best results, the as-deposited dot height should be twice the clearance between component and board.

small components (such as chips and SOTs) to perhaps 0.25 mm (0.010 in) for larger components (such as SOICs) that can accept a larger adhesive dot. Components such as PLCCs or leaded chip carriers are seldom adhesively mounted unless the package includes a pedestal on the underside to reduce the clearance to acceptable limits.

One technique for reducing the effective component standoff height is to place a "dummy land" underneath the component at the location of the adhesive, as shown in Fig. 12.25. If the land is covered with solder mask, the effective standoff height can be reduced by as much as 0.125 mm (0.005 in). On densely populated boards it is often necessary to route conductor traces underneath components, in which case dummy lands are not necessary.

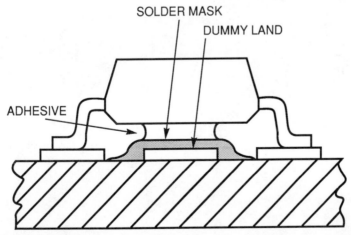

FIG. 12.25 The effective component standoff height can be reduced by adding a dummy land under the component. Covering the land with a permanent solder mask serves to further reduce the gap.

REFERENCES

1. Klein Wassink, R. *Soldering in Electronics*, Electrochemical Publications, Ltd., Ayr, Scotland, 1984.
2. Manko, H. *Soldering Handbook for Printed Circuits and Surface Mounting*, Van Nostrand Reinhold Co., New York, 1986.
3. Coombs, C. *Printed Circuits Handbook*, McGraw-Hill Book Co., New York, 1979, p. 15–15.
4. Drain, K., and Grant, S. "The Curve of Bonding Energy," *Circuits Manufacturing*, Aug. 1986, pp. 56–61.

13

Post-solder cleaning

The quality and reliability of a printed wiring assembly is a strong function of its initial cleanliness level. Inorganic residues such as flux activators cause a reduction in insulation resistance and an increase in current leakage. In combination with atmospheric moisture, they promote corrosion of metallic surfaces. Organic residues, such as rosin, greases, or oils, form an insulating film that can prevent proper electrical contact between mating surfaces of connectors, switches, or relays. For all but the most benign operating environments, these contaminants must be thoroughly removed.

Cleaning processes can be divided into two basic categories: *aqueous* and *solvent*. Aqueous processes use water as the primary cleaning fluid, while solvent processes use chlorinated or fluorinated hydrocarbon liquids. In this sense the term "solvent" cleaning, although widely used within the electronics industry, is somewhat misleading. Chemists are quick to point out that even water can be considered a solvent, and a more correct term would be *halogenated hydrocarbon solvent* cleaning. Because of its wide acceptance within the industry, this book will use the abbreviated term *solvent* to refer strictly to organic solvents.

The most important consideration in selecting a cleaning process is to insure that it does an adequate job of removing the anticipated contaminants. For printed wiring boards the major contaminant is flux residue from the soldering operation, so the choice of cleaning method depends largely on the type of flux used. Rosin-based and synthetic fluxes are best removed in a solvent cleaning process. Aqueous processes are employed when water-soluble organic acid fluxes have been used. They can also be used to remove rosin fluxes if suitable additives are included in the water.

Several other factors must be considered in selecting a cleaning process. Of primary importance is compatibility with the components to be cleaned. Some types of plastics and marking inks are dissolved by the more aggressive chlorinated solvents, while certain other components are not suitable for water cleaning. When used with an incompatible cleaning process, such components must be laboriously hand-soldered after cleaning has been completed.

Another concern is the ability to comply with local environmental regulations. Solvent processes release potentially harmful chlorofluorocarbons into the atmosphere, while aqueous processes discharge heavy metals into the local water supply. Variations in local laws may tend to favor one process over another.

Energy efficiency and operating costs are also important considerations. Aqueous systems, for instance, require large amounts of water, which may be in short supply in certain geographic locations; solvents are expensive and must be used in complex cleaning equipment. Finally, operator safety must be carefully considered, and appropriate steps must be taken to eliminate any potential health hazards.

13.1 TYPES OF CONTAMINATION

The contaminants found on printed wiring assemblies are either soluble films or nonsoluble particulates. Particulate matter is removed by mechanically flushing the board with the cleaning liquid. Since the particulate does not dissolve, the exact choice of liquid is not particularly critical. The removal of soluble films, on the other hand, depends entirely on the properties of the liquid. The bulk of the contamination normally encountered in flux residues is soluble, so the principles behind its removal should be thoroughly understood.

Soluble films can be classified as being either *polar* or *nonpolar* in nature. Polar films consist of molecules which possess an electric dipole moment. When subjected to an electric field, polar molecules tend to align with the field. Many types of polar films easily dissociate into free ions when combined with the small amount of moisture invariably found within the atmosphere. Such residues create paths of electrical conductivity that degrade circuit performance. They also promote corrosion and therefore should be entirely removed.

Nonpolar films consist of molecules with zero (or nearly zero) dipole moment. They are generally good insulators and do not promote corrosion. Such films are objectionable only if they cover areas of the circuit, such as connector contacts or test probe points, that must be electrically accessible.

Within the electronics industry, polar residues are often called *ionic*, while nonpolar residues are described as *organic*. This is another practice that causes no small amount of consternation to the theoretical chemist, for while the correlation is strong, it is not absolute. Technically, an ionic molecule is one that, in solution, forms an ion pair (the other extreme being a *covalent* molecule in which electrons are equally shared). Organic molecules are those containing carbon. It is entirely possible for a material to be both organic and ionic; alcohols are a good example. Conversely, sugar is an example of a polar compound that is not ionic. Fortunately, for the materials normally found in electronic applications, it is generally safe to interchange the term "polar" with the term "ionic" and the term "nonpolar" with the term "organic." It should always be remembered, however, that in certain instances there can be important differences.

13.1.1 Rosin flux residues

Rosin fluxes consist primarily of nonpolar organic compounds with small amounts of ionic halides added to improve activity level (Section 5.4.3). During soldering, complex reactions occur that alter the structure of the residue. Reaction products can include polymerized rosin, decomposed activators, and metal salts. It is usually easy to remove the unaltered rosin and activator and relatively difficult to remove the potentially more harmful reaction products.

13.1.2 Organic acid flux residues

Organic acid fluxes consist entirely of water-soluble polar materials and would seem ideally suited for removal in an aqueous cleaning system. Unfortuantely, they are less soluble after soldering than before. Certain reaction products generated during soldering are quite insoluble, so if water alone is used, large quantities are required. As an alternative, an alkaline neutralizing agent can be added to the water to convert these residues into more soluble salts.[1] Since the neutralizing agent is itself a highly caustic material, it must be totally removed in a subsequent rinse. It should be noted that while alkaline neutralizers are most often recommended, the use of acidic solutions has occasionally been advocated.[2]

13.1.2 White residues

This term is widely used to describe any residual film remaining on the board after cleaning. White residues (Fig. 13.1) can be caused by any number of problems in the PWB manufacturing and assembly process, and chemical compositions can vary widely. Even the color varies, ranging from yellow, brown, or gray to pure white. Some problems can be traced to defects in the manufacture of the laminate or bare printed wiring board. These can usually be identified on the incoming board material even before soldering. More commonly the residues are flux by-products. These are of particular importance in the surface mount assembly process.

The most frequent flux-related white residues are polymerized rosin, unreacted activators, and lead chloride or bromide by-products of the flux–solder reaction. Fluxes made from natural wood rosins are particularly

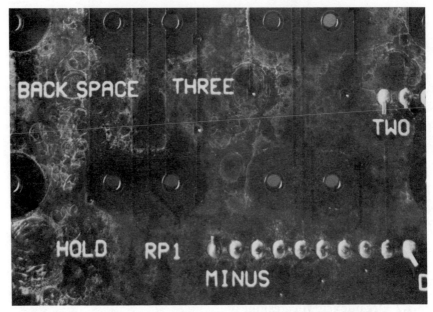

FIG. 13.1   White residues on printed wiring board. (Photograph by the author.)

prone to polymerization when exposed to heat. Simply subjecting the flux to the normal soldering process is enough to cause an appreciable amount of polymerization; if overheated or left at elevated temperatures too long, the problem can be acute.

The polymerized rosin is exceedingly difficult to remove even with aggressive solvents. Some success has been reported in re-dipping the board into liquid flux. The fresh flux dissolves the polymerized flux, which can then be washed away.[3] The best approach, however, is to prevent polymerization in the first place.

With natural rosin, the rate of polymerization increases rapidly at temperatures above about 145 °C. Therefore, natural rosin fluxes should not be used for reflow soldering because the flux can remain above 145 °C for several minutes. Instead, chemically modified fluxes should be employed. Through chemical means, it is possible to alter both the rate of polymerization and the temperature at which rapid polymerization begins to occur. Modified rosins show less tendency than natural rosins to leave white residues.

Fig. 13.2 illustrates the effect of chemical modification. The onset of rapid polymerization has been moved above 200 °C and the rate has been considerably reduced. Even better results can be achieved with a synthetic flux formulated to prevent polymerization under normal conditions.[4]

Activator residues are primarily a problem in solvent cleaning systems when the polar component of the fluid is depleted. Most commonly, this occurs because the polar component evaporates at a different rate than the

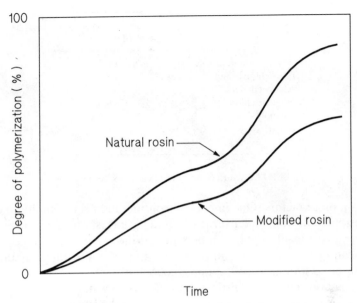

FIG. 13.2 Typical polymerization profiles of commercial rosin fluxes. (Adapted from Ref. 3.)

nonpolar component. The problem can be eliminated by selecting a solvent that is a constant boiling blend or *azeotrope* (discussed later in Section 13.3.2). The presence of excessive moisture can also be a contributing factor, so the use of a water separator (Section 13.3.6) is recommended.

13.2 CLEANING PROCESS SELECTION

The fundamental rule in selecting a cleaning process is: *like dissolves like.* This means that polar solvents should be used to remove polar contamination and nonpolar solvents to remove nonpolar contamination. If both polar and nonpolar contaminants are present, a solution that has both polar and nonpolar properties should be chosen.

It is this principle that is the basis for why solvent cleaning systems are recommended for rosin fluxes and aqueous systems for organic acid fluxes. In reality, however, all real flux residues include both polar and nonpolar contamination, so whichever system is chosen, it must be adapted to remove both constituents. Many commercially available solvent systems employ small amounts of ethyl or methyl alcohol to improve their ability to dissolve polar compounds. In aqueous systems, chemicals added to the water convert the nonpolar contamination into a water-soluble soap.

13.2.1 Cleaning under surface mount devices

An aqueous system that uses a saponifier is perfectly capable of removing rosin fluxes. The choice of solvent or aqueous processes must therefore be

Fluid	Surface tension @ 25 °C (dynes/cm)
Trichlorotrifluoroethane	17.3
1,1,1-trichloroethane	25.9
Trichloroethylene	32.3
Methylene chloride	28.0
Methanol	22.6
Ethanol	22.3
Water	72.1

TABLE 13.1   Surface tensions of various solvents

based on other factors. One important consideration is the ability to clean flux residues out from under surface mount packages. The gap between the underside of a leadless chip component and the top of the printed wiring board can be less than 0.05 mm (0.002 in). Even for integrated circuits the gap can be as little as 0.1–0.25 mm (0.004–0.010 in).

Organic solvents have a distinct advantage over water in penetrating this gap because of their much lower viscosities and surface tensions (Table 13.1). Although the surface tension of water can be lowered by the addition of a surfactant, a basic problem remains. The surfactant must eventually be washed away in a pure water rinse, so although it is able to penetrate under the device, it may not be washed away. High-pressure solvent sprays have been determined to be most effective in penetrating under surface mount devices.[5]

The ability of various solvents to clean flux residues from inside gaps of various distances has been studied experimentally.[6] In the study, a small drop of solder paste was placed between two glass slides separated by shim stock of known thickness. The paste was dried and reflowed in a vapor phase reflow oven to simulate actual production processing. The slide assemblies were then subjected to various cleaning solvents and processes. Efficiency was determined by recording the time required to obtain a visually clean assembly.

Table 13.2 reports the results obtained by immersing the slide assemblies in vigorously boiling solvent. As expected, chlorinated solvents were more aggressive than fluorinated solvents, while water-based solutions were essentially unable to remove the flux residues.

Of particular note is the performance of the alcohol/water solution in Column F of the table. This solution is specified in the MIL-P-28809 cleanliness test. In this test, the previously cleaned board is immersed in the alcohol/water solution to dissolve any remaining ionic residues. The electrical conductivity of the resulting solution is a measure of the amount of contamination left on the board.

The success of this test depends on the solution being able to dissolve residual ionic contamination on the board. However, as seen in Table 13.2,

| | Time to obtain visually clean substrates (min) | | | | | | |
| | Solvent (see note 1) | | | | | | |
Clearance (in)	A	B	C	D	E	F	G
0.001	21	16	14	18	17	note 2	note 2
0.003	14	8	9	11	9	note 2	>90
0.006	10	7	8	8	7	>30	note 2
0.015	5	5	6	3	3	note 2	note 2

Notes:
1. Solvents:
    A: Trichlorotrifluoroethane/methanol/nitromethane
    B: Trichlorotrifluoroethane/methylene chloride
    C: Trichlorotrifluoroethane/methylene chloride/methanol
    D: 1,1,1-trichloroethane
    E: Methylene chloride
    F: 75/25 isopropanol/water
    G: Water/detergent
2. Not tested

TABLE 13.2 Cleaning effectiveness of various solvents. Solder paste was deposited between glass slides separated by a known thickness. After reflowing in a vapor phase system, the time necessary to obtain a visually clean assembly was recorded. Solder paste was "Formon" 8625 fused in FC-70 vapor phase fluid for 22–28 sec. (Used by permission. W. P. Steinacker, E.I. Dupont de Nemours & Company, Inc.)

the solution is not able to penetrate narrow gaps to dissolve entrapped contaminants. The cleanliness test specified in MIL-P-28809 is therefore ineffective in measuring the contamination level of SMT boards.

Several other tests were performed in this study, with anticipated results. Findings include:

- Vigorously boiling solvent is more aggressive than slowly boiling solvent.
- High-pressure spray provides considerable improvement over boiling solvent alone.
- Ultrasonic agitation of a fluorocarbon–methanol blend can reduce the time necessary to obtain visually clean slides by a substantial amount (to under 1 minute).

13.3 SOLVENT CLEANING

Solvent cleaning makes use of chlorinated or fluorinated hydrocarbon solvents as the cleaning fluid. Chlorinated solvents such as methylene chloride or 1,1,1-trichloroethane are more aggressive than the fluorinated solvents but have several drawbacks. They are more likely to damage plastics or elastomers used in certain components, and they are more hazardous to operators. Methylene chloride, for instance, is a suspected carcinogen. Fluorinated solvents are less aggressive but considerably safer and easier to use. Newer blends of fluorinated solvents and alcohols have become increasingly popular in post-solder cleaning operations.

13.3.1 Solvent power

In developing a cleaning process, it is desirable to select a solvent that is aggressive enough to dissolve contamination without damaging the assembly. Several indices have been used in an attempt to grade solvent cleaning power. These include the Kauri–butanol value, Wetting Index, and solubility parameter. Unfortunately, the complex nature of flux residues makes these rather simplistic indices only marginally useful in the selection of a suitable solvent.

Kauri–butanol value

This parameter measures the comparative ability of a solvent to dissolve nonpolar contamination. it makes use of Kauri gum, a petrified resin from New Zealand. The test, defined in ASTM Standard D1133, depends on the fact that the solubility of Kauri gum in l-butanol is higher than in other solvents. As the solvent under test is added to a solution consisting of 20 g of Kauri gum dissolved in 100 ml of l-butanol, the solubility limit of the combined solution is reduced. Eventually, the amount of dissolved Kauri gum exceeds the solubility limit and it precipitates out, causing a visible clouding of the solution. The amount of solvent that can be added prior to precipitation determines the solvent's Kauri–butanol value. Kauri–butanol values for selected solvents are listed in Table 13.9.

Wetting Index

The Wetting Index is a figure of merit that compares the inherent ability of different solvents to penetrate the narrow gap between a component and board. It is defined as:

$$WI = \frac{1000\ D}{V\ S}$$

where WI = Wetting Index
   D = density of liquid
   V = liquid viscosity
   S = liquid surface tension

Although the Wetting Index can be used to compare the relative ability of solvents to penetrate narrow gaps, it is not a direct measure of cleaning effectiveness. Even though a solvent may be able to penetrate the gap, it may not be active enough to dissolve the flux residues.

To address this concern, a parameter called the Efficiency Index has been proposed.[7] This parameter combines a solvent's Wetting Index, Kauri–butanol value, and boiling point into a number intended to represent total cleaning effectiveness. The Efficiency Index is defined as:

$$EI = \frac{WI \times KB \times BP}{10000}$$

where EI = Efficiency Index
  KB = Kauri–butanol value
  BP = solvent boiling point, °K

Solubility parameter

The interaction between a solvent and a solute can be characterized by means of solubility parameter theory.[8] Although the exact details of this theory are beyond the scope of this book, the results are relatively easily understood. Every chemical compound can be characterized by a set of solubility parameters comprised of three partial parameters: a polar term, a nonpolar term, and a hydrogen bonding term. In general, maximum solubility occurs when the solubility parameters of the solvent match those of the solute.

By representing the respective solubility parameters of solvent and solute as points in three-dimensional space, the relative ability of different solvents to dissolve a solute can be compared. The distance between the points is termed the *radius of interaction*, ^{ij}R, where i refers to the solute and j refers to the solvent. The radius of interaction between abietic acid (the principal component of rosin fluxes) and various solvents has been calculated and is presented in Table 13.3. Solvents with smaller radii of interaction are presumably better able to dissolve abietic acid than those with larger radii of interaction.

Unlike the Kauri–butanol value and Wetting Index, solubility parameters take into account both polar and nonpolar performance of the solvent.

Solvent	^{ij}R
Methanol	19.4
Acetone	13.4
Isopropanol	11.5
Fluorocarbon 113	10.0
Fluorocarbon 113—Methanol Blend	8.4
1,1,1-Trichloroethane	5.4
1,1,1-Trichloroethane—Alcohol Blend	4.8
Trichloroethylene	1.5

TABLE 13.3 Radius of interaction between abietic acid and various solvents. (Used by permission. W. L. Archer, Dow Chemical Company.)

However, solubility parameters for many materials have not been determined, so the theory is difficult to apply to residues with a variety of constituents.

Effect of cleaning process

None of the cleaning indices described above takes into account many parameters that can have a profound impact on cleaning effectiveness. These include such factors as physical agitation, ultrasonics, and high-pressure spray velocity. Furthermore, the Kauri–butanol value and Wetting Index do not evaluate the ability of a solvent to remove ionic contaminants. These indices are useful in determining the gross characteristics of the solvents being evaluated, but by themselves they do not tell the whole story. Final selection should be made only after careful testing under conditions that closely match the anticipated production environment.

13.3.2 Fluorinated solvents

Nearly all fluorinated solvents are based on the compound trichlorotrifluoroethane (TTE), chemical composition $CCl_2F-CClF_2$. (A few are based on trichlorofluoromethane.) TTE is produced by several companies under various trade names; two examples are Freon® TF by E.I. Du Pont de Nemours and Co. and Genesolv®-D by Allied-Signal Corporation.

Originally developed as a refrigerant, TTE is also designated FC-113. Under this nomenclature, the number of carbon, hydrogen, and fluorine atoms in the molecule can be determined by adding 90 to its designation number:

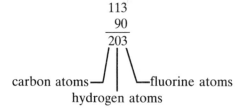

The chemical structure of this molecule is therefore:

$$\begin{array}{c} \quad F \quad Cl \\ \quad | \quad | \\ F-C-C-F \\ \quad | \quad | \\ \quad Cl \quad Cl \end{array}$$

Physical characteristics

The physical properties of TTE are included in Table 13.9. Some of its important advantages are as follows:[9]

- It has low surface tension, enabling it to easily wet surfaces and penetrate small gaps.
- It has high density, which helps it displace contaminants and float them to the surface of the solvent for easy removal.
- Its latent heat of vaporization is low, minimizing the energy required to generate vapor.
- Its low boiling point minimizes thermal damage to assemblies and eliminates the risk of exposing operators to high temperatures.

Materials compatibility

Most of the materials normally found in electronics applications are unaffected by immersion in TTE. Tables 13.4 and 13.5 describe its impact on elastomers, while Tables 13.6 and 13.7 describe its impact on plastics.

The effect of TTE on metals can be divided into two categories: metals used in the construction of the electronics components on the PWB assembly (which are immersed for short periods), and metals used in the cleaning equipment (which are continuously exposed for prolonged periods). For all metals normally used in the construction of components, except highly reactive metals such as sodium and lithium, the effect of short exposures is essentially unmeasurable. For long exposures, the effects on reactive metals such as aluminium, zinc, beryllium, and magnesium can be significant, particularly in the presence of moisture. Cleaning equipment should therefore avoid the use of these materials. Stainless steel is recommended for all metal parts, while plastics such as phenolic resins can safely be used in valves and fittings.

Because TTE reacts with aluminium, it is not recommended for cleaning unsealed aluminium electrolytic capacitors. Small amounts of TTE can penetrate inside the component body, where it is not easily extracted. Over time, as atmospheric moisture enters the body, it accelerates corrosion of the capacitor electrode. This effect can be reduced by employing only hermetically sealed capacitors (at greater expense) or by using a fluorocarbon blend that includes a stabilizing agent to prevent this reaction.

Fluorocarbon blends

Pure TTE is a relatively mild solvent with no ability to dissolve polar contaminants. To improve its effectiveness, it is usually blended with polar solvents, typically methanol or ethanol. Some blends obtain their polar component by incorporating a surfactant dissolved in water.

Solvent blends in which the composition of the vapor is exactly the same as

| | TEST A | | | | | | TEST B | |
| | % linear swell during immersion at room temperature for hours shown | | | | % permanent effects after 168 hours of immersion* | | % maximum linear swell regardless of immersion time required | |
Elastomer	1/12	1	4	168	Permanent Swell**	Extraction***	75°F	130°F
Neoprene W	—	0	1	2	-4	-8	1	3
Buna N	1	0	0	1	0	—	1	1
Buna S	1	2	8	13	-2	-8	9	9
Silicone	6	13	29	33	-1	-2	34	36
Butyl	—	1	4	16	0	4	21	23
Natural Rubber	2	9	21	31	-1	-4	17	19
"Thiokol" FA or ST	—	0	0	0	0	-1	1	1
"Hypalon" 40	—	0	1	2	-2	-2	1	5
"Viton" A	—	0	0	2	1	0	5	6
"Adiprene" L urethane rubber	—	0	1	4	1	-1	—	—
"Nordel" hydrocarbon rubber	—	4	11	12	4	-9	—	—
"Adiprene" C	—	1	2	7	1	-3	—	—

*Samples air dried until dimensions and weight stabilized

**Negative result indicates shrinkage.

***Negative result indicates loss in weight

— indicates no test run.

"Hypalon", "Viton", "Adiprene", and "Nordel" are registered trademarks of E.I. Du Pont de Nemours & Co.

"Thiokol" is a registered trademark.

TABLE 13.4 Effect of trichlorotrifluoroethane on Elastomers. (Used by permission. E.I. Du Pont de Nemours & Company, Inc.)

Elastomer	"Freon" TF		Stoddard Solvent		Methylene Chloride		1,1,1-Tri-chloroethane		Trichloro-ethylene	
	75°F	130°F	75°F	130°F	75°F	130°F	75°F	130°F	75°F	130°F
Neoprene W polychlorobutadiene	1	3	10	11	43	38	35	49	43	46
Buna N Butadiene/acrylonitrile	1	1	1	1	52	65	24	33	26	36
Buna S (SBR) Butadiene/styrene	9	9	28	D	26	D	44	D	65	D
Silicone polysiloxane	34	36	29	26	27	31	33	37	49	35
Butyl Isobutylene/isoprene	21	23	37	60	19	26	35	41	42	67
Natural Rubber	17	19	50	29	34	60	59	58	67	41
"Thiokol" FA organic polysulfide	1	1	1	1	59	D	12	11	27	48
"Hypalon" 40 synthetic rubber (chlorosulfonated polyethylene)	1	5	12	17	39	39	34	46	36	51
"Viton" A fluoro-elastomer (hexafluoro-propylene/vinylidine fluoride)	5	6	1	1	8	10	4	9	3	4

D—Disintegrated
"Hypalon" and "Viton" are registered trademarks of E. I. du Pont de Nemours & Co.
"Thiokol" is a registered trademark.

TABLE 13.5 Percent maximum swell of elastomers immersed in various solvents at 75°F and 130°F. (Used by permission. E. I. Du Pont de Nemours & Company, Inc.)

Table — left half

Plastic	"Freon" TF Solvent			Per-chloro-ethylene			Tri-chloro-ethylene			1,1,1-Tri-chloro-ethane		
	A	B	C	A	B	C	A	B	C	A	B	C
Delrin" Acetal Resin	0	0	0	0	0	0	0	0	0	0	0	0
"Zytel"–101 Nylon Resin	0	0	0	0	0	1	0	0	0	0	0	0
"Teflon" TFE Fluorocarbon Resin	0	0	0	0	0	1	0	0	1	0	0	0
Alathon"–7050 Linear Polyethylene	0	0	1	1	6	1	1	1	1	0	2	1
Polypropylene	0	0	2	0	6	2	1	5	2	0	4	2
Polyvinyl Chloride (Unplasticized)	0	0	1	0	4	4	2	4	4	0	4	4
Polyphenylene oxide	0	0	0	5	6	6	6	6	6	3	4	5

Table — right half

Plastic	"Freon" TF Solvent			Per-chloro-ethylene			Tri-chloro-ethylene			1,1,1-Tri-chloro-ethane		
	A	B	C	A	B	C	A	B	C	A	B	C
Polysulfone	0	0	0	0	5	0	4	5	6	0	3	2
"Geon"–8750 (Normal Impact PVC)	—	—	0	—	—	—	—	—	5	—	—	5
"Kralastic" ABS Polymer	0	0	0	4	4	4	5	6	6	4	5	6
Polystyrene	0	3	6	5	6	6	6	6	6	6	6	6
"Lexan" Polycarbonate Resin	0	0	0	2	4	2	4	6	5	4	4	4
"Lucite" Acrylic Resin (Cast)	0	1	0	1	4	4	6	5	5	1	4	6
"Surlyn" A Ionomeric Resin	0	1	2	—	—	—	—	—	—	—	—	—
"Tenite" Polyterephthalate	*	—	—	—	—	—	—	—	—	—	—	—

Test Conditions: A = 4 hrs at 75°F   B = 4 hrs at Solvent boiling point   C = 100 hrs at 130°F.

Effect Key: — = No test run. 0 = No visible effect. 1 = Slightly pliable, no significant swelling. 2 = Slightly swollen and pliable or slightly shrunk and softened. 3 = Stress cracked and brittle. 4 = Swollen, curled and rubbery. 5 = Partially dissolved or disintegrated. 6 = Totally dissolved or disintegrated.

* No effect 5 min. at boiling point.

"Delrin", "Zytel", "Teflon", "Alathon", "Lucite" and "Surlyn" are registered trademarks of E.I. Du Pont de Nemours & Co. (Inc.). "Geon", "Kralastic", "Tenite" and "Lexan" are registered trademarks.

TABLE 13.6   Effects of various solvents on unstressed plastics. (Used by permission. E.I. Du Pont de Nemours & Company Inc.)

Plastic	Cracking or crazing caused by stress
"Delrin" acetal resin	0
"Zytel"–101 nylon resin	0
"Teflon" TFE fluorocarbon resin	0
"Alathon"–7050 linear polyethylene	0
Polypropylene	0
Polyvinyl chloride (Unplasticized)	0
Polyphenylene oxide	3
Polysulfone "Geon"–8750	0
(Normal Impact PVC)	—
"Kralastic" ABS polymer	1
Polystyrene	3
"Lexan" polycarbonate resin	1
"Lucite" acrylic resin (cast)	2
"Surlyn" A ionomeric resin	0
"Tenite" polyterephthalate	0

Effect Key: 0 = None. 1 = Slight. 2 = Moderate. 3 = Severe. Test Conditions: Specimens stressed to almost 100% of yield and immersed in boiling solvent 5 min.

TABLE 13.7   Effect of trichlorofluoroethane on stressed plastics. (Used by permission. E.I. Du Pont de Nemours & Company Inc.)

the composition of the liquid are called *azeotropes*. Because the rate of evaporation of all components of the blend are identical, azeotropes have a constant boiling point. On the other hand, nonazeotrope blends lose individual components at different rates, so their boiling points and chemical properties change over time. For this reason azeotropes are preferred over nonazeotrope blends.

To prevent interaction between TTE and reactive metals, solvent blends often include an inhibiting agent such as nitromethane. These so-called "stabilized" blends are considered compatible with virtually all available electronic components.

A typical example of a widely used fluorocarbon blend is Freon® TMS, manufactured by E.I. Du Pont de Nemours & Co. It consists of 94.05% TTE, 5.7% methanol, and 0.25% nitromethane. Although not a true azeotrope, the composition of the vapor is very nearly the same as the liquid, and its boiling point is essentially constant. A similar blend that is a true azeotrope is marketed by Allied-Signal Corporation under the trade name Genesolv® DMSA. It consists of 94% TTE, 4% methanol, 0.5% ethanol, 0.5% isopropanol, and 1% nitromethane. Compositions of several fluorinated and chlorinated solvent blends are described in Table 13.8. Physical properties of various solvents are presented in Table 13.9.

Composition (percent)

Solvent Trade name	Manufacturer	TTE	TCE	Methylene Chloride	Methanol	Ethanol	Iso-propanol	Nitro-methane	Iso-hexane	Acetone
TMS	Du Pont	94.05	—	—	5.7	—	—	0.25	—	—
TES	Du Pont	95.2	—	—	—	3.8	—	1.0	—	—
TMC	Du Pont	50	—	50	—	—	—	—	—	—
DMSA	Allied-Signal	94.0	—	—	4.0	0.5	0.5	1.0	—	—
DFX	Allied-Signal	91.1	—	—	5.9	—	—	0.2	1.9	0.9
Prelete	Dow Chemical	—	94.0*	—	—	6.0**	—	*	—	—

* Stabilized.
** Total alcohol content.

TABLE 13.8 Chemical compositions of various halogenated hydrocarbon solvents

Property	TTE	TCE	TMS[1]	TES[1]	TMC[1]	DMSA[2]	DFX[2]	Prelete[3]	Methylene chloride	Trichloro-ethylene	Methanol
						Value					
Boiling point (°C)	47.6	74.1	39.7	44.4	36.2	40.3	39.9	73.3	39.8	86.9	64–66
Density (g/ml)	1.57	1.32	1.48	1.50	1.42	1.46	1.43	1.26	1.32	1.46	0.79
Evaporation rate (ether = 1)	1.3	2.7	—	—	—	2.0	2.0	—	0.7	3.1	0.23
Flashpoint (°C)	none	none	none	none	none	none	none	none	none	none	12.2
Flammable limit in air (wt %)	non-flammable	6.8–10.5	non-flammable	non-flammable	non-flammable	non-flammable	non-flammable	7.0–15.5	15–21.	8.0–10.5	6.0–36.5
Surface tension @ 20 oC (dynes/cm)	17.3	25.9	17.4	17.2	21.4	18.4	17.8	25.2	28.0	31.6	22.6
Latent heat of vaporization (btu/lb)	63.1	102	90.7	76.7	104.0	89.5	92.6	103.7	142	103	473
Specific heat of liquid (btu/lb/°F)	0.21	0.25	0.24	0.23	0.26	0.24	0.26	0.30	0.28	0.23	0.60
Toxicity–ACGIH TLV (ppm)	1000	350	475	770	140	510	480	350	100	50	200
Kauri-butanol value	31	124	45	37	86	49	46	124	115	130	—

Notes:
1. E.I. Du Pont de Nemours & Co.
2. Allied-Signal Corp.
3. Dow Chemical Co.

TABLE 13.9 Physical properties of various halogenated hydrocarbon solvents

13.3.3 Chlorinated solvents

Chlorinated solvents can be based on several halogenated hydrocarbons. The most common are 1,1,1-trichloroethane, trichloroethylene, and methylene chloride. Because of their high toxicity, neither trichloroethylene nor methylene chloride are commonly used to clean printed circuit assemblies. Instead, the solvent is usually based on 1,1,1-trichloroethane (TCE), chemical composition CH_3CCl_3. As with fluorinated solvents, polar additives are often included to enhance the cleaning power of the blend.

Physical characteristics

The more aggressive nature of chlorinated solvents makes them attractive for removing tenacious rosin residues. A commercially available example is a patented blend of TCE, alcohols, and stabilizer manufactured by Dow Chemical Company under the trade name Prelete.™ The physical properties of this solvent are included in Table 13.9. It is a more active solvent than fluorocarbon blends, as indicated by its higher Kauri–butanol value.

Solvents based on TCE have several characteristics that must be considered in the selection process. Compared to TTE blends, they have slightly higher surface tension, making them less able to penetrate very narrow gaps. They have higher heats of vaporization and higher boiling points, so they require greater energy input to reach the boiling point. This impacts operating costs by increasing the cost of electricity to heat the solvent.

Materials compatibility

Plastics and elastomers are more likely to be attacked by TCE than by TTE. Styrene plastics and polycarbonates are particularly susceptible to damage. It is suggested that materials compatibility tests be run prior to employing TCE-based solvents in a production environment.

13.3.4 Health and safety aspects

Most fluorinated and chlorinated solvent blends are nonflammable and have no flash point. However, blends that include alcohols can have a flammable limit in air. Electrical equipment used internal to the tank should therefore be approved for use in an explosive environment. This need not apply to circuitry that is external to the tank itself.

Fluorinated solvents are generally low in toxicity (refer to Table 13.9). The toxicity limits are determined more by the polar component of the blend than by the TTE itself. Chlorinated solvents are somewhat higher in toxicity, as evidenced by their lower exposure limits. Methylene chloride and trichloroethylene have been indicated as carcinogenic and are not recommended for general use.

When exposed to extremely high temperatures, organic solvents decompose into toxic and corrosive compounds. Equipment designed for use with solvents should include safeguards to prevent high-temperature exposure. Adequate ventilation is also necessary to dilute the concentrations of any decomposition products generated by contact with such sources as space heaters or soldering irons.

The greatest risk of injury is to maintenance workers responsible for cleaning and maintaining the equipment. These personnel should be thoroughly trained in proper maintenance procedures and should be provided with proper maintenance equipment, including protective clothing, eye protection, and respirators. A complete discussion of safety procedures is beyond the scope of this book. Refer to material provided by solvent manufacturers and government agencies for additional information.

13.3.5 Environmental impact

Fluorocarbon solvents have been linked to the theory of the depletion of the Earth's ozone layer, and it is likely that the US Environmental Protection Agency will soon limit production. One scenario under consideration is to initially cap production at 1987 levels and phase them out entirely over a protracted period. While the overall impact of such a regulation is uncertain, it is not expected to have any immediate discernible impact. Over the longer term, material shortages would be likely to occur.

While the environmental concerns must obviously be addressed, there is no evidence that the problem is yet acute. Government agencies seem willing to work with industry to limit the near-term regulatory impact while alternative solvents are developed. Ozone depletion is linked to the chlorine content of the solvent, and manufacturers are actively developing new solvent formulations that do not depend on chlorine. Such compounds are not expected to affect the ozone layer. At present, several formulations have proven technically feasible but have not yet reached the point of being economical to manufacture.

13.3.6 Water extraction in solvent systems

The presence of water in a solvent system is detrimental for two reasons. Moisture exacerbates chemical reactions between the solvent and various metals. This can lead to damage of both the cleaning equipment and the circuit board components. Water will also absorb alcohol from the solvent, dramatically reducing its ability to remove polar contamination.

Water can be extracted from the system in one of two ways. The simplest technique is to use a *gravity water separator*. In this approach, the water–solvent mixture flows by gravity into a separator sump. Because of its lower specific gravity, the water floats to the top of the sump where it drains out of an orifice. The relatively pure solvent can then be recycled into the system.

A gravity water separator should not be used with solvent blends containing alcohols. The alcohol has a high affinity for water, so as it attaches to the water molecules, it is lost when the water is extracted. To avoid this problem, a *molecular sieve water separator* should be used.[10] In this approach, the solvent–water mixture is passed through a bed of 3 Å molecular sieves. The relatively small water molecule is trapped between the sieves while the larger alcohol molecules pass through.

The molecular sieve can hold up to about 15% of its weight in water. At this level, the entrapped moisture must be removed through a relatively simple drying procedure. Refer to Ref. 10 for a complete description of this procedure.

13.4 SOLVENT CLEANING PROCESSES

The basic principle behind solvent cleaning is that when a cool board is immersed into hot solvent vapors, some of the vapor condenses onto the board. The resulting liquid dissolves contamination and then drains back into a sump of boiling solvent, carrying the contaminants with it. As the temperature of the board approaches the vapor temperature, condensation ceases and cleaning activity degrades markedly.

All contamination collects in the boiling sump, which must occasionally be cleaned. The vapor zone consists of distilled solvent whose individual components are presented in fixed ratios. In the case of an azeotrope, the composition of the vapor is identical to that of the liquid. In a well-designed system, the solvent is continually recycled, so the actual rate of consumption is low. Losses are primarily due to evaporation and dragout on printed wiring boards.

Many systems include a high-pressure spray to increase cleaning efficiency. This adds a mechanical scrubbing action that forces solvent into narrow openings and aids in flushing away residues. The liquid spray also cools the board so that condensation can again occur when it reenters the vapor zone. The most effective equipment includes several cycles of vapor and spray, as well as a zone in which the board is immersed directly in boiling solvent.

Solvent cleaning can be performed in either a batch mode degreaser or an in-line system. The relatively inexpensive batch mode approach is suitable for small volume prototype or production runs. In-line systems are preferred for higher volume production. In-line systems generally provide more aggressive washing cycles than batch vapor degreasers and result in boards with better and more uniform cleanliness levels.

13.4.1 Batch vapor degreasers

A representative batch vapor degreaser is illustrated in Fig. 13.3. It consists of a boiling sump and an adjacent cool solvent reservoir contained inside a deep stainless steel tank. The boiling solvent forms a vapor zone above the

2-SUMP VAPOR DEGREASER

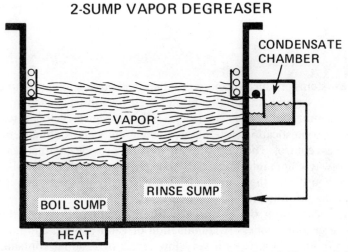

FIG. 13.3 Batch vapor degreaser. (Used by permission. E. I. du Pont de Nemouts & Co., Inc. "Freon" Products Division.)

liquid; a set of cooling coils at the top of the tank reduces evaporative loss. As the solvent condenses, it fills the solvent reservoir and spills over into the boiling sump. The reservoir thus consists of relatively clean solvent, while the boiling sump serves as the collection point for contaminants. Often, a manually operated spray wand is included to allow an operator to accentuate cleaning of particularly dirty areas on the board.

The cleaning process normally begins by placing the boards vertically in a basket and lowering them into the vapor zone. Solvent vapors condense on the cool board, dissolving contaminants and carrying them away as the solvent drips back into the tank. After 2–3 minutes, the board warms to the vapor temperature and condensation ceases.

The basket is then lowered into the cool liquid reservoir (not the dirty boiling sump!) for an additional 2–3 minutes. During this time, the solvent continues to act on the contaminants while simultaneously lowering the board temperature.

After 2–3 minutes in the reservoir, the basket is withdrawn and held in the vapor zone. At this time, the spray wand can be used to direct a stream of solvent onto critical areas of the boards. After a 20–30-second spray, the board is left in the vapor for a final 60–90-second phase. The basket is then slowly lifted out of the tank, tipping it slightly to allow any remaining solvent to drain back into the tank. The entire process is normally performed manually, but overhead conveyors can frequently be purchased to automate the cycle.

It is important that boards be mounted vertically in the basket. If mounted horizontally, solvent will not freely drain away, leaving obvious streaks and residues.

13.4.2 In-line cleaning

In-line systems produce cleaner assemblies and provide greater throughput than batch systems, making them preferred for most production applications. Commercial equipment (Fig. 13.4) has been developed to a high degree of sophistication. Internal microcomputers are routinely employed for process control. The most complex systems provide complete capability for two-way communications with an external computer, receiving setup information from the computer and passing back real-time process-monitoring information.

In a typical system, boards are carried horizontally via conveyor through a series of cleaning zones. A combination of vapor, spray, and immersion zones produces boards with very low levels of residual contamination. Individual zones can be classified into one of the following categories (not every zone is found on any single machine):[11]

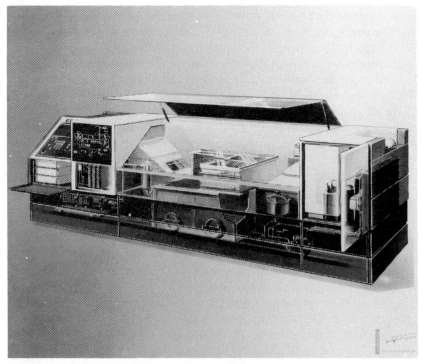

FIG. 13.4 In-line solvent cleaner. (Used by permission. OSL (Outillages Scientifiques et de Laboratoires), France.)

- vapor
- horizontal spray
- inclined spray
- immersion
- spray over immersion

Vapor

The vapor zone is similar to that in a batch degreaser. The cool board is carried into the hot vapor, which condenses onto the board. Contaminants are dissolved and carried away as the liquid drains back into the reservoir. Compared to spray or immersion zones, a vapor zone provides relatively mild cleaning action. It is usually employed only at the entrance and exit zones of the cleaner.

Horizontal spray

In this zone, the board is carried through a vapor zone that includes a solvent spray. Distilled solvent is directed onto the board via a set of nozzles. Spray pressures typically range from 20–30 psi. Pressures as high as 200 psi have been found to provide superior cleaning action, but such high pressures run the risk of damaging the circuit board or components.[12]

Typical spray nozzles are shown in Fig. 13.5. The configuration of the nozzle has a large impact on cleaning efficiency. An angled, flat spray is superior to a downward-directed fan spray. Nozzles should be directed at both the top and bottom sides of the board.

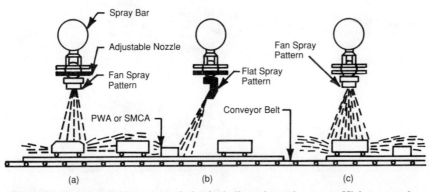

FIG. 13.5 Variations in spray nozzle design for in-line solvent cleaners: a. High pressure fan spray nozzle for pressures up to 200 psi, b. Flat spray designed to penetrate under component bodies, c. Standard low-pressure fan spray. (Used by permission. D. R. Gerard, Detrex Chemical Industries.)

Inclined spray

This is similar to the horizontal spray except that the board is carried at an angle, typically 10–20°, through the spray. By inclining the board, solvent can more readily drain away, improving cleaning efficiency over the horizontal spray.

Immersion

In this zone, the board is immersed into boiling liquid. The boiling provides a mechanical scrubbing action that can help dislodge tenacious soils. The main concern with immersion is that boards tend to "float" on the conveyor. Depending on the exact liquid level, they may actually float entirely off the conveyor or become wedged in internal parts of the system.

Spray over immersion

This zone combines both spray and immersion in a single zone. The additional turbulence introduced by the spray is even more effective than boiling alone. The spray also tends to hold the boards down and prevent them from floating on the conveyor.

An in-line cleaner that incorporates a number of these zones in a highly efficient sequence is illustrated in Fig. 13.6. Upon entry to the system, the board is carried into an initial vapor zone and subsequent pre-clean spray, which removes gross contamination. It then proceeds through an extended

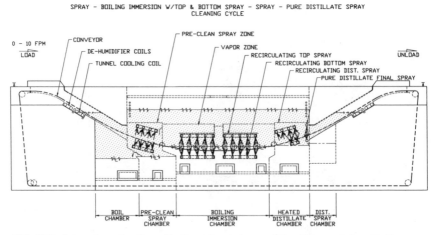

FIG. 13.6 Internal construction of in-line solvent cleaner. (Used by permission. D. R. Gerard, Detrex Chemical Industries.)

spray-over-immersion zone that removes the bulk of the contamination. After a final spray rinse, it travels through an exit vapor zone, which dries all remaining liquid. Using this system with a compatible flux, boards with surface insulation resistance values in excess of 10^{12} ohms per square can routinely be obtained.

13.4.3 Ultrasonic agitation

By adding ultrasonic agitation to a liquid immersion zone, the time required to reach a specified level of cleanliness can be cut by more than a factor of five. Such an improvement in performance has naturally led to interest in employing this technique on both batch and in-line systems. At present, this is still a subject of considerable controversy. The concern is that the ultrasonic energy will couple internal to integrated circuits and cause wirebonds to fracture.[13] US government specifications specifically exclude the use of ultrasonic agitation to clean printed wiring boards, and many commercial manufacturers have followed suit. Since most of the fears seem based more on conjecture than on hard data, a well-conceived experimental plan could demonstrate the feasibility of the technique. Such a plan is now under development, sponsored by the Electronics Program Office at the Naval Weapons Center.[14] Results of this activity are expected to become available in 1989–1990.

13.4.4 Selection of a suitable solvent cleaning process

The solvent cleaning process must be developed as a total system that includes both solvent and cleaning equipment. In the author's opinion, published literature has overemphasized the issue of solvent cleaning power while underemphasizing the impact of the cleaning process. Claims that a solvent with a higher Kauri–butanol value or one that performs better in static tank tests will result in cleaner assemblies neglect the very real importance of the cleaning cycle and equipment. An aggressive cleaning system that uses a relatively mild fluorinated solvent may outperform a stronger chlorinated solvent used in a poorly designed process. Furthermore, it must always be remembered that real-life contaminants are a complex combination of polar and nonpolar materials. Much of the published literature emphasizes the performance of a solvent only on pure rosin without addressing the more complex real-life situation.

When selecting a solvent, several factors must be kept in mind. Choose as mild a solvent as possible while still meeting the specified cleanliness objectives. Facilities that must build many different boards in large quantities should consider using fluorinated solvents with an in-line system employing multiple spray and immersion cycles. This will minimize the risk of damaging circuit components through interaction with the solvent, while still assuring a high level of cleanliness. The selected solvent should include both polar and nonpolar components to insure complete removal of both organic and ionic contaminants. Operating costs should also be evaluated. Factors to be considered here include solvent cost, rate of evaporation, and energy requirements.

Smaller facilities employing batch degreasers may wish to consider the use of more active chlorinated solvents. The more active solvent can compensate for the less aggressive action of the degreaser. In this case, components that are incompatible with the solvent must be identified and loaded in a subsequent process step.

Fluorocarbon blends of TTE and alcohols are good choices for general-purpose cleaning. In situations where a higher level of cleanliness is required, a blend of TCE and alcohol is suggested.

13.5 AQUEOUS CLEANING

In through-hole technology, aqueous cleaning has become popular for the removal of both water-soluble and rosin flux residues. As through-hole production facilities have begun to incorporate surface mount processes, there has been strong incentive to continue the use of existing cleaning processes.

Unfortunately, the relatively high viscosity and surface tension of water make it less suitable than organic solvents for removal of residues from the tight spaces under SMCs. Because of this concern, aqueous cleaning has not gained widespread popularity in the surface mount arena. It has primarily been used to clean wave soldered SMCs in relatively benign commercial and consumer applications.

The following discussion is intended as a general overview of aqueous cleaning. A comprehensive review of the process has recently been published by IPC.[15] Although targeted for through-hole applications, it contains extensive discussions of a number of factors critical to the success of the process. It is suggested that the material in this document be reviewed prior to installing any aqueous cleaning process.

13.5.1 Water hardness

The hardness of water is a measure of the level of calcium and magnesium ions it contains. High levels of these metals are undesirable because they reduce the ability of the water to dissolve contaminants. They can also form scales on the cleaning equipment and water supply pipes.

Water hardness is typically defined as the equivalent level of dissolved calcium carbonate in parts per million (ppm). Suggested limits for water hardness in aqueous systems are as follows:[15]

- rough cleaning: 250 ppm
- commercial cleaning: 85 ppm
- high cleanliness: 0.5 ppm

If the incoming water supply exceeds these levels, it may be necessary to soften the water. Water softeners do not actually remove ions but rather exchange the "hard" calcium and magnesium for "softer" sodium or potassium ions. Although this process is satisfactory for many applications, it will not meet the demands for extremely high cleanliness levels. In these situations, deionized water must be used.

13.5.2 Aqueous solutions

Rarely does the process use water alone. To improve cleaning effectiveness, various chemicals are added. Chemical additives can be classified as follows:

- neutralizers
- saponifiers
- surfactants
- dispersants
- anti-foaming agents

Neutralizers

Neutralizers are employed when water-soluble organic acid fluxes have been used. Although such fluxes as received are entirely water-soluble, exposure to soldering temperature causes relatively insoluble reaction products to form. Alkaline neutralizers are used to convert these compounds into more soluble forms that are easier to wash away. As their name implies, they also neutralize any remaining acid flux residues.

Since they often contain ammonia or other strong alkaline materials, neutralizer residues are often nearly as corrosive as the original flux. Their main purpose is to assist in dissolving insoluble compounds; it is imperative that they be thoroughly removed in subsequent rinse cycles.

Saponifiers

Rosin flux residues are insoluble in water. However, by adding certain chemicals to the water, such residues can be converted through the process of *saponification* into water-soluble soaps. Strong alkaline solutions having a pH in the range of 10.5–11.8 are effective saponifiers. Below this pH range, the rate of saponification is markedly reduced. Above this range, the solution can dissolve component markings or damage plastic components.

Surfactants

Surfactants ("*surf*ace *acti*ve *agents*") are added to reduce the surface tension of the water. This improves its wetting characteristics and increases its ability to penetrate into narrow crevices. A variety of ionic and nonionic materials can be used as surfactants. Nonionic surfactants are most commonly used because they are relatively immune to variations in water hardness.

Although it may seem that a surfactant can be beneficial in cleaning surface mount assemblies, this is only partially true. The surfactant assures that the solution is able to reach the residues and dissolve them. Ultimate removal, however, is accomplished in a final rinse consisting of pure water. Since water alone may not reach all areas of trapped residues, this rinse may be only partially effective.

Dispersants

These materials are added to assist in the removal of insoluble particulates. They possess relatively high charge densities that attract particulate matter. Once brought into suspension, the particulates tend to remain attracted to the soluble dispersant. They are then easily removed in a subsequent rinse cycle. Typical dispersants include organic and inorganic phosphates and organic polymers.

Anti-foaming agents

When exposed to the high-pressure sprays typically encountered in the cleaning systems, saponified rosin tends to generate significant amounts of foam. Anti-foaming agents are added to the water to limit the amount of foam to within an acceptable range. Typical anti-foaming agents are nonionic surfactants that lower the surface tension of the liquid and thereby reduce its propensity to form bubbles.

13.5.3 Aqueous cleaning systems

Both batch and in-line aqueous cleaning systems are commercially available. For both types, cleaning efficiency is considerably improved through the use of hot water in the range 60–70 °C (140–160 °F). Although most systems include elements to heat the water, these are intended only to maintain water temperature rather than to serve as the primary heat source.

Batch systems are basically industrial versions of household dishwashers. A typical system is illustrated in Fig. 13.7. Boards are loaded vertically so that they are totally accessible to a rotating spray nozzle. A mechanical timer controls the washing cycle and water temperature.

Batch systems have rather limited control over the washing parameters. Temperature is usually fixed, as is the nature of the washing cycle. The spray nozzles, being located at a considerable distance from the board, are usually less effective than the spray zones of in-line systems. For these reasons, batch systems are best used in prototyping and small-volume production environments where high cleanliness levels are not essential.

In-line systems have more aggressive wash cycles that can be tailored to

FIG. 13.7 Batch aqueous cleaning system. Systems of this type are derived from commercial dishwashing equipment. (Photograph by the author.)

the needs of a specified production line. A typical system (Fig. 13.8) consists of an initial prewash zone to remove gross contamination, followed by a recirculating detergent wash zone. Several cascaded rinse zones complete the cleaning cycle, and a final drying zone removes all excess water. Certain commercial systems include air knives to speed the drying process and reduce overall energy consumption.

FIG. 13.8   In-line aqueous cleaning system. (Hewlett-Packard Co.)

13.5.4 Environmental considerations

The primary environmental concern with aqueous cleaners is discharge of pollutants into the public sewer system. Although levels are generally small, they could exceed federal standards in several areas. Use of detergents can cause the effluent to exceed the standards for biochemical oxygen demand (BOD) and chemical oxygen demand (COD). The use of a neutralizer can affect the level of total suspended solids and the pH of the effluent. Appreciable levels of copper and lead can be produced as the flux reacts to remove oxides on the conductors. When washed into the sewer system, the amount of metal can exceed government standards.

The need for treatment of the effluent depends on such factors as volume of effluent, exact chemical composition, and the precise requirements of local laws. Treatment equipment is readily available and not technologically difficult to operate. Since local environmental standards may differ appreciably from federal standards, it is essential that local authorities be contacted prior to the installation of any facility.

13.5.5 Safety considerations

The saponifiers and detergents used in aqueous systems are potentially dangerous to humans, particularly in their concentrated forms prior to dilution. The highly alkaline saponifier is extremely caustic and should never be allowed to come in direct contact with skin. The threshold limit value (TLV) for monoethanolamine, one of its key ingredients, is only 3 ppm. (As used in the cleaner, it is diluted to much lower levels, typically 2–5% saponifier in water.) Operators must be thoroughly trained in the handling of chemicals, and proper protective clothing must always be worn.

13.6 MEASUREMENT OF CLEANLINESS LEVELS

The cleanliness levels of the finished product should be continually monitored on a sample basis to ensure that the process remains in control. Early detection of cleanliness variations is essential if problems are to be identified and corrected before a large number of defective products is produced.

The most commonly used tests fall into one of the following categories:

- visual inspection
- solvent extract resistivity
- insulation resistance

13.6.1 Visual inspection

The simplest way to measure board cleanliness is to visually examine the board. Fluxes and white residues in appreciable quantities are readily identified and are indicative of gross failure of the process.

Unfortunately, visual requirements are extremely subjective. Contamination overlooked or deemed acceptable by one inspector may be rejected by a second. An even greater concern is that visual inspection only catches the gross problems. Residues that are imperceptible even under a microscope can be sufficient to cause serious insulation resistance or corrosion problems. Visual inspection alone is only applicable for products that do not have critical long-term reliability requirements.

13.6.2 Solvent extract resistivity

A widely used technique for measuring the cleanliness of through-hole boards is to soak the cleaned board in an ionic solvent and measure the conductivity of the resulting solution. The higher the conductivity, the greater the level of residual ionic contamination. A standard test is described in MIL-P-28809 and IPC-S-815.

The solution used to dissolve contamination is a mixture of 75% isopropanol and 25% deionized water. A known volume of solution is introduced into the container and the board under test is immersed for a predetermined length of time. The conductivity of the solution is then measured, and by knowing the surface area of the board, the level of cleanliness can be determined. Cleanliness is specified as the equivalent amount of sodium chloride remaining on the board per unit area, in micrograms per square inch.

Extreme caution is advised in relying on this test to indicate the cleanliness of surface mount boards. It measures only ionic contamination that can be dissolved by the test solution. For surface mount boards, much contamination resides in the narrow gaps between devices and the board, where the test solution, with its high surface tension, cannot easily reach. Even though the test may not indicate residual contamination, the board may in fact have unacceptable levels remaining.

13.6.3 Insulation resistance

This is the most effective method for measuring the level of contamination on a surface mount board, but it must be carefully controlled to avoid large errors. The test is nondestructive and can be run either on production boards or on test coupons incorporated into the PWB panel.

Insulation resistance is defined as the ratio of the voltage applied between two electrodes and the current through the electrodes. It depends upon both surface resistance (impacted by the level of ionic contamination) and volume resistance of the board. Although the test is often referred to as a "surface insulation resistance" test, the impact of volume resistivity of the substrate should not be overlooked.

The test makes use of an interdigitated series of conductors known as a "comb pattern" (Fig. 13.9). Voltage is applied across the two electrodes and the resultant leakage current is measured. Insulation resistance can be

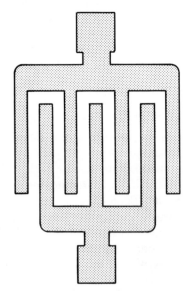

FIG. 13.9 Comb pattern used for testing board insulation resistance.

reported either as a straight resistance value or as an equivalent *ohms per square*. The former is a direct function of the specific comb pattern used and is not useful in comparing boards with different configurations. The latter eliminates the effect of comb geometry. It depends on the fact that the resistance across a homogeneous square of material is identical regardless of the size of the square. To determine ohms per square, the gap between the electrodes is converted into an equivalent fraction of a square. The measured resistance is then divided by this number to determine ohms per square.

For example, suppose the distance between the electrodes is 1 mm and the length of the electrodes is 10 mm. The gap is therefore 10 times longer than it is wide, or 0.1 square total. if the measured insulation resistance were 5×10^{10} ohms, the equivalent ohms per square would be:

$$\frac{5 \times 10^{10} \text{ ohms}}{0.1 \text{ square}} = 5 \times 10^{11} \text{ ohms per square}$$

Insulation resistance is frequently measured with a DC voltage, but this may not always be optimal. Ions, depending upon their charge, tend to migrate towards either the positive or negative electrode. This can result in a nonuniform distribution of charge that alters the measured resistivity. Ion migration can be avoided by using alternating current that has a net zero DC potential.

13.7 CLEANING PHILOSOPHY: WHEN IS IT NECESSARY?

As important as the selection of cleaning solvents and equipment is the need to establish a basic cleaning philosophy. Poorly cleaned boards can, in some instances, be even less reliable than boards which have not been cleaned at all. It is important to understand the factors that contribute to an effective cleaning philosophy.

Solidified rosin is surprisingly effective in capturing ionic activators within its residue. Polymerized rosin has a "glassy" surface that prevents the activator from migrating to areas where it can cause corrosion. A poorly designed cleaning process may only partially dissolve the rosin, and the activator, rather than being totally removed, may instead be dispersed across the board. Manually operated batch-mode vapor degreasers are prone to this type of problem. Impatient operators may tend to "short-cut" the process, inadvertently creating a bigger reliability problem than if they had not bothered to clean at all.

The cardinal rule of cleaning is *clean as soon as possible after soldering*. The longer the residues remain on the board, the more difficult they are to remove. Ideally an in-line cleaning system should be used, with the soldering station located so that no more than a few minutes elapse between soldering and cleaning. Boards that sit for even as little as an hour can be considerably harder to clean than those that have been cleaned without delay. Many alleged cleaning problems would undoubtedly disappear if this axiom were followed religiously.

A particularly relevant question is whether it is even necessary to clean at all. Although there are many instances where thorough cleaning is essential, in some cases, cleaning does not measurably improve board reliability and may well be unnecessary.

Boards soldered with Types R or RMA flux, used in a consumer or industrial application that does not encounter large environmental variations, are least likely to need cleaning. Boards soldered with more active fluxes should be cleaned regardless of final application.

Any hand-soldering should be done with a wire solder employing a Type RMA flux core. Residues can safely be left on the board in all but the most demanding applications. If cleaning is essential, an in-line cleaner is recommended. When using a batch degreaser, an active chlorinated solvent, such as a blend of 1,1,1-trichloroethane and alcohol, is advised. Under no circumstances should inexpensive aerosol cans of solvent be used. Such an approach is virtually guaranteed to disperse residues throughout the board, causing more problems than it solves.

REFERENCES

1. Coombs, C. *Printed Circuits Handbook*, McGraw-Hill Book Co., New York, 1979, p. 16–17.
2. Kenyon, W. "Part 1—Water Cleaning Assemblies: Wave of the Future or Washout?" *Insulation/Circuits*, Feb. 1978.
3. Westerlaken, E. "Rosin Solder Flux Residues Shape Solvent Cleaning Requirements," *Electronic Packaging and Production*, Feb. 1985, pp. 118–124.
4. Kenyon, W. "Synthetic Activated (SA) Flux Technology: Development, Commercialization, Benefits and Future Applications," *Proceedings of the Sixth Annual International Electronics Packaging Conference*, San Diego, CA, Nov. 1986, pp. 204–281.
5. Musselman, R. and Yarbrough, T., "The Fluid Dynamics of Cleaning Under Surface Mounted PWA's and Hybrids," *Proceedings of NEPCON/West '86*, Anaheim, CA, Feb. 1986, pp. 207–220.
6. Hale, J., and Steinacker, W. "Complete Cleaning of Surface Mounted Assemblies," *Proceedings of NEPCON/West '85*, Anaheim, CA, Feb. 1985, pp. 304–313.
7. Brous, J., and Schneider, A. "Cleaning Surface-Mounted Assemblies With Azeotropic Solvent Mixtures," *Electronics*, Apr. 1984.
8. Archer, W. "Examination of Solvent Cleaning For Printed Wiring Board Applications," *Electri.onics Electronic Edition*, May 1987, pp. 11–14.
9. "Freon® TF Solvent," *Bulletin No. FST-1*, E.I. Du Pont de Nemours & Co., (Inc.), Wilmington, DE, Apr. 1977.
10. "Separation of Water from Freon® TMS Solvent," *Tech Brief TB-EQ-7*, E.I. Du Pont de Nemours & Co. (Inc.), Freon Products Division, Wilmington, DE, Jan. 1985.
11. Gerard, D. "Choosing the Proper Cleaning Cycle for Cleaning Surface Mounted Assemblies". Presented at *NEPCON/Northwest*, San Mateo, CA, Oct. 1984.

12. Lermond, D. "Key Process Design Factors For Efficient Fluorosolvent Spray Cleaning of SMAs," *Printed Circuit Assembly*, May 1987, pp. 20–26.
13. Harman, G. "Metallurgical Failure Modes of Wire Bonds," *Proceedings of the 12th Annual IEEE Reliability Physics Symposium*, Las Vegas, NV, 1974, pp. 131–141.
14. Johnson, K. "Ultrasonic Defluxing of Military Electronic Assemblies—A Re-valuation; Part I: The Test Plan," *Proceedings of NEPCON/West '86*, Anaheim, CA, Feb. 1986, pp. 389–392.
15. "Post Solder Aqueous Cleaning Handbook," *ANSI/IPC-AC-62*, Institute for Interconnecting and Packaging Electronic Circuits, Lincolnwood, IL, Dec. 1986.

Inspection and test

One of the basic tenets of modern manufacturing theory is that a process left to its own devices will tend to go out of control. To avoid the prospect of building large quantities of defective products, immediate feedback on process performance is essential. By understanding the current behavior of the process, problems can be anticipated and corrective action taken before defects arise.

Within the surface mount factory, there are two primary techniques for obtaining process feedback. The first is by monitoring physical characteristics, such as solder bath temperatures, conveyor speeds, and the like. The second is by examination of the end product through physical inspection and electrical testing. Both approaches are essential in a well-run factory. The former, however, is largely driven by the specifics of the process equipment and does not lend itself to generalized treatment. This chapter is concerned with the issues involved in physical inspection and electrical testing of the completed assembly.

Inspection and testing address two different aspects of product performance. The inspection process focuses on physical variations that could lead to mechanical reliability problems. Although often associated with simple visual inspection, several other approaches can be employed. These include machine vision, X-ray, and infrared techniques.

Electrical testing confirms that the assembly is electrically functional by comparing circuit performance against predetermined limits. The two most common approaches are functional test, which simulates the actual operating environment seen by the assembly, and in-circuit test, which measures the performance of each component on an individual basis.

Neither inspection nor test, by itself, can identify all defects that are likely to occur. Many electrical defects are not manifest as obvious physical anomalies and so would escape detection at a physical inspection point.

Conversely, many reliability problems do not show up as immediate electrical problems but are readily apparent when visually inspected. Well-run factories make intelligent use of both techniques to efficiently collect the optimum amount of data.

14.1 INSPECTION PHILOSOPHY: TO INSPECT OR NOT TO INSPECT

It is often taught that inspection adds no value to the finished product; companies that fall into the trap of "inspecting" quality in, rather than preventing defects in the first place, are doomed to failure in the face of more enlightened competitors. This philosophy is sometimes interpreted to mean that all inspection is bad and has no place in a world-class factory.

Such an interpretation, while based on good intentions, misses the basic intent of the philosophy. Inspection as a means only to locate and correct defects *is* bad, for it diminishes the incentive to identify and solve the root cause of the problem. Inspection as a means for continuous process monitoring, however, is not only good but essential.

At first, the differences may seem subtle. The distinction is not necessarily in *how* inspection is performed, but *what* is done with the data. In the former case, data gathered at inspection is used to fix defects but has little other value. In the latter case, the primary motivation for collecting data is to gain early insight into process variations. Potential problems can be identified before they become serious. Corrective action can often be taken even before actual defective assemblies are produced.

14.1.1 Control charts

A basic tool of the process engineer is the *control chart*, which provides a graphical record of process performance over time. A typical process might be monitored by several charts tracking the key process variables. Trends observed in the charts provide valuable insight into how the process is currently performing.

It is not the intent of this chapter to provide an entire course in control charts and process control theory; readers who desire to learn more are referred to one of the many texts on the subject, such as Refs. 1, 2, and 3. The following paragraphs describe certain basic principles that will help in formulating a viable inspection philosophy.

Several forms of control charts have been devised. The choice of which to use depends on the type of data being collected. Two of the simplest charts are the *p chart* and the *pn chart*, which are most often used to plot pass–fail data. The pn chart tracks the number of defective units in a specified subgroup, while the p chart tracks the percentage of defective units. The pn chart is used with constant subgroup size and the p chart when the subgroup size varies. The use of these charts can best be understood by example.

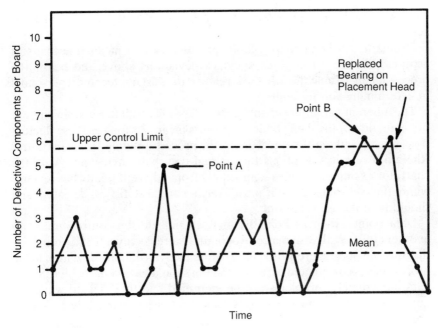

FIG. 14.1 pn-chart for example in text.

Consider a visual inspection station located immediately after the component-placement operation. Its intent is to confirm proper operation of the placement machine.

One way to collect data is to simply record the number of components on each board that have not been acceptably placed per the specified acceptance criteria (see Appendix A). This would suggest the use of a pn chart in which the measured parameter is the number of defective placements per board and the subgroup is the total number of components on the board. This simple chart can be maintained directly by the inspector. After inspecting each board, he or she immediately plots the data on the chart. A hypothetical chart is shown in Fig. 14.1.

Several features of this chart can be observed. First is the fact that the data shows a certain amount of variability. This is unavoidable in any real process and represents the inherent limit of process capability. Next is the dashed line labeled *mean*. This is the average number of defects per board based on the long-term performance of the process. It is determined when the control chart is first instituted by averaging a large number (at least 25) of initial data points. Thereafter, the process mean is not adjusted unless the process itself changes.

The dashed line labeled *upper control limit* marks the boundary within which the process is defined to be in control. It also is a calculated quantity and is determined coincident with the process mean. In many cases, the chart will also have a *lower control limit*. In this example, the lower limit is zero.

Ordinarily, 3-sigma control limits are used, which means the limits of acceptability are set at three standard deviations above and below the process mean. (Tables have been developed to assist nontechnical personnel in determining control limits.)

The inherent variability of any real process will result in a certain amount of fluctuation of the data about the process mean. As long as these fluctuations remain within the control limits, the process is defined to be in control (there are certain exceptions for unusual data patterns). Point A on the chart, for example, deviates significantly from adjacent points but remains within the control limits. It is most likely a normal statistical deviation and should be no cause for alarm.

Data points, such as Point B, that fall outside the control limits are another story. With 3-sigma control limits, there is only a 0.3% probablity that this will occur merely by chance. More likely, a definite deviation in the process has occurred, and corrective action should be taken. By plotting the data immediately, problems can be identified and investigated while the important information is still fresh and the suspect assembly is readily accessible.

The pn chart is useful in determining whether a particular process is under control, but it is rather limited in its ability to identify what has gone wrong. More insights can be gained from charts that plot continuously variable data. This is done on $\bar{X}$ (*X-bar*) and *R charts*. The $\bar{X}$ chart records variations in the mean value of a process, while the R chart records variations in dispersion.

To obtain the data, successive measurements are collected into subgroups of fixed size. The mean of each subgroup is plotted on the $\bar{X}$ chart, and the *range* (the difference between highest and lowest value) is plotted on the R chart. The R chart is thus a simplified way of looking at the instantaneous standard deviation of the process.

Consider how $\bar{X}$ and R charts could be used to track the performance of the component-placement machine. One solution would be to simply group the pass–fail data recorded above into subgroups of perhaps three or four readings and plot the mean and range of each subgroup. In this case, however, we desire more insight than such a graph would provide. For simplicity, assume that only a single process variable, component rotation, is important. (Component rotation is defined as rotational deviation from target orientation.)

To collect the data, the inspection station is outfitted with an optical comparator that measures actual component orientation against the target. Since the inspection step is intended to monitor process performance rather than identify every defect, a sample inspection plan is employed. The operator randomly selects five components on each board and measures their orientation (the exact number of samples is not critical but should be the same from board to board). This set of readings forms one subgroup.

From this data, the operator first computes the mean rotation for the subgroup. This point is plotted on the $\bar{X}$ chart. Next, the operator determines the range by subtracting the smallest value from the largest. This number is plotted on the R chart.

For example, suppose the readings for the five components on a specific board were as follows:

$+7°$
$-10°$
$-3°$
$-14°$
$0°$

The mean value is then:

$$\frac{(+7-10-3-14+0)}{5} = -4°$$

and the range is:

$$7-(-14) = 21°$$

Hypothetical $\bar{X}$ and R charts are shown in Fig. 14.2. In this example, an increase in the range is easily observed even before it reaches the control limit. This type of trend would trigger an investigation to determine the root cause—in this case, the replacement of a worn bearing on the placement head.

A key to the success of control charts is knowing which of the many process parameters to track. There is no general answer to this question, and the best advice is to start conservatively by tracking a large number of variables. As insight is gained over time, it is usually possible to eliminate many of the charts and track only those few variables that provide the best indication of present performance.

As evidenced from the preceding examples, control charts can be valuable tools to help track process performance. While they do not totally eliminate the need for human interpretation, they make it easy to separate true process problems from ordinary statistical variations.

14.2 IN-PROCESS INSPECTION POINTS

The decision for how and where to inspect must be based on economics. The cost of inspecting must be weighed against the potential cost of not identifying defects until a later process step. Those processes with greatest overall impact on the finished product are the ones most likely to benefit from immediate feedback. The most common inspection points are illustrated in Fig. 14.3. In order of priority, they are:

• final inspection

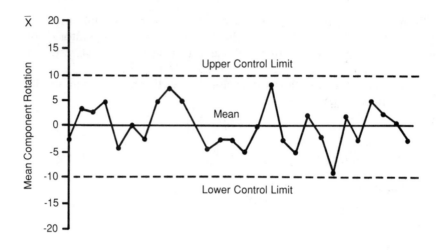

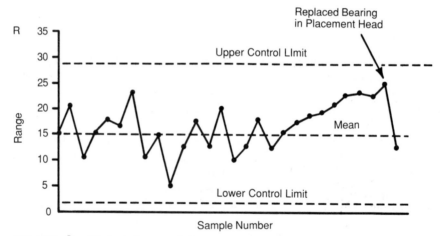

FIG. 14.2 X̄ and R charts for example in text.

- post-solder inspection
- post-placement inspection
- post-screen printing inspection

Final inspection

This is the last opportunity to catch defects before shipping the product and is the most common inspection point. It is performed after all processing has been completed, usually in conjunction with a final electrical test.

Final inspection is not an ideal point to monitor process performance. The observed defects are a composite of the entire process, making it difficult to ascribe a specific defect to a particular process step. Often, final inspection is

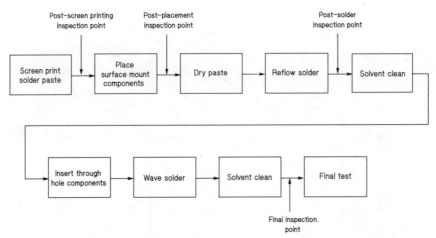

FIG. 14.3 Typical in-process inspection points.

used primarily as a "gate" to prevent defective products from escaping. In light of the previous discussion, it would seem that this type of inspection is at odds with world-class manufacturing philosophy. Technically this may be true, but the practicalities of real-world manufacturing often make such an inspection essential.

Consider a surface mount manufacturing facility that achieves defect levels of 100 parts per million on a per-joint basis. This means that out of every 1 million joints produced, it can be expected that about 100 of them will be defective. (This defect level, while not extraordinarily low, would be an aggressive goal for many factories.) The probability that a given joint will be acceptable is thus:

$$P_j = 0.999900$$

and the probability that any given board will be acceptable is determined by the binomial probability distribution:

$$P(n) = P_j^n$$

where n = number of joints per board.

The probability of a given board being defective is then just:

$$P_d = 1 - P(n) \tag{14.1}$$

Figure 14.4 plots eqn. [14.1] for various process defect levels. For example, if the above process were used to assemble boards with 5000 joints per board (typical of a computer memory board), about 40% of the boards produced would contain at least one defect. The need for a comprehensive final inspection is then readily understood—it is of little comfort to know the process is in control if nearly half the boards shipped are defective! Until process performance can be improved by several orders of magnitude, a final outgoing inspection will continue to be mandatory.

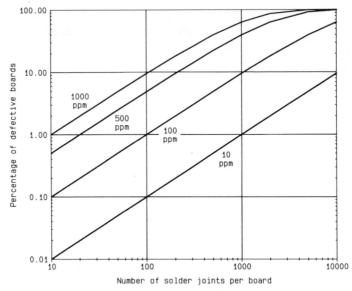

FIG. 14.4 Impact of soldering process defect levels on final assembly yield. The ppm defect levels refer to the process yield on a per-joint basis.

Post-solder inspection

This station is designed to monitor the quality of the SMT soldering process. It tracks solder joint defects, such as inadequate solder volume, poor wetting, solder bridges, solder balls, etc. These types of defects are exceedingly difficult to inspect automatically, so human vision is most often used. Some success has been reported with X-ray (Section 14.3.4) and infrared (Section 14.3.5) techniques.

Post-solder inspection suffers from limitations similar to those at final inspection: since it is so far downstream in the process, it is difficult to tell whether a particular defect is due to the soldering operation or a previous process. For example, if a component is missing, did it fall off during the soldering process or was it never mounted by the component-placement machine? To minimize uncertainty, the soldering system should be preceded by a post-placement inspection step. In this way, the quality of the product prior to soldering can readily be determined.

A question that often arises is how to account for defects that are most probably due to problems at previous processes. If a reflow-soldered joint is defective because it apparently never received solder paste, should it be counted as a soldering defect or a screen printing defect? According to one school of thought, the inspector should make an intelligent determination of which process step was the probable cause and ascribe the defect to that process. Another school of thought argues that regardless of where the defect actually occurred, since it was first observed at the post-solder inspection step, it should be counted as a post-solder defect.

The author tends to favor the latter approach. Process monitoring is intended to identify potential process problems, not to place blame on a particular machine or operator. By counting the defect at the point where it was first observed, someone is assured of taking ownership of the problem. Otherwise it is easy for an inspector to dismiss it as being caused by another process step upstream without following up to confirm his or her suspicion.

For this approach to be effective, it is essential the operators understand that their performance is not judged solely by the results of inspection. A much more important metric is how actively they respond to solve problems when they arise. The real measure of the success of a production line is whether the operators work as a team to ensure that the products exiting the line are of consistently high quality.

Post-placement inspection

This step provides feedback on the quality of the component-placement process. It looks for placement-related errors, such as missing, skewed, and incorrect components, and polarized parts installed backwards. Although often performed manually, it is easier to automate than post-solder inspection.

Post-screen printing inspection

The one point in the process where rework is actually easy is immediately after screen printing. If a defect is found, the paste is simply washed away and the board rescreened. The inspection process at this point need not be exotic. Frequently it consists of a straightforward visual examination by the screen printer operator. If this person doesn't like the results of the print, he or she simply sets the board aside for later washing and reprinting.

It is easy to let this inspection point remain informal and not record the data. However, it is good to consider the possibility of maintaining a simple control chart to track the process. This might be nothing more than a pn chart that plots the number of consecutive good boards produced before discovering a defect. The advantage of the control chart is that it helps identify evolving problems that may escape the notice of an operator whose primary concern is to meet the production schedule.

14.3 INSPECTION TECHNIQUES

Once the need for inspection has been established, the next step is to select the appropriate inspection techniques. The decision should be based on a combination of economic and technical issues. Inspection must always provide an economic benefit; the increased expense of inspecting must be more than offset by the resulting improvements in process control. Unfortunately, the tradeoffs are not always easily analyzed. How does one compare the potential cost of future defects against the very real ongoing cost of inspecting? What investment in inspection is justified to prevent this intangible future cost? The technical issues are somewhat easier to resolve. Sample boards with a variety of representative defects can be used to evaluate the capabilities of various inspection techniques.

Caution is advised when considering some of the more exotic approaches. Many products have only recently reached the market and, despite manufacturers' claims, their performance in a wide range of manufacturing environments has not been demonstrated. These products should be thoroughly evaluated in a way that determines their performance across the entire range of expected operating conditions.

The most common inspection approaches are:

- visual inspection
- machine vision
- three-dimensional vision
- X-ray inspection
- infrared inspection

14.3.1 Visual inspection

This is by far the most popular inspection technique. One reason for its popularity is that it does not require expensive and complicated capital equipment. Trained operators using relatively simple optical aids are all that are needed to inspect even the most complicated boards. Another benefit is that acceptance criteria can include detailed specifications that would be virtually impossible to program into a computer algorithm.

Visual inspection has several drawbacks. The first is its fundamental premise that a product that meets certain visual requirements will therefore be reliable in the field. In some cases, such a connection is tenuous at best. A solder joint may appear ideal, yet have a potentially disastrous void hidden just below the surface. Conversely, levels of flux residue that would trigger a visual reject may in fact be harmless rosin that would pose no threat to reliability. Since there is no easy way to visually identify these types of exceptions, there is no choice but to rigidly apply standard inspection criteria to all situations. Representative criteria are presented in Appendix A.

Another drawback is the high inherent variability of the technique. Visual inspection depends entirely on subjective interpretation of the specifications. A component lead that is determined as being 20% off its land by one operator may be judged 30% off by another. If the specification limit is 25%, this variance would be the difference between acceptance and rejection. Even a single operator could judge the same product differently at different times depending on such factors as lighting, fatigue, and subconscious concerns about meeting production schedules.

Where possible, equipment operators should visually inspect their own work before sending it to the next assembly step. This provides the most immediate feedback to the person best able to take corrective action. If the workload is excessive, it may be necessary to maintain separate inspection stations with full-time operators.

It is not usually practical to inspect surface mount boards with the unaided eye. The physical features of components and solder joints are small enough to cause rapid operator fatigue in the absence of optical aid. For intermittent use, a large illuminated magnifier is adequate. For prolonged use, a stereo microscope equipped with a continuously variable zoom magnification feature is strongly recommended. The most elaborate equipment includes specialized optics and fixturing to facilitate rapid inspection of all sides of a component (Fig. 14.5).

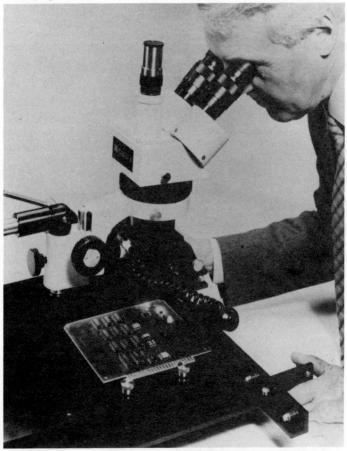

FIG. 14.5 Visual inspection using stereo zoom microscope. This fixture permits the board to be comfortably viewed at an oblique angle. (Used by permission. Assemtest.)

The low initial investment required of visual inspection must be weighed against the rather limited technical information that is obtained. It works best when the defects are readily identifiable, such as after solder paste deposition where there are few defect categories and problems are usually obvious. It is also reasonably useful after component placement. However, the positions where it is most commonly used, after soldering and at final inspection, are those where it is least effective. Defects at these steps are often difficult or impossible to see, so conservative criteria must be applied.

14.3.2 Machine vision

This approach builds on simple visual inspection by eliminating operator subjectivity. Instead of using human vision, the board is scanned by a video camera or series of cameras. The black-and-white image is digitized and analyzed by an internal computer, which compares it against predefined limits. A typical system is illustrated in Fig. 14.6.

FIG. 14.6 Machine vision system. (Used by permission. International Robomation/ Intelligence.)

The primary benefits of this technique are the higher inherent repeatability and much faster cycle time compared to manual methods. Depending on the accuracy required, commercial equipment can inspect between 5 and 25 surface mount components per second. Statistical data can also be easily obtained, either through the internal computer or by electronic transfer to an external process control system. As a result, machine vision is especially useful in highly automated factories.

As with manual inspection, defects must be visually recognizable. This is more of a concern with machine vision, however, because the video image is in black-and-white. Two objects of similar luminance but different color would be easily distinguished visually but may blend together in the video image.

Another concern is that the video image reduces a three-dimensional surface to a two-dimensional image, so all information relative to the vertical dimension is lost in the process. Finally, vision systems are expensive, ranging from abut $100,000 up to $500,000 or more, depending on capability.

Machine vision is ideally suited for inspecting solder paste and component placement, two situations where defects are visually obvious. The comparatively simple inspection requirements at these points can be met with relatively inexpensive machines. Machine vision can frequently be justified at these points even for factories with production volumes as low as 1 million components per month.

Solder-joint quality has proven much more difficult to inspect. Not only are joints difficult to view, but the algorithms for acceptance are extremely complex. One of the primary concerns is lighting. Illumination must be free of "hot" spots and be consistent from joint to joint. At the same time, the illumination must provide high contrast between the object being inspected and its background. Considering that much of the important information is internal to the joint and not visually observable, the long-term viability of machine vision for inspecting solder-joint quality is questionable.

14.3.3 Three-dimensional vision

Three-dimensional imaging was developed to overcome two limitations of conventional machine vision: the difficulty in analyzing low-contrast images and the inability to measure height. Of several possible approaches, the technique known as *structured light* is most commonly used for printed wiring board inspection.[4,5]

The concept of structured light is illustrated in Fig. 14.7. Light from a laser is spread into a thin horizontal stripe by rapidly scanning the beam. The stripe is projected onto the printed wiring board and viewed by a video camera mounted at a 45° angle. The image of the stripe is digitized into a series of points called *pixels*, which are sent to a computer for processing. Commercial cameras typically employ either 256 or 512 horizontal pixels.

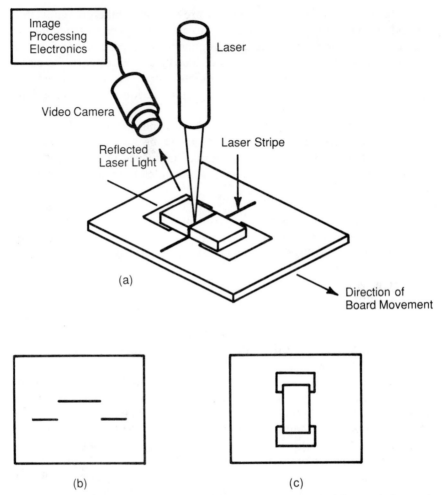

FIG. 14.7 Concept of structured light inspection system: a. Mechanical diagram, b. Image of a single video frame, c. Video image of component after processing.

As illustrated in Fig. 14.7b, the observed vertical position of each pixel depends on the height of the object at that point. The digitized camera output is processed by the computer to determine the profile of the stripe. The board is then moved a short distance vertically and the process repeated. By scanning across the entire board, a three-dimensional profile can be obtained. The speed of computation is such that one stripe can be processed during each 1/30-second TV camera frame time. A 200 × 400 mm printed wiring board can typically be fully analyzed in about 60 seconds.

Structured light systems have both advantages and disadvantages compared to conventional machine vision. A primary advantage is that by having three-dimensional information, analysis algorithms are considerably simplified. With conventional machine vision, for example, component outlines are determined by studying contrast information contained within the image. In low-contrast situations, this information can be extremely difficult to interpret. Structured light provides a much higher level of resolution, because rather than depending on contrast, component positions are determined by their vertical profiles.

One drawback is that contrast information is difficult to obtain. Unlike white light, laser light is comprised of a very narrow band of wavelengths. The reflectivity of an object illuminated by the laser may be very different from its reflectivity in white light. This makes it impractical in situations where contrast information is essential, such as reading bar code labels or component markings. Conventional machine vision is preferred in these situations.

Another drawback is that the TV camera views the image from an oblique angle. For certain component orientations, the laser stripe is hidden from view and no data can be obtained. Viewing the board from several orientations may therefore be necessary in critical situations.

Structured light systems have been successfully employed to inspect after solder paste deposition and component placement. Their ability to determine solder-joint profiles also makes them attractive for post-solder inspection. However, as with all vision systems, only the exposed portions of a joint can be inspected. Gull-wing leads are easy to inspect, but J-leads and I-leads are much more difficult.

14.3.4 X-ray inspection

The advantage of X-ray inspection is that it looks at the internal structure of a joint rather than just at its surface. Voids within a joint or solder missing from underneath a component can readily be detected. Tin–lead solder is quite opaque to X-rays, so even small defects are easily observed. In the past, systems using photographic film were common. For printed wiring board inspection, these have now largely been supplanted by *real-time X-ray* systems, which provide a live view of the board on a TV screen.

Fig. 14.8 shows a representative commercially available machine; its operating principles are illustrated in Fig. 14.9. The beam is generated in an X-ray tube and directed such that it illumines only a small portion of the board, typically 12×12 mm to 25×25 mm square. The rays pass through the board and are attenuated in proportion to the absorptivity of the material. The transmitted beam strikes a screen that fluoresces in proportion to the X-ray intensity, generating a visible image of the object. This image is viewed by a high-resolution video camera system, which digitizes and processes the information. Algorithms have been developed to inspect for a number of common defects, including component misalignment, solder-joint profile, solder voids, bridging, and solder balls.

The time required to analyze all joints in a single image is roughly 0.5–1

FIG. 14.8 X-ray inspection system. (Used by permission. Nicolet Instrument Corporation.)

second. After each image is processed, an X-Y table moves the board to the next location. Depending on the number of images required, a typical printed wiring board may take anywhere from 30 seconds to 5 minutes to inspect. To save time, areas of the board that do not contain components are not inspected.

X-ray equipment is targeted primarily at post-solder inspection. It has been used for years to inspect through-hole boards and has been successfully extended to single-sided surface mount applications. It is less successful for double-sided assemblies because of its inability to distinguish features on one side of the board from those on the other. A variety of techniques have been explored to address this difficulty, including viewing the board from several angles and requiring that top and bottom component locations be offset. To date, none of these solutions has proven entirely successful. Three-dimensional X-ray systems that should solve this problem are currently under development but not yet commercially available.

Another concern that has been raised is the effect that X-ray exposure can have on semiconductors. In the vast majority of all applications, this should not be a factor. Calculations performed by X-ray manufacturers uniformly indicate that even the most sensitive components should be undamaged

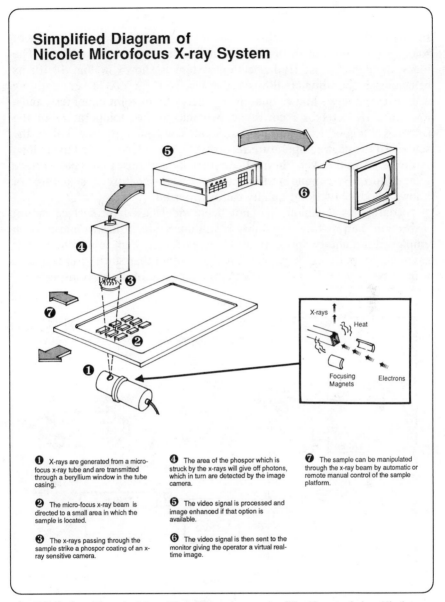

Simplified Diagram of
Nicolet Microfocus X-ray System

X-rays

Heat

Focusing
Magnets

Electrons

❶ X-rays are generated from a micro-focus x-ray tube and are transmitted through a beryllium window in the tube casing.

❷ The micro-focus x-ray beam is directed to a small area in which the sample is located.

❸ The x-rays passing through the sample strike a phospor coating of an x-ray sensitive camera.

❹ The area of the phospor which is struck by the x-rays will give off photons, which in turn are detected by the image camera.

❺ The video signal is processed and image enhanced if that option is available.

❻ The video signal is then sent to the monitor giving the operator a virtual real-time image.

❼ The sample can be manipulated through the x-ray beam by automatic or remote manual control of the sample platform.

FIG. 14.9 Operating principles of X-ray inspection system. (Used by permission. Nicolet Instrument Corporation.)

after many hours or days of continuous exposure. However, it is still a good idea to minimize total exposure. This is primarily a concern on products that are inspected multiple times.

14.3.5 Infrared inspection

Infrared inspection is a specialized technique used to assess the quality of solder joints on both through-hole and surface mount assemblies.[6] The block diagram for an IR inspection system is shown in Fig. 14.10; its principles of operation are illustrated in Fig. 14.11. A YAG laser operating at 1.06 μm applies a known quantity of energy to the joint under test, and a low-noise IR detector records the dynamic surface temperature of the solder. On a good joint, the heat is rapidly conducted into the bulk of the solder, so the peak temperature recorded by the detector is relatively low. An internal void lowers thermal conductivity and raises the peak surface temperature. By comparing the actual thermal signature to signatures of known good joints, joint quality can be inferred.

To date, this technique has not been widely used for surface mount inspection, and its total capability is still uncertain. It has primarily been employed in military applications where extremely high joint reliability is essential. Since it cannot examine attributes other than solder-joint quality, it must be used in conjunction with another form of physical inspection.

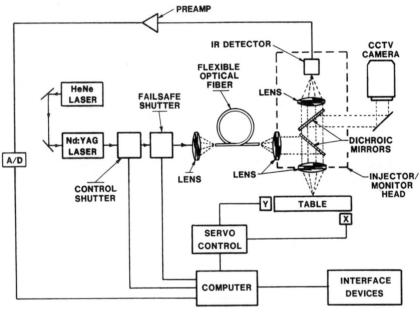

FIG. 14.10   Block diagram of IR inspection system. (Used by permission. E. Doucette, Vanzetti Systems.)

14.4 ELECTRICAL TEST

While physical inspection can verify the mechanical reliability of an assembly, it cannot guarantee that the circuit will function electrically. This can be

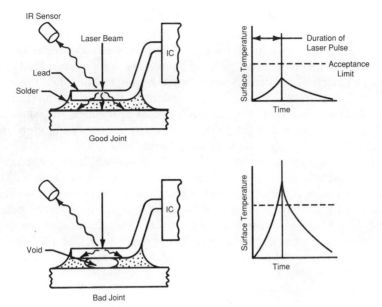

FIG. 14.11   Thermal characteristics of normal and defective solder joints tested with IR inspection system. (Hughes Aircraft.)

done only through some form of electrical test. The two most common electrical test techniques are *functional testing* and *in-circuit testing*. Both methods have unique advantages and disadvantages, and the choice of which to use depends on the specific nature of the anticipated defects.

14.4.1 Functional testing

In this method, the performance of the entire circuit is analyzed on a system that simulates the intended operating environment. All electrical contact is normally made through the board edge connector. A series of input signals serves as stimuli, and the output responses are measured and compared against acceptance limits. The result is a pass/fail indication of board performance.

Functional testing can take on several forms. The simplest, termed *hot mock-up*, employs an actual end product that has been modified to allow boards to be easily interchanged for testing. The test is a direct simulation of actual operation and identifies defective boards to a very high level of confidence. However, a separate test system may be required for each board type, making it a very expensive and inflexible solution.

Commercial systems that perform more generic functional tests are also available. Such equipment can test a variety of boards with relatively little setup time. The tradeoff, however, is that some faults may be overlooked because the test may not exactly duplicate the operating environment.

Digital circuits, for example, may not be tested at full rated speed, so certain timing problems could be missed.

A third form of functional testing is self-test, in which additional diagnostic circuitry is included directly on the board. The complexity added to the board can often be justified through a reduction in test time and the use of simpler test systems. An additional advantage is that field failures can be diagnosed by technicians using relatively simple equipment. An example of this approach is the self-check routine that many personal computers automatically execute every time they are powered up.

One disadvantage common to all forms of functional testing is a limited ability to diagnose failures. It is usually possible to trace a problem only to a particular region of the circuit, rather than to a specific component. Some functional testers have no diagnostic capability at all, but merely indicate whether the board has passed or failed the test. Another concern is with the time required to write the test program for a new board. Complex assemblies may require anywhere from a few weeks to as long as nine months for program development.

14.4.2 In-circuit testing

In-circuit testing does not check the performance of the circuit as a whole but rather of each component individually. The board is accessed by a series of probes (called a *bed-of-nails fixture*) that make contact with all circuit nodes. Test signals are applied across successive combinations of nodes and the responses measured. Defects can ordinarily be traced to a specific component or small cluster of components. A commercially available in-circuit tester is illustrated in Fig. 14.12.

The principle of analog in-circuit testing is shown in Fig. 14.13. The unkown impedance of the device under test is used as the input impedance of an inverting operational amplifier circuit. One end of the device, Node S in the diagram, is excited by a known source. The other end, Node I, is connected to the inverting input of the operational amplifier. This point operates as a virtual ground. The value of the unknown impedance can be calculated from the standard relationship for an inverting operational amplifier circuit:

$$Z_x = -R_{ref} \frac{V_s}{V_o}$$

Digital components are tested by applying a series of test patterns, called *test vectors*, to the component inputs. The outputs are measured and compared to the expected truth table for the device. Many digital in-circuit testers can function at clock rates similar to those encountered in actual operation. The block diagram of a digital in-circuit tester is shown in Fig. 14.14.

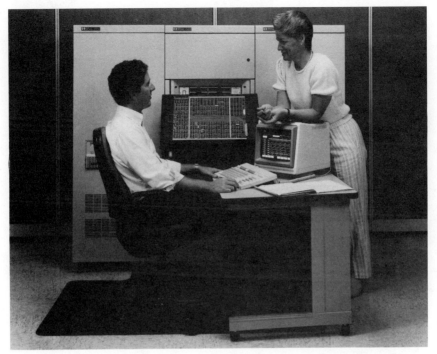

FIG. 14.12   In-circuit test system. (Used by permission. Hewlett-Packard Company.)

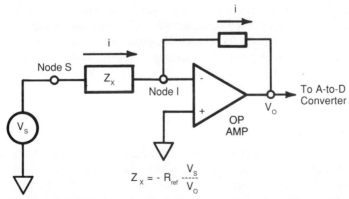

FIG. 14.13   Schematic diagram of analog in-circuit test configuration. (Used by permission. Hewlett-Packard Company.)

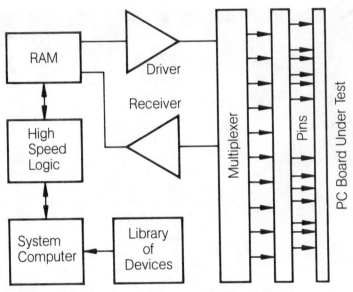

FIG. 14.14 Block diagram of digital in-circuit test configuration. (Used by permission. Hewlett-Packard Company.)

The advent of surface mount technology has forced users and manufacturers of in-circuit testers to rethink their test strategies. Some of the problems and potential solutions are as follows.

Probing on close centers

Traditional in-circuit testers employ probes located on 0.100-in (2.54-mm) centers. This has not proven sufficient for surface mount technology, where component lead pitches of 0.050 in (1.27 mm) or even 0.025 in (0.63 mm) are common. New probes have been developed for 0.050-in and 0.040-in (1.0-mm) spacings, but these are fragile and must be replaced more often than 0.100-in center probes.

Node visibility

A node that can be probed by the bed-of-nails fixture is said to be *visible*. With through-hole technology, all nodes are automatically visible to a traditional fixture that probes only the underside of the board. Surface mount component leads do not penetrate the board, so there is no guarantee that a node connecting two components on the topside will naturally be visible on the underside. As a result, either the complexity of the test must

FIG. 14.15   Double-sided in-circuit test fixture. (Used by permission. Hewlett-Packard Company.)

be increased by probing both sides of the board (Fig. 14.15) or the board must be modified to bring all nodes through to the underside.

Functional failures

Standard in-circuit testers do an excellent job of identifying process-related faults, such as solder shorts or opens. They can also readily identify defective components. They are not, however, effective in locating circuit interaction problems. To address this limitation, new machines that include both functional and in-circuit capabilities are now entering the market. They employ a technique known as *cluster testing* to verify the performance of high-density boards.[7] Cluster testing treats specified component groups as though they were a single entity. An in-circuit test of the cluster thus becomes the equivalent of a functional test of the total circuit. Cluster testing combines the high test confidence of functional testing with the excellent diagnostic capabilities of in-circuit testing.

14.4.3 Test strategy development

The first step in selecting an appropriate test system is to develop a total test strategy. It makes little sense to invest hundreds of thousands of dollars on a test system unless an obvious economic payback can be demonstrated. In developing the strategy, the following considerations must be understood.

- anticipated fault profile
- production volume and mix
- anticipated level of repair
- test throughput/test thoroughness tradeoff

Anticipated fault profile

The measure of success for a test technique is how well it detects the types of faults most likely to occur. The distribution of anticipated faults, called a *fault profile*, varies somewhat depending on the assembly process employed. Table 14.1 describes a number of common faults and their relative importance for wave and reflow soldering processes.

	Relative importance	
Fault type	Wave soldering	Reflow soldering
Solder bridging	High	Medium
Solder balls	Low	High
Unsoldered joint	High	High
Missing component	Medium	Medium
Incorrect component	Medium	Medium
Misplaced component	Low	Medium
Reversed polarity	Medium	Medium
Damaged component	Low	Low
Component out of specification	Low	Low
Circuit interaction problems	Depends on design	

TABLE 14.1 Typical fault profiles for wave soldered and reflow soldered surface mount components

The most frequently encountered problems in wave soldering are solder bridges and unsoldered joints. As described in Section 12.4.1, bridges occur when the solder does not cleanly peel away as the board exits the wave. Unsoldered joints, also called "opens," are usually the result of solder shadowing. They are sometimes caused by poor solderability of components or boards.

In the reflow process, unsoldered joints are also a problem, but for a different reason. They are usually caused by bits of foreign matter that clog some of the openings on the solder stencil, preventing solder from flowing through the stencil and onto the board. Solder balls are another frequent problem, caused both by oxides in the solder paste and variations in the soldering process.

Both wave and reflow soldering processes experience a variety of problems related to component placement. Missing components are perhaps the most common of these faults. In most cases, the component is initially placed acceptably but falls off later. When wave soldering, the primary cause is insufficient adhesive quantity, which allows the component to be washed away by the solder wave. With reflow soldering, the problem is due to the comparatively weak holding force of dried solder paste. During the time between component placement and reflow soldering, the assemblies are quite susceptible to damage either by physical abrasion or mechanical shock.

In both processes, board warpage is especially troublesome. During component placement the board is forced flat against supports, but upon exiting the machine it springs back to its original warped configuration. In extreme cases, the amount of flexure is sufficient to eject components from the board.

Because many SMCs are not marked, an incorrect component can be a very difficult problem to identify. The most obvious cause occurs when the wrong feeder is loaded onto the placement machine. This concern can usually be managed by careful process control and thorough operator training. A more insidious problem occurs when the component supplier loads the wrong part onto the reel or reverses the orientation of the parts in the tape. While this may seem almost incomprehensible, one subcontract assembly facility found that over an extended period, nearly 5% of all reels purchased did not contain the parts indicated on the reel!

Placement accuracy problems tend to be greater in reflow soldering than in wave soldering. This is not due to any inherent limitation of the process but rather to the fact that wave soldered components are primarily chip resistors and capacitors that can tolerate large placement deviations. More complex components with higher accuracy requirements are generally reflow soldered.

One of the biggest variables is the impact of component interactions. Included in this category are such concerns as timing problems on digital circuits and parasitic reactances on high-frequency analog circuits. Although each individual component may perform to specification, the circuit as a whole may fail to operate as required. Designs that push the margins or that depend on unspecified component parameters frequently experience interaction problems. Conservative designs that include generous design margins are relatively unaffected.

The precise impact of the various faults depend on the specifics of the board design and manufacturing facility. For many manufacturers, a fault profile similar to that in Fig. 14.16 has been found to be representative. Defects from the printed circuit production and soldering processes account for about half of all defects. Assembly and wiring faults account for another 30%, while defective components are the cause about 13% of the time. Functional failures account for only about 7% of all defects.

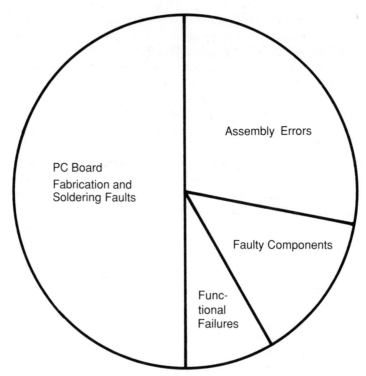

FIG. 14.16 Typical fault profiles for printed wiring boards. (Used by permission. Hewlett-Packard Company.)

Production volume and mix

A factory that builds many different board types in small quantities needs a flexible test system. The changeover time from one board to another must be extremely rapid, and the investment in unique fixtures, test programs, etc., must be low. The time taken to build fixtures and write test programs for new boards should be measured in days or weeks, not months. In-circuit testing has a definite advantage in this environment.

High-volume factories that build only a few board types have a different set of needs. Fixture development and programming times may not be nearly as important as rapid cycle time and high test reliability. Depending on the specific set of requirements, either functional or in-circuit testing may be indicated.

Anticipated level of repair

If boards are inexpensive and only rarely fail, it may be more economical to discard the defective units rather than repair them. A functional test that makes a simple pass/fail decision may be the best choice in this situation.

Complex products are usually too expensive to discard, and it is important to rapidly identify and repair the defects. An in-circuit test capable of diagnosing faults to the individual component level is preferable for these boards.

Test throughput/test thoroughness tradeoff

As a general rule, the more thorough the test, the longer the test time. Between the two extremes of no testing at all and finding every possible defect lies a point that optimizes the tradeoff between throughput and thoroughness.

This optimum point varies depending on the type of product being manufactured. High-reliability products require extremely thorough testing and can absorb the associated increase in manufacturing cost. Cost-sensitive consumer products are more likely to accept the increased risk that comes with less extensive testing.

For low levels of defects, the throughput of functional testing exceeds that of in-circuit testing (Fig. 14.17). However, as the number of defects increases, the efficiency of functional testing falls off rapidly. This is related to the poor diagnostic capability of functional testing and the fact that each defect may need to be repaired before the test can continue. The throughput of in-circuit testing falls off much more slowly because components are tested in isolation and a failure in one component does not usually affect the remainder of the test.

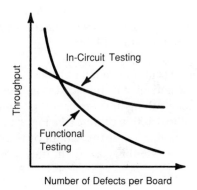

FIG. 14.17 Efficiencies of in-circuit and functional tests. (Used by permission. Hewlett-Packard Company.)

14.4.4 Guidelines for in-circuit testing

At the present time, in-circuit testing, either alone or in conjunction with a functional test, has proven to be the most viable approach for the majority of surface mount assemblies. Testing of these assemblies, however, is more complex than through-hole testing. Certain additional guidelines should be observed to ensure that the full capability of the tester is efficiently used.[8, 9] These guidelines are summarized in the following paragraphs.

1. Avoid using double-sided fixtures
Registration and accuracy problems are compounded when both sides of the board must be probed simultaneously, especially when using 0.050-in probes. Double-sided fixtures also cost more and require more maintenance than single-sided fixtures. Where possible, avoid double-sided probing by adding test pads to bring all nodes to the underside. If a double-sided fixture must be employed, use only 0.100-in center probes.

2. Always probe test pads, never the component or solder joint
If the probe contacts the component, either the component or probe can be damaged. For similar reasons, the probe should not contact the solder joint—tolerances in the component-placement operation may result in the component body intruding into the probe area. Even if this is not the case, the steep angle of the solder fillet may cause the probe to slide off the solder or even bend or break. Another problem with probing components or joints is that the pressure exerted by the test probe may force an open joint to make temporary contact and appear acceptable.

In most cases, requiring test pads is not a significant burden on the board design. Much of the requirement can be fulfilled by naturally occuring via holes, so the only pads that must be overtly added are for nodes that would not otherwise be visible. Studies have shown that the higher the total number of nodes, the greater the likelihood that they will be naturally visible to a single-sided test fixture (Fig. 14.18).

3. Avoid using 0.050-in center or smaller probes
Such probes are fragile and must be replaced more frequently than standard 0.100-in probes. When probing 0.050-in center or smaller components, try to fan the test pads out to 0.100-in centers (see Fig. 1.9). The loss in available board area is often more than compensated for by the reduction in test cost. If miniature probes are essential, use them only where they are actually required.

4. Coat test pads with solder to insure reliable contact
In order to make reliable electrical contact with the board, the probe must puncture through any oxide layer that may exist on the pad surface. The soft solder provides a pliable surface that is easily penetrated. The probe is also less likely to slip off a solder-coated surface than a bare copper surface.

5. Test pad diameters should be large enough to accommodate normal manufacturing tolerances
Pad diameters for 0.100-in center probes should be at least 0.9 mm (0.035 in) in diameter. For 0.050-in center probes, the recommended pad diameter is

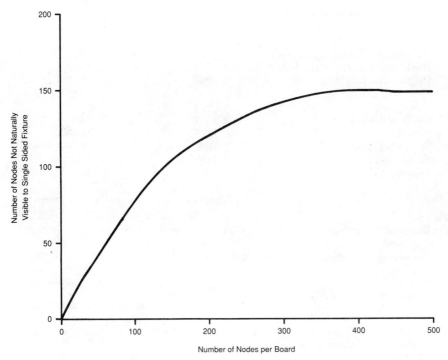

FIG. 14.18 Node visibility as a function of circuit complexity. The more complex the board, the more likely that all nodes will be naturally visible to a single-sided fixture. (Used by permission. Hewlett-Packard Company.)

even larger, being 1.0 mm (0.040 in). This apparent anomaly is explained by the fact that with current manufacturing techniques, 0.050-in probes have a larger tolerance between the plunger and outer barrel of the probe (Fig. 14.19). A complete error analysis is presented in Table 14.2.

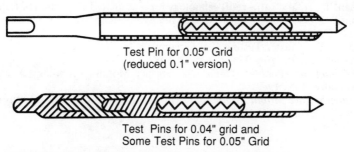

Test Pin for 0.05" Grid
(reduced 0.1" version)

Test Pins for 0.04" grid and
Some Test Pins for 0.05" Grid

FIG. 14.19 Construction of test probes for 0.050-in and 0.040-in probing applications. (Used by permission. Hewlett-Packard Company.)

Fixture	Tolerance	√Variance
Probe location in tooling hole	± .0030″	.0010″
Due to angle of socket in hole	± .0030″	.0021″
Due to angle of drilled socket hole	± .0030″	.0010″
Due to fixture plate bow	± .0014″	.0007″
PCB		
Pad to tooling hole	± .0030″	.0010″
Pad size	± .0020″	.0007″
Tooling hole clearance to pin	± .0030″	.0021″
Tooling hole size	± .0030″	.0010″
Tooling pin size	± .0005″	.0003″

	.100″ Center Probes		.050″ Center Probes	
Probe	Tolerance	√Variance	Tolerance	√Variance
Due to angle of plunger in barrel	± 0.002″	.0014″	± .005″	.0035″
Due to angle of probe in socket	± .001″	.0007″	± .001″	.0007″
Straightness of probe	± .001″	.0003″	± .001″	.0003″
Estimate of 1 standard diviation		.004″		.005″

TABLE 14.2   Tolerance analysis for single-sided in-circuit test fixture. (Used by permission. Hewlett-Packard Company.)

REFERENCES

1. Leavenworth, R., and Grant, E. *Statistical Quality Control*, McGraw-Hill Book Co., New York, NY 1980.
2. Ishikawa, K. *Guide to Quality Control*, Asian Productivity Organization, Tokyo, 1976.
3. *Statistical Quality Control Handbook*, Western Electric Co., Newark, NJ, 1956.
4. Simmons, J. "Applications for Real Time Three Dimensional Vision Systems," *SME Technical Paper MS86-1042*, Society of Manufacturing Engineers, Dearborn, MI, 1986.
5. Juha, M. *Improving Automated SMT Inspection with 3-D Vision*, Photonic Automation, Inc., Santa Ana, CA, 1986.
6. Doan, T., et. al. "Infra-red Technology for Automated Inspection of Lap Solder Joint," *Proceedings of 11th Annual Soldering/Manufacturing Seminar*, China Lake, CA, Feb. 1987.
7 Caplow, S. "Cluster Testing Can Circumvent In-Circuit Testability Problems," *Electronic Engineering Times*, Feb. 2, 1987, pp. 60–65.
8. *Designing for Testability Handbook*, Surface Mount Technology Association, Los Gatos, CA, 1987.
9. *Testing Surface Mount Technology*, Hewlett-Packard Co., Manufacturing Test Div., Loveland, CO, 1985.

15

Repair of surface mount assemblies

The goal of the repair process is to economically replace a defective component without negatively impacting an assembly's overall performance or reliability. Even before the advent of surface mount technology, repairing a printed wiring board was a difficult task. Repair equipment and technology have always been poorly developed compared to the remainder of the manufacturing process, relying mainly on crude manual techniques. With the introduction of surface mount components, the difficulties have only been compounded.

In part, this can be traced to the rapid acceptance of the so-called "world-class" manufacturing philosophy, which among other things, stresses the importance of "doing it right the first time."[1] Rather than wasting time finding and fixing defects, managers are learning that it is more efficient to use that time to control the process and prevent defects in the first place. The arguments in favor of this approach are so compelling that some companies find it embarrassing to admit that they even need a process that so obviously conflicts with this strategy. As a result, they have been reluctant to invest in developing efficient repair processes.

As often happens in such instances, the problem is not an error in fundamental philosophy but rather a disregard for the practicalities of real manufacturing environments. Printed wiring assembly processes have not yet reached a level of control that eliminates the need for repair. Even in the most well-controlled processes, the impact of defect levels can be appreciable, as was shown in Section 14.2. Until manufacturing defect levels can be reduced by several orders of magnitude, repair will remain an integral part of the process. It should not be ignored merely because it is perceived to be unbecoming. Instead, every effort should be made to reduce the cost of repair without increasing the incentive to rely on it.

Repair processes that have worked well for through-hole assemblies are not adequate for SMT. This chapter reviews the current state of repair technology and examines the issues involved in repairing surface mount assemblies. Topics that are addressed include the following:

- design for repairability
- repair processes
- design modifications
- field repair strategies

15.1 DESIGN FOR REPAIRABILITY

No matter how sophisticated the repair process, it will be ineffective if the board has not been designed to be repairable. Surface mount assemblies are even more sensitive than through-hole assemblies to the limitations of the repair process. Although the exact restrictions depend on the type of repair equipment employed, the following general guidelines should always be observed.

1. Allow clearances around components sufficient to permit proper operation of the repair tooling

The specific dimensions depend primarily on the design of the repair tooling. A hot-gas tool may not need as much clearance as a tool that depends on thermal conduction. A tool that accesses the component from the side (Fig. 15.1) requires more clearance than one that comes down from the top.

Many designers use SMT for size reduction, so constraints that force them to give up some of this benefit are not likely to be enthusiastically received. It is encumbent upon manufacturing engineering to stress the reasons for this compromise, but it is also important to avoid making it more restrictive than necessary. When selecting repair tooling, preference should be given to equipment that minimizes the required clearance area.

2. Ensure that component-mounted heat sinks do not interfere with repair tooling

Heat sinks are frequently used on high-power semiconductors and may become even more prevalent with the increased component densities of surface mount boards. To ensure that such components can be repaired, the heat sink must not extend beyond the periphery of the component. (see Fig. 15.2b). The repair collet can then readily access all solder joints on the component. Heat sinks such as shown in Fig. 15.2a should be avoided, since they prevent the collet from being lowered onto the joints.

FIG. 15.1 Modified soldering iron for repairing chip components. This design accesses the component from the side and requires more clearance than a tool which comes down from the top (compare to Fig. 15.4). (Photograph by the author.)

3. When using adhesive to mount components, select a relatively low-strength type

Adhesive selection is a compromise between high strength to hold the component during wave soldering and low strength to aid the repair process. The issues involved in adhesive selection are described more fully in Section 12.6. In general, acrylic adhesives have somewhat lower strength than epoxies and are preferred when repair is likely.

(a)

(b)

FIG. 15.2 Examples of unacceptable and acceptable heat sink design: a. This heat sink extends beyond the component periphery and would prevent the repair tool from accessing the leads. (Used by permission. Pace, Inc.) b. The smaller diameter of this heat sink is preferred because it does not interfere with the repair tool. (Used by permission. Pace, Inc.)

4. Design circuit ground planes to minimize thermal heat-sinking effects

Large ground planes on printed wiring boards can have a considerable heat-sinking effect. Removal of a component soldered directly to a ground plane may be difficult because heat applied to the joint is rapidly conducted away and into the ground plane. Not only will this delay the melting of the solder in the joint, but the additional heat input could damge the component or board.

Component lands connected to ground planes should be thermally isolated by a short length of conductor. Examples of preferred and non-preferred layouts are given in Fig. 7.4.

5. Protect all circuit traces with solder mask

Unlike the initial assembly process, the repair process is primarily a manual technique. As such, it is susceptible to the variations inherent in all manual processes. A common problem is solder splashes that occur during the removal or replacement of a component. To protect the board, all printed wiring conductors should be protected by an insulating solder mask that exposes only the component land patterns and test pads. It is especially important to protect conductors that are routed between successive IC lands.

As an alternative, a printed wiring technique known variously as *pads-only*, *buried traces*, or *glass pack* can be used. In this approach, the outer board layers contain only component lands. All conductors are confined to inner layers and are connected to the lands by vias. This approach is analogous to using solder mask, but it has advantages and disadvantages. The foremost advantage is an improvement in registration accuracy. Solder mask is difficult to align such that it completely covers a conductor routed between two IC lands without overlapping onto either land. When using a pads-only approach, this is not a problem because conductors are not routed on outer layers.

A major disadvantage is that since a via hole is required for every component land, drilling costs are dramatically increased. In effect, every board becomes a multilayer board, so the overall board fabrication costs can be significantly higher than an equivalent two-layer board.

6. When faced with the possibility of difficult repair problems, use a high-temperature board material

Ordinary epoxy-glass laminates do not readily tolerate long exposures to temperatures above their 125 °C glass transition temperature. Whenever an extended time at soldering temperature is anticipated, a high-temperature board material is recommended. Polyimide-based materials (Section 6.3.4) have glass transition temperatures of about 250 °C and are ideal for these applications.

For example, high-power devices are sometimes cooled by the use of *thermal vias*. A number of plated via holes under the component are connected to a large ground plane on the underside of the board. They conduct heat away from the device and into the board. Often, heat transfer is further increased by soldering the underside of the component to the vias. Although this approach is effective in reducing component temperatures, it also makes repair extremely difficult. The heat necessary to melt all solder under the component could easily damage an ordinary glass-epoxy board. In this case, a high-temperature polyimide-based material would be indicated.

15.2 REPAIR PROCESSES

A frustrating concern for the engineer chartered with developing a repair process is that no equipment yet on the market provides a total solution. Many machines do a credible job of removing defective components, but few are able to accurately position the replacement part. Even fewer address the problem of applying a repeatable quantity of fresh solder to the joint.

Since turnkey solutions are unlikely to become available in the near future, it falls to the manufacturing engineer to develop a total repair process. The highest priority must be to assure that the repaired assembly is reliable—ideally, its reliability should be indistinguishable from that of an original assembly. In reality, every cycle through the soldering process has a minute impact. Intermetallic compounds within the joint increase in thickness; microcracks in component plastic molding compounds grow in depth. The effect is essentially unmeasurable for the few cycles ordinarily encountered in assembly and repair, but it can become significant when the temperature gradients are large or the time at temperature is excessive.

The cost of repair must also be reasonable. Although the repair cost per component will inevitably be higher than the initial assembly cost, it will be incurred over a much smaller number of components. Whether to spend $5000 or $50,000 on a repair process is a decision that must be based on the economic return provided by the additional investment.

There is more to repair than simply removing the defective component and soldering a new one in its place. To meet the reliability objective, careful attention must be placed on the entire process, which consists of the following steps:[2]

- preparation
- preheating
- component removal and replacement
- cleaning

15.2.1 Preparation

Before the defective component can be removed, the board must be properly prepared. The attention placed on preparation can make the difference between a straightforward repair job and one that is fraught with problems. The following preparatory steps should be taken:

1. Clean the board to remove contamination

If the defective board has just come off the assembly line, this step may be unnecessary. If the board has been installed in an operating environment for any length of time, and especially if it has been returned from the field, cleaning is strongly advised. High-voltage circuits are particularly prone to attracting dust from the environment, although the effect occurs to a lesser extent with any operating circuit. If not removed, this contamination can hamper the reflow of solder on the defective component.

The process need not be elaborate. Since the primary objective is to remove particulate matter, considerable latitude exists in the selection of a cleaning fluid. Isopropanol applied locally and agitated with a brush or cotton swab is satisfactory. Immersion in a batch-mode or in-line solvent cleaner is also acceptable as long as all components on the board are compatible with the solvent.

2. Remove any components that would interfere with the repair process

This would include nearby tall components, such as transformers, switches, and potentiometers, that violate minimum spacing requirements. It might also include thermally sensitive components that cannot otherwise be protected. These components should be handled carefully so that they may be installed again after the repair is completed.

Every time a component must be removed, the risk of damaging the assembly increases. This risk is compounded when components other than the defective one must be removed. These additional complications serve to underscore the importance of abiding by the guidelines for minimum component clearances so that no components other than the defective one need be removed.

3. Protect adjacent components that could be damaged by the heat

The degree to which this is necessary depends on the sensitivity of nearby components and the design of the repair system. Hot-gas systems frequently employ a shroud that directs the heat only onto the joints of the defective components. Other systems are less selective and can melt the solder joints of all components within a 25-mm radius.

Components can be protected by forming sheet metal shrouds to direct the heat away from the undesired area. Although they do not afford indefinite protection, they are usually adequate for the short duration of a typical repair operation.

4. Apply flux to the solder joints of the defective component

The solder at the joint will melt much more quickly and evenly if the layer of oxide on its surface is removed. A Type RMA liquid flux is recommended because it is relatively active yet is mild enough to be left on the board if desired. In liquid form, it can be applied to the appropriate locations with an ordinary artist's brush.

15.2.2 Preheating

Thermal shock is just as damaging during the repair process as it is during initial assembly. Rapid heating causes a variety of problems, including separation of lead frames from plastic component bodies, broken device wirebonds, and cracked solder joints. Fracturing of ceramic capacitors is a well-documented failure mode (refer to Section 2.4.1).

The problem is compounded by the fact that during repair, heating is usually localized. This causes much larger differential stresses within the substrate than are seen during the production soldering process. Ceramic substrates are particularly prone to fracturing, but ordinary epoxy-glass materials can also be damaged.

As in wave and reflow soldering processes, the solution to these problems is to preheat the assembly immediately prior to soldering. Ideally the pre-heater should gradually raise the temperature of the assembly to within about 25–50 °C of the solder's melting temperature. For tin-lead alloys, this suggests a preheat temperature of about 125–150 °C. The rate of temperature increase to the preheat temperature should be held below about 4–5 °C.

The simplest way to preheat is to set the board on a reistance-heated hot plate. Fixturing to support the board may be required, especially with double-sided assemblies. Rather than attempting to precisely control the temperature gradient, it may be acceptable to simply set the room-temperature board directly on the hot plate and let the board thermal mass control the rate of temperature rise. For very small substrates, some additional means of limiting the temperature gradient may be necessary. The bord should be maintained at the preheat temperature throughout the removal and replacement process.

15.2.3 Component removal and replacement

The sequence of removing and replacing a component actually consists of the following five steps:

- application of soldering heat
- removal of defective component
- application of fresh solder
- placement of new component
- solder reflow

In principle, any of the three basic heating methods—convection, conduction, and radiation—could be used during repair. However, the two most popular approaches are conduction and convection. Reflow by direct infrared radiation, although popular as a production soldering process, has not found widespread application for repair purposes.

Thermal conduction techniques

Most thermally conductive repair is performed with handheld tools that depend heavily on the manual dexterity of the operator. They are best suited for the repair of small devices with relatively few leads. Equipment ranges from ordinary soldering irons to complex tools designed for specific component types. Their primary advantage is low capital cost and portability. The reliability of the repair is a strong function of operator skill.

The ordinary soldering iron is of limited usefulness in surface mount repair because it is not able to simultaneously heat all leads. Even so, it is sometimes used to remove and replace 2-lead passive devices (Fig. 15.3). Irons with modified tips (Figs. 15.1 and 15.4) are more practical for removing devices up to about 16-lead SOICs.

For larger ICs, handheld tweezer tools, such as shown in Fig. 15.5, are recommended. This type of tool essentially consists of two connected soldering irons controlled by a temperature controller. The tips are specially configured for a single type of component or small range of components.

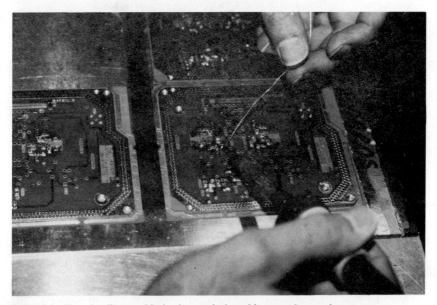

FIG. 15.3 Use of ordinary soldering iron and wire solder to replace surface mount component. To make soldering easier, component should be mounted to the board with adhesive. (Photograph by the author.)

FIG. 15.4 Soldering iron with modified tip. This tool
is designed to remove SOICs and requires a minimum
amount of clearance. (Used by permission. Pace, Inc.)

Thermal convection techniques

Thermal convection, more commonly known as "hot gas reflow," has
become extremely popular for removing and replacing integrated circuits
and other multileaded packages. Equipment has evolved to a rather high
degree of sophistication, which has improved the process repeatability and
reduced the skill level required of the operator.

A typical machine is pictured in Fig. 15.6. In operation, air or nitrogen is
blown across a resistance-heated element that raises the gas temperature
above the melting point of the solder. The heated gas is directed via a
nozzle onto the component to be removed. With a simple system, the nozzle
may direct the gas onto the entire component and perhaps nearby components as well. More elaborate systems employ interchangeable nozzles
shaped so that the gas is directed only onto the component solder joints.

To prevent the assembly from overheating, the temperature of the gas
must be carefully controlled. A thermocouple mounted in the path of the

FIG. 15.5 Conductive tweezers being used to remove PLCC package. (Photograph by the author.)

FIG. 15.6 Hot gas repair station. (Used by permission. Pace, Inc.)

heated gas is usually employed as the temperature-sensing element. Its output is used to control the current through the heater element. Gas flow must also be regulated; too low a flow will result in excessively long repair times, while too high a flow can cause the heated gas to spread out over a large area of the board.

Many machines include a spring-actuated vacuum tool mounted concentric with the nozzle to automatically remove the component. In the rest position, the tool is retracted. To remove a component, the tool is lowered and the vacuum is actuated. Air pressure holds the tool in place on the component body. The flow of hot gas is initiated and, when all solder has melted, the upward force exerted by the spring lifts the component away from the board. The tool can also be tied to a switch to automatically shut off the heat once the component is removed.

A problem common to many hot-gas machines is that they require a different nozzle for every component shape. Nozzles are not always easy to change, especially if the one mounted on the machine is still hot from recent use. Many machines also have rather crude capability to align the replacement component to its land pattern. Frequently, an operator must visually examine the alignment and manually adjust it as necessary to match all leads to their corresponding lands. With multileaded ICs, this can be a challenging task.

Fig. 15.7 shows what could be considered the first of a second generation of machines designed to address these problems.[3] Rather than using inter-

FIG. 15.7 Advanced hot gas repair station with programmable matrix heater and video-assisted component placement. (Used by permission. SRTechnologies, Inc.)

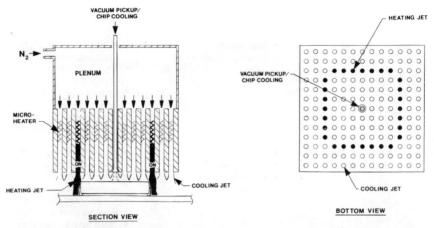

FIG. 15.8 Concept of programmable matrix heater used on the equipment illustrated in Fig. 15.7. Refer to text for details of operation. (Used by permission. SRTechnologies, Inc.)

changeable nozzles, it uses a programmable matrix heater to determine where the heated gas will flow. The concept of the heater is illustrated in Fig. 15.8. Nitrogen is blown into a plenum that introduces it into a matrix of microheater nozzles. Within each nozzle is a heater element that can be turned on or off programmatically. The nitrogen blows through all heaters at all times, but it is heated only by the nozzles that are turned on. In this way, the system can be rapidly reconfigured for a new component. An additional advantage is that the nitrogen blowing through the unheated elements serves to cool those areas where heat is undesired.

Another feature of this machine is an improved mechanism for positioning the new component. It employs a high-resolution video camera to allow an operator to precisely align the component to its land pattern. Routine placement accuracy of better than ± 0.075 mm (0.003 in) has been reported.

Comparison of heating methods

The differences between thermal conduction and thermal convection stem not so much from an inherent difference in capability but rather from differences in equipment design. Modified soldering irons, for instance, are an inexpensive solution that is attractive for use in field repair situations. However, they are highly dependent on operator technique. If the tool is not applied evenly to all joints, some areas of the board will overheat before solder in other areas has fully melted. The component should never be forced off the board before all joints melt, as this can cause circuit lands to separate from the laminate, destroying the board.

A mechanized hot-gas repair station affords much greater control over the process and in most cases produces more consistent results. Its main limita-

Repair Technique	Advantages	Disadvantages
Standard soldering iron	• Inexpensive • Easily portable	• Heavily dependent on operator technique • Easy to overheat component or board • Cannot heat all joints simultaneously • Component placement must be done manually
Soldering iron with specialized tip	• Inexpensive • Easily portable • Heats all joints simultaneously	• Heavily dependent on operator technique • Easy to overheat component or board • Component placement must be done manually • Each tip accommodates only a limited range of components
Hot plate	• Good control over maximum temperature • Moderately portable • Moderately inexpensive • Frees operator's hands to remove & replace component	• Melts all joints on entire board • Requires flat surface on bottom of board • Component placement must be done manually
Hot gas	• Very repeatable process • Well-controlled thermal profile • Mechanically assisted component placement • Localized heating	• Expensive • Physically large and heavy • Nearby components may need protection from heat

TABLE 15.1   Comparison of several common repair techniques

tions are high capital cost, low portability, and difficulty in reconfiguring for a new component type. It is also more suited for replacing multileaded ICs than for small chip components. Advantages and disadvantages of several repair techniques are summarized in Table 15.1.

Solder application

An often-overlooked aspect of repair is the need to apply fresh solder to the joint. It has sometimes been suggested that the solder remaining on the land pattern is sufficient and no new solder need be added. In the author's opinion, this is a dangeous perception. Roughly half of the solder from the original joint is carried away with the defective component, and the amount left on the board can vary widely from land to land. The only reliable way to assure that an adequate amount is available is to apply new solder to each joint.

Solder can be applied in several ways. The simplest approach is to use a conventional low-wattage soldering iron, feeding wire solder to the joint by hand as was illustrated in Fig. 15.3. This is also the least repeatable technique and the one most likely to cause overheating.

One problem with using a soldering iron is that it is difficult to keep the component properly positioned while simultaneously manipulating the iron and feeding wire solder. It is tempting to use the soldering iron to maneuver the component into position, but this increases the risk of overheating the component or board. The easiest way to address this problem is to mount the component to the board with adhesive prior to soldering. A relatively low-strength heat-cure acrylic is satisfactory since it need not withstand significant stresses. It may even be possible to use the preheat stage of the repair process to simultaneously cure the adhesive.

Another approach, suitable for IC packages with leads on all four sides, makes use of fine-diameter (0.4-mm) wire solder. The first step is to construct solder preforms by wrapping the wire solder a number of times around a square mandrel whose outer dimensions match those of the component. The coil of solder is cut lengthwise (preferably with a fixture designed to protect the operator) to form a number of square preforms. After positioning the replacement component on the board, the preform is dropped over it, liquid flux is applied, and the solder is reflowed either by hot gas or on a hot plate. The molten solder cannot wet the spaces between the component lands, so it flows entirely to the joints. The technique depends on good component solderability and uniform heating to assure that the solder is distributed evenly to all joints. For this reason, a hot-gas reflow technique should be used.

It is also possible to use a handheld syringe to dispense solder paste onto individual component lands. Although somewhat affected by variations in operator technique, it is generally able to accurately dispense a repeatable volume of solder. When using solder paste, a hot-gas reflow approach should be used. Soldering irons or other methods of thermal conduction can cause the paste to spatter and eject solder balls.

A somewhat similar approach, used primarily with gull-wing leads, is to run a continuous bead of solder paste along the row of leads. When reflowed, the solder retracts away from nonwettable areas of the board and onto the lands. Again, uniform heating and good component solderability are essential.

15.2.4   Cleaning

Many specifications require that flux residues be removed after the repair process has been completed. It is important to understand that cleaning should not be performed haphazardly. As described in Chapter 13, a poorly controlled cleaning process may serve only to distribute flux residues across the entire board, where they are free to cause rapid corrosion. If Type R or RMA rosin fluxes are used, it may actually be better to avoid cleaning altogeher.

The best way to clean the board is with an in-line solvent system such as used for original assembly. If this is not practical, and cleaning is still required, a batch vapor degreaser may be used. A chlorinated solvent should be used to compensate for the less aggressive cleaning cycle. Solvent packaged in aerosol spray cans should not be used because of the difficulty in maintaining adequate control over the process. If this is the only choice (such as in on-site repair), it is strongly suggested that a Type R or RMA flux that does not require cleaning be used.

15.3 DESIGN MODIFICATIONS

Despite the most careful design analysis, it is occasionally necessary to modify the design of a board after it has entered production. Sometimes this is a result of unexpected circuit behavior under conditions only infrequently encountered. At other times it may be due to spurious oscillations or performance deviations as components vary across their tolerance extremes. Whatever the cause, there are times when it is impractical to discard the inventory of assemblies already manufactured and wait for a new board design to be produced.

Modifications made to production boards must meet all the performance and reliability objectives of the original board. Few guidelines for production-grade modifications have been established, and the tolerable level is a function of the end-use application. On critical high-reliability or life-support circuitry, only minor modifications (such as the addition of a single wire) may be acceptable. Even these should be undertaken only after extensive reliability qualification. In more cost-competitive markets, a significant level of modification may be acceptable, as shown in Fig. 15.9. The following guidelines can be applied when modifying boards used in consumer and general industrial applications.

1. Solder discrete wires to via holes rather than to components or circuit traces

By making the connection to a plated via, the joint reliability approximates that of a standard through-hole joint. Avoid soldering directly to a component lead, since the heat of soldering could easily damage the component. The strength of the resulting joint may also be marginal. Always use insulated wire and strip off only enough of the insulation to make the joint.

FIG. 15.9 Example of modifications on a production board. This board was contained in a compact disc player purchased at a local consumer electronics dealership. Besides the discrete wires around the quadpack, note the added surface mount potentiometer in the upper center of the photograph. (Photograph by the author.)

Although often called "jumper wires," the IPC preferred term for a wire added as the result of a design modification is *hay wire*. The term *jumper wire* is reserved for a wire, such as a zero-ohm resistor, that is included as part of the original board design. Jumper wires are most often used on single-sided boards to ease the complexities of conductor routing.

2. Affix discrete wires to the board with adhesive

This protects the wire from physical damage during handling and improves its resistance to shock and vibration.

3. If additional components must be added, select axial or radial lead through-hole types

Through-hole components are relatively easy to add to an existing circuit because their leads serve as the connections between component and board. Surface mount components, especially leadless devices, are much more difficult; they require that discrete wires be soldered directly to the components. Except in unusual circumstances, surface mount components should not be used for modifications.

4. Add only passive components and discrete semiconductors

Avoid the temptation to add integrated circuits. The usual technique is to adhesively attach the IC to the board in an inverted position and solder individual wires from each lead to the corresponding board locations. This greatly increases the risk of damaging IC or board either by electrostatic discharge or by overheating during soldering. In many cases, the damage will not become evident until long after the board has entered service.

5. Use teminals as junction points for multiple wires

When only a single wire must be added, it should be soldered to a via hole. When multiple jumpers must be added to a single node, they should be attached to a terminal pin (see Fig. 15.10).

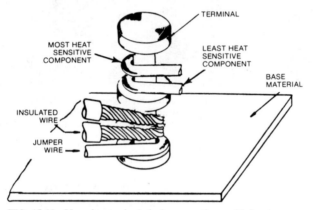

FIG. 15.10   Use of a terminal pin for mounting multiple wires. (Published with permission of the Institute for Interconnecting and Packaging Electronic Circuits (IPC).)

It is sometimes possible to insert the terminal into a via hole and solder the wires to it. When no via is conveniently available, it may be necessary to drill a hole in a blank area of the board and rivet the terminal in place. A single wire can then connect the terminal to the appropriate via, and all additional wires can be routed to the terminal. On multilayer boards, ensure that the location selected for the terminal is free of conductors on inner layers as well as outer layers.

6. Use insulating sleeves to protect exposed wires

Discrete wires that cross printed wiring conductors should always be insulated either by using insulated wire or by protecting the wire in an insulating sleeve. Sleeves should not extend into the lead bend radius but should terminate 1.5–3 mm (0.062–0.125 in) behind the bend radius (see Fig. 15.11).

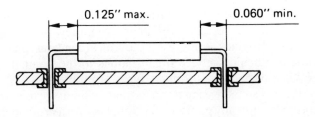

(a) Supported Holes — PTH or Eyelet.

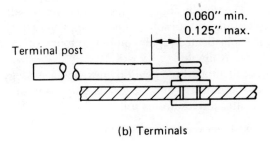

(b) Terminals

FIG. 15.11 Methods of mounting discrete wires. (Published with permission of the Institute for Interconnecting and Packaging Electronic Circuits (IPC).)

15.4 FIELD REPAIR STRATEGY

Any discussion of surface mount repair would be incomplete without describing the impact on field repair strategy. No longer are ordinary soldering irons practical for component-level repairs in the field. Large, expensive hot-gas systems are also impractical. To address the specialized needs of surface mount technology, it may be necessary to adopt an entirely new field repair strategy.

There are three basic objectives for field repair. Simply stated, they are as follows:

- high quality of repaired assemblies
- short downtime for customer
- cost-effective repair process

Above all else, repairs must be of consistently high quality. Ideally, the reliability of a repaired assembly should be indistinguishable from that of the original. Any compromise that markedly degrades reliability is unlikely to be tolerated by customers.

Rapid turnaround time is more important today than ever. Computers, for instance, have permeated the business world to the point they now control everything from manufacturing schedules to payrolls to customer invoicing. A system failure that results in even a few hours of downtime could prove catastrophic. To address these critical concerns, many manufacturers are strengthening service organizations to the point that they can guarantee same-day service for many types of problems.

Finally, there is an increasing trend to treat field service as a profit center that is expected to not only pay its own way but to turn a profit in the process. Cost-effective repair processes are critical to achieving this goal.

The technical problems with field repair are similar to those in the factory: smaller components are more difficult to remove and replace; heating and cooling cycles must be carefully controlled; components must be accurately positioned; controlled amounts of solder must be applied to the joints. In the field, however, the sophisticated repair equipment found on the production lines is unlikely to be available.

Repair strategies fall along three general lines, and a strategy that works for one segment of the industry may be totally inappropriate for another. The three strategic alternatives are as follows.

- on-site component-level repair
- board exchange program
- throw-away assemblies

15.4.1 On-site component-level repair

This approach has historically been employed in certain segments of the military and in the commercial instrumentation market. Defects are diagnosed to the individual component level and repaired while the equipment remains at the customer site. Often, the actual repairs are performed by technicians within the customer's own organization so as to achieve an extremely rapid turnaround time. This, in fact, is the chief benefit of the strategy.

On-site repair may have been successful for through-hole assemblies, but it has a number of problems when applied to surface mounting. It is a slow process that requires that defects be traced to individual components. Troubleshooting is difficult because service technicians usually have only rudimentary equipment at their disposal. Once defects are identified, the actual component removal and replacement must be performed manually with modified soldering irons. Finally, replacement parts must be readily available for all components used in the original product.

15.4.2 Board exchange program

It is usually much easier to identify a defective board than to locate the specific defective component. In a board exchange program, the field service technician simply isolates the defective board, replaces it with a good board, and returns the product to the customer. The defective board is returned to a central repair depot where it is restored to operating condition. It is then returned to the repair organization for use in subsequent repairs.

Board exchange is appealing because it reduces the skill level required to do on-site repairs while simultaneously improving turnaround time. Component-level repair is still performed, but it can be done at a more relaxed pace with proper equipment and trained operators. The approach is especially suited to situations where same-day or next-day service is required.

The main limitation is that a readily accessible inventory of replacement boards must be maintained. This can be a formidable challenge for small manufacturers or even for multinational organizations that must provide rapid worldwide support. Another limitation is that an efficient channel must be set up to ensure that defective boards are returned. If this does not happen, the inventory of spares must be filled by newly manufactured boards. This will rapidly drive repair costs to prohibitive levels.

15.4.3 Throw-away assemblies

Field repair labor rates often exceed $100–150 per hour. Under these conditions, it may be less expensive to simply discard a defective assembly rather than repair it. It makes little sense to spend two hours to locate a defective 25-cent component on a $100 board when the entire board could have been replaced in 15 minutes.

Like the board exchange program, this approach reduces the skill level required for on-site repairs and improves turnaround time. An adequate inventory of spares must also be readily available. However, no complex channels are required to ensure that defective boards make their way back to a central repair depot.

15.4.4 Selecting a field repair strategy

The selection of a field repair strategy is primarily an economic decision. Factors that enter into the analysis include average board cost, estimated average repair time, skill level within the service organization, and logistical complexity of supporting all customers. In general, the following guidelines should be observed:

- Avoid component-level repair at remote sites.
- Combine a policy of throw-away assemblies and board exchange program to provide the best combination of quality, cost, and customer service objecives.
- Work toward high reliability of SMT assemblies so that field repair is not necessary! This can be accomplished by using high-quality incoming parts, high-quality designs, and high-quality manufacturing processes.

REFERENCES

1. Schoenberger, R. *Japanese Manufacturing Techniques: Nine Hidden Lessons in Simplicity*, The Free Press, New York, 1982.
2. Holdway, J. "Guide for Removal, Replacement of Surface Mount Devices—Parts 1, 2, and 3," *Electri·onics*, Dec. 1984, Jan. 1985, Feb. 1985.
3. Rehkow, W. and Finocchario, M. "Development of Programmable Matrix Heating for Surface Mounted Boards," *Proceedings of NEPCON/East*, Boston, MA, June 1986.

Appendix A

Acceptance criteria for visual inspection of surface mount assemblies

1.0 OBJECTIVE

This document describes recommended visual inspection criteria for surface mount assemblies. The information herein pertains only to the unique requirements arising from the use of surface mount components. The document is intended to be used in conjunction with existing requirements for through-hole assemblies.

2.0 INSPECTION METHODS

All inspection should be performed using an optical magnification of 3–10×. Questionable areas may be inspected at 40×. A stereo zoom microscope having a magnification range of 7–40× is recommended. Alternatively, an illuminated magnifier mounted on an adjustable extension arm may be employed.

3.0 SOLDERING REQUIREMENTS

All solder joints must show visible evidence that the solder has wetted both the component termination and the circuit board land. Wetting is evidenced by a positive wetting angle and a concave meniscus of solder that blends cleanly into the body of the termination. There should be no evidence of cracking or peeling, and the joint should not have a lumpy appearance. A joint that exhibits a convex meniscus, or one in which the outline of the termination is not visible within the solder, should be rejected. (Refer to Fig. A-1.)

Although a shiny appearance is desirable, the actual appearance depends

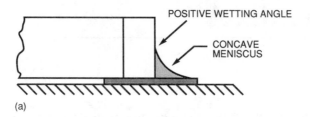

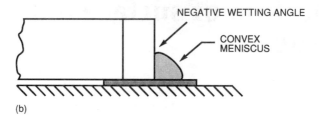

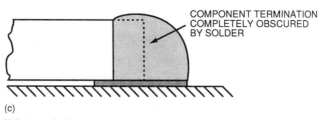

FIG. A-1   Solder joint visual appearance: a. Acceptable,
b. Unacceptable, c. Unnacceptable.

on the solder alloy and soldering process that have been employed. An otherwise acceptable joint should not be rejected simply because it does not look "shiny."

3.1 Leaded devices (see Fig. A-2)

The following criteria apply to J-leads, gull-wing leads, and I-leads:

A. The solder fillet must have wetted at least three of the four sides of the lead (all four sides for I-leads).
B. The fillet must cover at least 50% of the length of each of the wetted sides (75% for I-leads).
C. The solder must extend up the lead to a distance of 0.5 mm (0.020 in) or 50% of the lead height, whichever is less.

3.2 Leadless devices (see Fig. A-3)

The following criteria apply equally to chip components, MELFs, and leadless chip carriers:

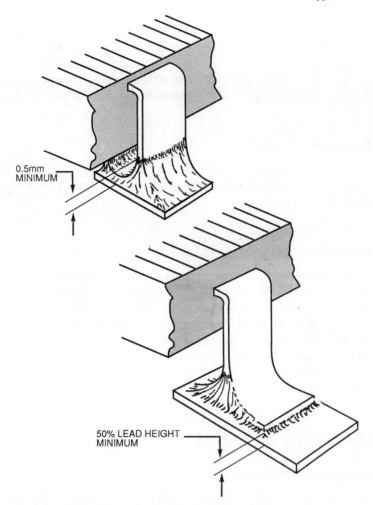

0.5mm
MINIMUM

50% LEAD HEIGHT
MINIMUM

FIG. A-2   Solder fillet acceptance criteria for leaded joints.

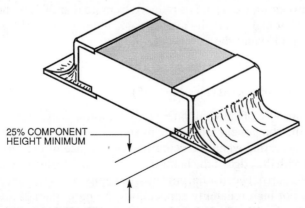

25% COMPONENT
HEIGHT MINIMUM

FIG. A-3   Solder fillet acceptance criteria for leadless joints.

A. The solder fillet must have wetted at least 50% of the face of the termination. It is not necessary that wetting occur on the sides of the termination.

B. The fillet must extend up the face of the termination to a distance of 0.5 mm (0.020 in) or 25% of the termination height, whichever is less.

3.3 Bridging

A. Any solder extending beyond the outline of the component land must not protrude so far as to reduce the gap between adjacent lands by more than 50%.

3.4 Solder balls

A. The maximum diameter of isolated solder balls on the board must not exceed half the narrowest gap between adjacent conductors or component lands or 0.15 mm (0.006 in), whichever is smaller.

B. The number of solder balls should not exceed one solder ball of diameter 0.15 mm per square centimeter of board area, or an equivalent volume of smaller balls. In no event should the localized concentration of balls be such as to reduce the gap between adjacent circuit traces or lands by more than 50%.

4.0 COMPONENT ALIGNMENT

4.1 Leaded components (see Fig. A-4)

No more than 50% of any component lead should extend beyond the outline of the component land. In no event should the lead extend to a point where the gap between adjacent lands is reduced by more than 50% of the intended dimension. For high-reliability applications, no more than 25% of the lead should extend beyond the outline of the land.

4.2 Leadless components (see Fig. A-5)

No more than 50% of any component termination should extend beyond the outline of the component land. The maximum permissible misalignment is defined as occurring when the centerline of the face of the termination is coincident with the edge of the land. In no event should the misalignment be such that the gap between adjacent lands or components is reduced by more than 50%. For high-reliability applications, no more than 25% of the termination should extend beyond the outline of the land.

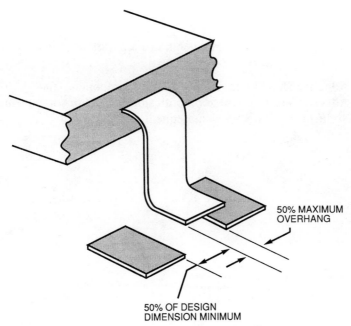

FIG. A-4   Acceptance criteria for leaded component alignment.

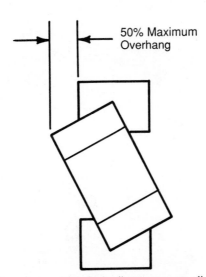

FIG. A-5   Acceptance criteria for leadless component alignment.

5.0 Adhesive

Adhesive used to secure components in preparation for wave soldering should meet the following requirements:

A. Adhesive should not extend onto any component land.

B. Adhesive must be visible on both sides of a chip component. (This requirement may be waived subsequent to the soldering operation.)

Appendix B

Glossary

AZEOTROPE: A solvent blend in which the individual components evaporate at rates such that the composition of the vapor is identical to that of the liquid. The boiling point of the solvent thus remains constant over time.

BLIND VIA: A via that connects an outer layer of a printed wiring board to an inner layer but does not continue through to the other side.

BRIDGE (Solder): A web of solder that shorts between adjacent conductors that are not otherwise connected.

BURIED VIA: A via that connects two inner layers of a printed wiring board but is not visible from either outer layer.

BUTT JOINT: See *I-LEAD*.

CHIP COMPONENT: Generic term for any two-terminal leadless surface mount passive device, such as a resistor, capacitor, or inductor.

CHIP-ON-BOARD TECHNOLOGY: Generic term for any component assembly technology in which an unpackaged silicon die is mounted directly on the printed wiring board. Connections to the board can be made by wire bonding, tape automated bonding (TAB), or flip-chip bonding.

CLAMSHELL FIXTURE: An in-circuit test fixture designed to probe both sides of a printed wiring board. The top probe plate is hinged to allow the board to be inserted and withdrawn.

CLUSTER TESTING: A variation of in-circuit testing in which a cluster of components is tested as a functional unit.

CONSTRAINING CORE SUBSTRATE: A composite printed wiring board consisting of epoxy-glass outer layers bound to a low thermal-expansion core material. The core artificially constrains the expansion of the outer layers to match the expansion coefficient of ceramic chip carriers.

CONTROL CHART: A chart that tracks process performance over time. Trends in the chart are used to identify potential process problems before they become serious.

COPLANARITY ERROR: The maximum deviation of component leads away from perfect planarity. Determined by placing the package on a flat surface and measuring the worst-case lead height off the surface.

CTE: Coefficient of thermal expansion. The rate of expansion of a material as temperture is increased. Expressed in parts-per-million per degree C.

CURIE POINT: The temperature at which the crystal structure of a ferroelectric material changes to a configuration of greater symmetry. Ferroelectric behavior ceases above this temperature.

DISPERSANT: A chemical added to water to improve its ability to remove particulate matter.

DOUBLE-SIDED ASSEMBLY: A fully assembled P/I structure with components mounted on both sides.

DOUBLE-SIDED BOARD: A P/I structure with conductor traces on both sides. Also called *TWO-LAYER BOARD.*

DRAWBRIDGING: See *TOMBSTONE.*

DUAL-WAVE SOLDERING: A wave soldering process that combines an initial turbulent wave with a subsequent laminar wave. The turbulent wave insures complete solder coverage and the laminar wave removes bridges and icicles. Designed expressly for surface mount soldering.

DUMMY LAND: A conductor on a printed wiring board that is not electrically connected to the rest of the circuitry. Frequently used as a way to reduce the gap between a component and board when using adhesive to mount the component onto the board.

EUTECTIC: The alloy of two or more metals that has the lowest melting point. Eutectic alloys, when heated, transform directly from a solid to a liquid, without experiencing a plastic region.

FAULT PROFILE: A description of the type and frequency of electrical faults most likely to be found on the assembled printed wiring board. Used to determine the most appropriate test technique for final electrical test.

FIDUCIAL MARK: A geometric shape incorporated into the artwork of a printed wiring board and used by a vision system to identify the exact artwork location and orientation. A minimum of two fiducial marks must be used per board.

FILLET: The web of solder that connects a component termination to the corresponding circuit land to form the actual solder joint.

FLATPACK: A component with two rows of leads that extend straight out from the device body. Various lead spacings may be employed, but 0.050-in pitch is most common.

FLIP-CHIP TECHNOLOGY: A chip-on-board technology in which the silicon die is inverted and mounted directly to the printed wiring board. The bonding pads on the die are first coated with a heavy layer of metal so that when inverted, they make contact with the corresponding board lands and the die rests slightly above the board surface.

FOOTPRINT: The outline of a component mounted on the printed wiring board. Sometimes used as a nonpreferred term for *LAND PATTERN.*

FUNCTIONAL TEST: An electrical test of an entire assembly that simulates the intended operating environment of the product.

GRAVITY WATER SEPARATOR: A system that uses gravity to separate water from a hydrocarbon solvent. The water floats to the top of the solvent where it is drained away by an orifice.

GULL-WING LEAD: A surface mount device lead that flares outward from the device body.

HAY WIRE: A wire added to a printed wiring assembly as a result of a design modification or error in the original board design. (Compare to *JUMPER WIRE.*)

ICICLE (Solder): A finger of solder that protrudes out of a solder joint but does not make contact with another conductor.

I-LEAD: A surface mount device lead that is sheared such that the end of the lead contacts the board land pattern. (Also called "butt joint.")

IN-CIRCUIT TEST: An electrical test of an assembly in which each component is tested individually.

INTERCONNECTIVITY: A measure of the number of solder joints that can be realized per unit area of printed wiring board. It is a function both of the component technologies used and the minimum conductor geometries achievable on the bare printed wiring board.

J-LEAD: A surface mount device that is formed into a shape resembling a "J" or an "L" with the tail folding under the device body.

JUMPER WIRE: A wire installed on a printed wiring assembly as part of the original board design. Typically used to jump across conductors on a single layer board as a way to simplify conductor routing. Also called *ZERO OHM RESISTOR.* (Compare to *HAY WIRE.*)

LAMINAR WAVE: A smoothly flowing solder wave with no turbulence. Minimizes the formation of solder bridges and icicles.

LAND: A metallized conductor on a P/I structure designed to accept a surface mount component lead.

LAND PATTERN: The complete configuration of lands to which a surface mount component is attached.

LCC: Nonpreferred term for "leadless ceramic chip carrier."

LCCC: Leadless ceramic chip carrier. Also called *LCC.*

LDCC: Leaded ceramic chip carrier.

LEACHING: The dissolution of a metal coating into liquid solder.

LEAD PITCH: The distance between successive centers of the leads of a component package.

MANHATTAN EFFECT: See *TOMBSTONE.*

MELF: *M*etal *EL*ectrode *F*ace component. A two-terminal cylindrical surface mount package primarily used for resistors and diodes.

MOLECULAR SIEVE WATER SEPARATOR: A system that separates water from an organic solvent by passing the solvent through a bed of fine molecular sieves. The large solvent molecules pass through the sieve, but the small water molecules are trapped within the sieve.

MULTILAYER BOARD: A printed wiring board that employs more than two layers for conductor routing. Internal layers are connected to the outer layers by way of plated via holes.

NEUTRALIZER: An alkaline chemical added to water to improve its ability to dissolve organic acid flux residues.

NODE: An electrical junction connecting two or more component terminations.

p CHART: A type of control chart that tracks the percentage of defectives in a specified subgroup. Used when the subgroup size varies over time.

PEEL BACK: In the wave soldering process, the point at which solder in the wave breaks away from the exiting board and returns to the wave.

P/I STRUCTURE: Packaging and interconnecting structure. Generic term describing any structure on which electronic components are mounted, including such materials as glass-epoxy boards, flexible substrates, constraining core substrates, ceramic substrates, and molded boards.

PCC: Nonpreferred term for *PLASTIC CHIP CARRIER.*

PIN GRID ARRAY: A through-hole integrated circuit package with multiple rows of pins protruding from the underside of the package.

PLCC: Plastic leaded chip carrier; a plastic package with J-leads on all four sides. Lead spacing is 0.050 in.

pn CHART: A type of control chart that tracks the number of defectives in a specified subgroup. Used when the subgroup size remains constant over time.

PRINTED WIRING ASSEMBLY: The generic term for a printed wiring board after all electronic components have been completely attached. Also called "printed circuit assembly."

PRINTED WIRING BOARD: The generic term for a completly processed board containing conductors onto which components will be mounted. It includes rigid or flexible boards (with single- or double-sided conductors) and multilayer boards. Also called "printed circuit board."

PWB: Printed wiring board.

QUADPACK: Generic term for SMT packages with leads on all four sides. Most commonly used to describe packages with gull-wing leads. Lead spacing varies by device type, normally metric pitch.

R CHART: A type of control chart that tracks the spread of values in a specified subgroup to indicate variations in process repeatability over time. Used in conjunction with an *X-BAR CHART.*

SAPONIFIER: An alkaline chemical added to water to improve its ability to dissolve rosin flux residues.

SCAVENGING: See *LEACHING.*

SELF-ALIGNMENT: The tendency for reflow soldered components to center themselves with respect to the land pattern when the solder melts, even if they were originally placed slightly off center. Results from surface tension forces of the molten solder.

SHADOWING (Infrared reflow): A condition in which component bodies block direct infrared energy from striking certain areas of the board. Shadowed areas receive less energy than their surroundings and may not reach a temperature sufficient to completely melt the solder paste.

SHADOWING (Solder): A condition in which solder fails to wet surface mount device leads during the wave soldering process. Affects leads on the trailing portion of the component because the component body blocks the proper flow of solder.

SINGLE-LAYER BOARD: A printed wiring board that contains metallized conductors on only one side of the board. Through-holes are un-plated.

SINGLE-WAVE SOLDERING: A wave soldering process that uses only a single, laminar wave to form the solder joints. Originally developed for through-hole soldering, it is of limited usefulness for surface mount soldering.

SMC: Surface mount component.

SMD: Surface mount device. Registered service mark of North American Philips Corporation.

SMOBC: Solder-mask-over-bare-copper. A printed wiring technology in which bare copper conductors are protected by solder mask and only the component land patterns are exposed.

SMT: Surface mount technology.

SOIC: Small-outline integrated circuit; a plastic package with gull-wing leads on two sides. Lead spacing is 0.050 in.

SOJ: SOIC package with J-leads rather than gull-wing leads.

SOLDER PASTE: A blend of flux, small particles of solder, and various additives. Also called "solder cream."

SOLVENT: Technically, any solution capable of dissolving a solute. Within the electronics industry, the term is primarily used to describe organic hydrocarbon solvents.

SOT: Small-outline transistor; any of various plastic semiconductor packages designed for surface attachment.

STONEHENGE EFFECT: See *TOMBSTONE.*

SUBPANEL: A printed wiring board panel containing multiple board images and used as the basic unit for assembly processing. Two or more subpanels are normally cut from the full panel used for bare board fabrication.

SURFACTANT: Contraction of "surface active agent." A chemical added to water to lower surface tension and improve wetting.

TAB: Tape automated bonding. A chip-on-board technology in which a miniature lead frame is gang-bonded directly from the silicon die to the printed wiring board.

TCE: 1,1,1-trichloroethane; also thermal coefficient of expansion. (Preferred term is *CTE,* "coefficient of thermal expansion.")

TERMINATION: The portion of a component that makes electrical contact to the printed wiring board; the leads of a leaded device or the metallized ends of a leadless device.

THERMAL VIA: A plated via under a component used to conduct heat away from the component.

TOMBSTONE: A condition in which a two-lead surface mount device has pulled into a vertical or near-vertical position with only one termination soldered to the board. Typically caused by force imbalances during reflow soldering. Also called "drawbridging," the "Manhattan effect," and the "Stonehenge effect."

TTE: Trichlorotrifluoroethane (FC-113).

TWO-LAYER BOARD: A printed wiring board in which both sides of the laminate contain metallized conductors. Metallized via holes connect traces between the layers.

VIA HOLE: A plated hole through a printed wiring board that serves only to connect conductors on different layers. Via holes are not designed to accept component leads.

X-BAR ($\bar{X}$) CHART: A type of control chart that tracks the mean value of a subgroup to indicate variations in the average capability of a process over time. Used in conjunction with an *R CHART.*

ZERO-OHM RESISTOR: An automatically insertable jumper wire used to connect between two points of a printed wiring board. It resembles a resistor and is often used on single-layer boards as a means of simplifying conductor routing.

Index

abietic acid, 381
acceptance criteria, 26, 461–6
  dip test, 136
acid number, 128
additive processing, 159–61
adhesive attach/wave soldering, 18–21,
    202, 204, 206, 207, 211–13, 363–71
  see also *wave soldering*
adhesives, 19, 363–71
  acrylics, 19, 365–6
  component compatibility, 370–1
  curing of, 364, 366
  dispensing, 366–70
  epoxies, 365
  physical properties, 363–4
  selection of, 363–4, 441
  thermoplastic, 364
  thermoset, 364
aging of dielectric materials, 53–4
aging of terminations, 144–7
aircraft avionics, 170
air knife, 212, 344–5, 356
Alloy-42 lead frame, 66–7
alumina, 170
aqueous cleaning, see *cleaning*
arimid-fiber boards, 167
area-of-spread test, see *spread factor
  test*
area source emitter, 337–40
ASIC (application-specific integrated
  circuit), 111
assembly processes, see specific process
  technologies impact on reliability,
  171–5
azeotrope, 387

barrier layer, 34, 49, 149–50
barium titanate dielectric material, 48–
  9, 50–1, 52–3
bed-of-nails tester, 16, 428–31
  see also *testing, electrical*
Bell Laboratories, 173
beryllia substrates, 171
Bingham body, 229
binomial probability distribution, 415
bridging, see *wave soldering*
Brookfield viscometer, see *viscometer*
bulk feeding of components, 310–11
buoyancy (wetting balance), 137–8,
  139, 140
buried traces, 443
butt joint see *I-lead joint*

capacitors, fixed, 48–59
  aluminum electrolytic, 55, 59
  capacitance formula, 52
  ceramic, 48–55
  dielectric classes, 50–1, 53–5
  size codes, 49–50
  plastic film, 59
  tantalum electrolytic, 48, 55–9, 190
capacitors, variable, 59
ceramic hybrids, see *hybrid circuits*
ceramic substrates, 170
chip-and-wire packaging, 99
chip-on-board technology (COB), 99–
  102, 166
cleaning after soldering, 174–5, 373–
  406
  aqueous, 174–5, 373, 377–9, 398–403
  see also *water*

cleaning after soldering—*cont.*
  cleanliness levels, 378–9, 403–5
  compatibility of fluxes, 175
  efficiencies of various solvents, 378–9
  philosophy, 405–6
  process selection, 377–9, 397–8
  solvent, 125, 175, 210, 373, 379–98
    theory, 392
    water separator, 391–2
  types of contamination, 374–7
  under SMT devices, 377–9
cleaning systems, aqueous, 400–2
  environmental concerns, 402
  safety, 402–3
cleaning systems, solvent, 392–7
  batch vapor degreaser, 392–4
  in-line, 394–7
  ultrasonic agitation, 397
cluster testing, 431
CMOS integrated circuits, 15
coefficient of thermal expansion, 14,
    154–5, 157, 159, 168–9, 342
colophony, 125, 127
compliance, see *lead compliance*
compliant layer materials, 170–1
component feeders, 262, 275–6, 277,
    279–80, 297, 301–12
component land patterns, see *land
    patterns*
component placement
  accuracy requirements, 263–70
  component centering, 293–6
  impact on reliability, 173
  steps in, 261
component placement equipment
  accuracy, 263–70
  centering jaws, 284, 294–5
  centering nests, 295–6
  classification, 278–86, 287–8
  communications protocol, 299
  component verification, 299–301
  computer control, 297–9
  coordinate registration, 292–6
  data storage, 299
  equipment design, 261–3, 274–8,
    286–301
  flexibility, 274–8
  general purpose, 279–81
  high speed, 282–4
  in-line, 286, 288
  optical centering, 296
  placement head, 262–3, 278
  placement tool, 263, 279–80, 282
  precision, 284, 285

  sequential, 278–84
  setup, 276–8
  simultaneous, 286–7
  speed, 271–4
component terminations, 124, 147–50
  pretinning, 148–9, 172, 258
components, passive, 33–62
  see also individual component types
connectors, SMT, 105–111
constraining core materials, 167, 168–
    70
contamination on printed wiring
    boards, 129, 374–7
control charts, 410–13, 414
  control limits, 411–12
  p chart, 410–12
  pn chart, 410–12
  R chart, 412–13, 414
  X̄ chart, 412–13, 414
coplanarity error, 87, 131, 173
copper-clad Invar, 168
copper lead frame, 66–7
cost, 13, 103, 417–18
  component, 103
  factory, 13, 222–4
C-quad package, 97–8
CTE, see *coefficient of thermal
    expansion*
Curie point, 52–3, 54
cycle rate (of placement machine),
    272

defect levels, 415–16
Department of Defense, 27–8
design factors, connectors, 107–10
design guidelines, 177–98
  component land patterns, 187–98
  component layout, 184–6
  conductor routing, 182, 183
  fiducial marks, 181
  printed wiring board dimensions,
    177–80
  repairability, 440–44
  testability, 186–7
  tooling holes, 180, 181
  via holes, 182–4
dewetting, 124
die passivation, 75–6, 103
dielectric classifications, 51
DIP (dual-in-line package), 6–8
dip test for solderability, 133, 134–6
discrete semiconductors, see
    semiconductors
double-pass reflow, see *reflow*

double-sided SMT, 10, 21–3, 202, 206, 210–15
drag soldering, 360–1
drawbridging, see *tombstoning*
dross, 363
dry film solder mask, 161, 165
dual-in-line package, 6–8
dual-layer passivation, 75–6
dual-line terminator, 46–7
dual wave soldering, see *wave soldering*
dummy land, 371

electrical testing, see *testing, electrical*
Electronic Industries Association
    (EIA), 28–9, 35, 48, 49–50, 56–7,
    61, 141, 299
electroplated leads, 148–9
epoxy, see *adhesives*
    electrically conductive, 41
epoxy-fiberglass boards, 166, 433
equipment placement rate, 272
eutectic, 119, 123

factory cost, see *cost*
factory design
    considerations in, 201–2, 215–26
    fully automated, 215–21
    layout, 216–21
    process flows, 202–15
    recommendations, 225–6
    semiautomated, 221–2
    serial vs. parallel equipment, 219–21
failure modes of solder joints, 153–5,
    432–4
fan out, 17
fault profiles, 432–4
federal specifications, 27, 120, 125
feeder compacting, 275
ferroelectric properties of barium
    titanate, 53–4
fiducial marks, 181, 293
fine-pitch chip carrier, see *plastic quad
    flat pack*
firmware, 297
flatpack, 3, 4
flexible disks, 276, 299
flexible printed wiring boards, 168
flexural failure, 154–5
flood bar (screen printer), 252
floppy disks, see *flexible disks*
flux, 124–8
    activity, 143–4, 242–3
    efficacy, 127–8
    for solderability testing, 133

for wave soldering, 349
organic acid, 127, 349, 373
polymerization, 375–7
rosin, 125–7, 237–8, 373
solvent soluble, 125–7
synthetic, 127
testing, 143–4
Type R, 125, 133
Type RA, 125, 133
Type RMA, 126, 133
Type RSA, 126
water-soluble, 127, 349
flux application, 258, 349–51
flux removal, see *cleaning*
flux residues, 375–7
forming gas, 341
functional modules, 24–5
functional testing, 17–18, 409, 427–8

glass-epoxy boards, see *epoxy-fiberglass
    boards*
glass pack, 443
globule test, 133, 142
gold surface finishes, 172
graphite-based materials, 168
grey tin, see *tin pest*
gull-wing lead, 84–6, 96, 107–8

hay wire, 455
heat sinks, 440, 442
host controller, 297–8
hot gas reflow, 448–51
hot mock-up testing, 427
HTC Corporation, 23
hybrids, ceramic, 3, 24, 55

I-lead joint, 84, 86–7, 97
icicling, see *wave soldering*
IEC, see *International Electrotechnical
    Commission*
IEEE, see *Institute of Electrical and
    Electronic Engineers*
in-circuit test, see *test, electrical*
indium solders, 122, 123, 172
inductors, 59–62
    multilayer, 61–2
    wirewound, 59–61, 190–1
inert environment, 150, 326, 341
infrared reflow, 19, 131, 174, 322–3,
    334–41, 345–6
    advantages, 334–5
    color selectivity, 336
    disadvantages, 335–7
    equipment design, 337–40

infrared reflow—*cont.*
  inert atmosphere, 341
  shadowing, 336–7
  temperature profile, 340–1
infrared sources, 337–40
inspection of solder joints, 409–26
  infrared (laser), 416, 426, 427
  inspection criteria, 461–6
  inspection points, 413–17
  machine vision, 420–21
  philosophy, 410
  three-dimensional vision (structured
      light), 421–3
  three-dimensional X-ray, 424
  visual, 107, 173, 409, 416, 418–20
  X-ray, 416, 423–5
Institute for Interconnecting and
    Packaging Electronic Circuits
    (IPC), 23, 24, 26–7, 134, 145, 147,
    398
  classification scheme, 24
Institute of Electrical and Electronic
    Engineers (IEEE), 156
Institute of Printed Circuits, see
    *Institute for Interconnecting and
    Packaging Electronic Circuits*
insulation resistance, 404–5
integrated circuits, 83–103
  C-quad, 97–8
  chip-on-board (COB), 99–101
  flatpack, 3, 4, 83
  gull-wing, 84–6
  I-lead (butt joint), 84, 86–7
  J-lead, 84, 86
  LCCC, 94–5, 103, 155, 157
  LDCC, 95, 103, 157, 171
  lead configuration, 84–7
  lead coplanarity, 87
  leaded, 84
  leadless, 84
  pinout configuration, 84
  plastic quad flatpack (PQFP), 96–7
  PLCC, 90–1, 92–3, 103
  quadpack, 91–3, 96, 168
  selection criteria, 102–3
  SOIC, 47–8, 88–90, 103
  SOJ, 89–90
  TAB, 99, 100–2
  Tape Pak®, 98–9
interconnectivity, 6–10, 91
  defined, 6
  of various component packages, 10,
      91
intermetallic compounds, 172

International Electrotechnical
    Commission, 29–30, 48, 147
ionic contamination, 374–5
ionograph testing, see *solvent extract
    resistivity test*
IPC, see *Institute for Interconnecting
    and Packaging Electronic Circuits*
islands of automation, 215, 221

J-lead joint, 84, 86, 107
JEDEC standards, 29, 90, 94, 95, 97
jumper wire, 455
junction temperature, semiconductor,
    64, 73

Kauri-butanol value, 380, 389
Kevlar®, 167

lambda wave, 355
laminar wave, see *wave soldering*
land patterns, 27, 187–98, 268–9
laser soldering, 323, 341–4, 345–6
  advantages, 342
  disadvantages, 342–3
  sources, 341, 343–4
laser trimming, 35, 39
LCCC, see *leadless ceramic chip carrier*
leaching, 122, 130, 141–2
lead compliance, 64, 107, 156, 171
lead coplanarity, 87, 131, 173
lead finish, 110, 129–31
lead frames, IC, 66–7, 98, 100
lead screw, 289, 290
leaded ceramic chip carrier, 95, 103,
    156, 171
leaded joints, 153, 156
leadless ceramic chip carrier, 94–5, 103,
    154, 156, 171
leadless components, 6, 14, 166
leadless joints, 153, 155–6
light-emitting diodes (LEDs), 77

magazine feeders, 275, 276, 304–10
Manhattan effect, see *tombstoning*
Manson-Coffin equation, 157–8
Martin-Marrietta Aerospace, 167
matrix-tray feeding, 311–12
MELF components, see
    semiconductors; *resistors*
Meniscograph, see *wetting balance*
mesh size
  of screens, 248–9
  of solder paste, 236
metal-core materials, 168–70

microcracking, 167
military specifications, see *standards*
mixed assemblies, 21–2, 207–10
modules, see *functional modules*
molded boards, 168
molecular sieve, 392
motherboard, 24

National Machine Tool Builders
    Association, 270
Newtonian fluids, 228, 254
nickel barrier, see *barrier layer*
nitromethane, 387
nodes, 16, 428, 430–1
nonpolar contamination, 374–5

off-line programming, 277, 298
omega wave, 357, 360
organic acid flux, see *flux*
organic-based substrates, 159–68
organic contamination, 374–5
oxidation, 129

p chart, 410–12
package propagation delay, 11
packaging and interconnection (P/I)
    structure, 158–71
pads-only board, 443
panel emitter, 337–9
paper-based boards, 166
parasitic reactances, 11, 155
peel back, 355
PFIB (perfluoroisobutylene), 327
phase diagram for tin-lead solder, 119–
    20
pick-and-place, see *component
    placement*; *component placement
    machines*
pin-grid-array package (PGA), 8–9
pin transfer dispensing of adhesives,
    368–70
pixel, 421–2
placement accuracy, 263–71
plastic leaded chip carrier (PLCC), 47–
    8, 90–1, 92–3, 103
    thermal resistance, 70, 72
plastic molding compound, 67, 74–5,
    108–9
plastic quad flatpack (PQFP), 96–7
plated finishes, 148–9
pn chart, 410–12
polar contaminants, 374–5
polyimide-fiberglass boards, 166, 443–4
polyimide-quartz boards, 167
polymerization of flux, 375–7

potentiometers, see *resistors, variable*
power cycling, 154
preheating, 55, 131, 174, 315
printed wiring boards, 158–71
    also see individual board types
    panel sizes, 177–80, 216–17
probability of defective joints, 415, 416
process flows, 202–15
    see also *factory design*; *surface mount
        technology*
pseudoplastic fluids, 228, 229

QQ-S-571, 120, 125, 237
quadpack, 91–3, 96, 168
quantization error, 269

R chart, 412–13
reflow soldering, 19–23, 203–6, 207,
    211–15, 313–46
    see also individual soldering methods
    comparison of methods, 345–6
    double pass, 213–14
    infrared reflow, 19, 131, 174, 322–3,
        334–41
        see also *infrared flow*
    laser, 323, 341–4
        see also *laser soldering*
    modified soldering irons, 324, 447
    single pass, 214–15
    self alignment, 317
    skewing, 317
    temperature profile, 174, 314–17,
        327, 340–1
    theory, 314–17, 325–8, 335
    thermal conduction, 322, 323–4, 447,
        451–2
    thermal convection, 322, 345–6, 448–
        52
    vapor phase, 19, 131, 322, 325–33
        see also *vapor phase reflow*
relays, SMT, 116–17
reliability
    assembly, 153–8, 159, 171–5
    cleanliness, 405–6
    package, 63–76, 93, 94–5
repair, 9, 26, 439–59
    cleaning, 453–4
    design for repairability, 440–4
    design modifications, 454–7
    field repair, 457–9
    heating methods, 447–52
    of pin-grid-array packages, 9
    philosophy, 439–40
    processes, 444–54

resistance to dissolution test, 141–2
resistor networks, 45–8
    power derating, 47
resistors, fixed, 34–41
    carbon film, 39
    metal film, 39
    power derating, 36, 37
    MELF, 37–40
    rectangular chip, 34–37
    size codes, 35–6
    termination configuration, 40–1
resistors, variable, 41–5
    open element construction, 41, 43–4
    sealed construction, 41, 42–3
rheology, 227–30
Rho'lix® Drive, 289, 291
ROM (read-only memory), 112
rosin flux, see *flux*
rotary dip test, 133, 142–3
rotational error (placement machine),
    264–6

saponifier, 377, 399
scavenging, see *leaching*
screen printing, 244–54, 366–7
    board registration, 252
    contact mode, 245–6
    equipment design, 246–54
    mesh orientation, 249
    mesh sizes, 248–9
    of adhesives, 366–7
    off-contact mode, 245–6
    screen holder, 250
    screens, 248–50
    setup time, 218–19, 244–5
    snap-off rate, 245
    stencils, 250
    substrate holder, 251–2
    theory, 245–6
SECS-II communication protocol,
    299
selection criteria
    for IC packages, 102–3
    for solder alloys, 122–3
self alignment, 317
SEMI (Semiconductor Equipment and
    Materials Institute), 299
semiconductor die, 74, 75–6
semiconductors, discrete, 76–83
    DPAK, 79, 81
    MELF, 80–2
    selection criteria, 81–3
    small outline transistor (SOT), 76–9,
        80, 82–3

setup time
    of SMT line, 216–19
    screen printer, 218–19, 244–5
shadowing, infrared, 336–7
shadowing, solder, 357, 358
shingling of ICs, 310
silicon nitride passivation, 75–6
single-pass soldering, 214–15
size codes for passive devices, 35–6, 49–
    50
skewing, 317
small outline integrated circuit (SOIC),
    76–9, 80, 82–3
    thermal resistance, 69, 70, 71
small outline transistor (SOT), 76–9,
    80, 82–3
    SOT-23 (TO-236, SC-59), 76–7, 82–3
    thermal resistance, 68
    SOT-89 (TO-243), 68, 78–9
    SOT-143 (TO-253), 68, 79, 80
SMOBC, see *solder-mask-over-bare-
    copper process*
socket, IC, 111–14
SOIC, see *small outline integrated
    circuit*
solder
    tin-lead, 120–22, 147, 148, 172
        alloys, 120–22
        grain structure, 131
        mechanical properties, 73
    tin-lead-silver, 122–3
    tin-silver, 123
    lead-indium, 123
solder balls, 238, 241–2
solder bump process, 257–8
solder columns, 171
solder cream, see *solder paste*
solder-dipped leads, 148–9
solder joint, 14, 72–3, 105, 153–8
    as mechanical support, 109, 153, 154
    stresses, 106–7, 156–8
    temperature impact on reliability,
        72–3
    volume impact on reliability, 172–3
solder mask, 161, 165, 443
solder-mask-over-bare-copper process
    (SMOBC), 165
solder paste, 131, 144, 227–44
    cleaning, 238, 373–406
    composition of, 233–8
    drying, 174, 316–17
    fluxes, 237–8
    mesh sizes, 236–7
    oxide content, 235, 237

particle shape, 235–6
particle size, 236–7
percent metal, 239–40
powders, 233–7
rheological modifiers, 238
shelf life, 243–4
slump, 240
solvents, 238
specifications and tests, 144, 238–40,
    258–9
stringing, 238
thinning of, 244
viscosity, 227–9, 240
wicking, 131, 234
working life, 243
solder thief, 182
solderability, 41, 110, 123–4
causes of problems with, 128–31
important factors, 147–50
specifications, 132–3
tests, 133–44
soldering irons, see *reflow soldering,
    thermal conduction*
soldering process (see also individual
    process types)
impact on reliability, 173–4
reflow, 313–46
repair, 444–54
temperature profile, 174
solubility parameter, 381–2
solvent cleaning, see *cleaning*
solvent extract resistivity test, 403–4
solvent power, 380–2
solvents (organic), 373–4, 379–92
azeotrope, 377, 387
chlorinated, 390–1, 406
    methylene chloride, 379, 390
    Prelete®, 390
    1,1,1-trichloroethane (TCE), 379,
        390, 406
    trichloroethylene, 390
efficiency index, 380–1
environmental impact, 391
fluorinated, 382–9
    blends, 383–7
    Freon® TMS, 387
    Genesolv® DMSA, 387
    trichlorotrifluoroethane, FC-113
        (TTE), 330–1, 382–9
health and safety, 390–1
Kauri-butanol value, 380, 389
materials compatibility, 383, 384–6,
    390
solubility parameter, 381–2

stabilized, 387, 390
water extraction, 391–2
wetting index, 380–1
SOT, see *small outline transistor*
specifications, see *standards*
spread factor test, 128, 133–4, 242–3
squeegee, 245, 252
standards and specifications, 16, 25–30,
    125, 134, 140, 192
cleanliness testing, 378–9, 403–5
component magazines, 306, 308
flux, 125
Kauri-butanol test, 380
safety, 327–8, 390–1
solders and soldering, 120, 134–6,
    140–1, 147–50
tape and reel, 302, 304
ultrasonic cleaning, 397
standoff height, 76–7, 171, 371
STAT technique, 258
steam aging, 145–6
stencil printing, 244, 245–6, 250
see also *screen printing*
step soldering, 326
Stonehenge effect, see *tombstoning*
stringing of solder paste, 238
structured light, 421–3
subcontract assembly, 15, 201
subtractive processing, 159–61, 164
surface mount technology
advantages, 3, 5–14
components, see individual
        component types
    size, 5–7
cost, 13, 15
definition, 5
history, 3–5
limitations, 14–18
of through-hole devices, 208–10
process flows, 18–23, 202–15, 225
quality/reliability, 13–14
size, 5–10
Type I, 23
Type II, 24
Type III, 24
surface tension
of solder pastes, 227, 229–30
of solvents, 175, 378
surfactants, 174–5, 378, 399–400
switches, SMT, 116
syringe dispensing
of adhesives, 367–8
of solder paste, 212–13, 215, 218–19,
    254–6

syringe dispensing—*cont.*
   air-driven syringe, 254
   peristaltic pump, 254–6
   positive displacement pump, 256

T-3 tungsten lamp, 337–9
TAB, see *tape automated bonding*
tape-and-reel packaging, 44–5, 275,
   302–4
tape automated bonding (TAB), 99,
   100–2
TapePak® package, 98–9
teach mode programming, 276–7, 298
Teflon® boards, 167
temperature profile
   reflow soldering, 314–17
   wave soldering, 351–2, 361–2
terminations, see *component
   terminations*
test clips, 114–15
test vectors, 428
testing, electrical, 16–18, 409
   fault profiles, 432–4
   functional, 17–18, 409, 427–8
   in-circuit, 16–18, 409, 428–31, 435–7
      bed-of-nails fixture, 428
      cluster testing, 431
      double-sided fixtures, 430–1, 436
      layout guidelines, 435–7
      node visibility, 430–1
      test vectors, 428
   probe design, 17, 437–8
   strategy, 431–5
thermal cycling, 64, 106, 153–4
thermal expansion mismatch, see
   coefficient of thermal expansion
thermal gradients, 131, 173–4, 327,
   340–1, 352
thermal management, 15
thermal mismatch, see *coefficient of
   thermal expansion*
thermal resistance, 15, 64–72
thermal shock, 106, 174, 206, 315, 351–
   2, 361–2, 446
thermal vias, 444
thixotropic fluids, 229
through-hole technology, 3–5
throughput (of placement machine),
   272–4
tin pest, 147
tin whiskers, 147
tin-lead solder, see *solder, tin lead*
tombstoning, 318–22
tooling holes, 180, 181, 292

translational error, 264, 266–7
trichlorotrifluoroethane, FC-113
   (TTE), 330–1, 382–9
true position radius, 264

ultrasonic cleaning, 397

vapor phase fluids, 327, 328–9
vapor phase reflow, 325–33, 345–6
   advantages, 325–6
   batch mode equipment, 329, 331–2
   disadvantages, 326–8
   dual-vapor system, 329–31
   equipment design, 329–33
   in-line equipment, 332–3
   safety, 327–8
   single-vapor system, 329–30
   temperature gradient, 327
   theory, 325–8
   wicking, 131, 234, 315, 327, 335
via holes, 10, 13, 161, 169, 182–4
viscometer
   Brookfield, 230–2, 258–9
   cone-plate, 232–3
   rotating spindle, 230–2
viscosity, 227–9, 240
   measurement, 230–2, 258–9
   of solder paste, 240
vision alignment, see *component
   placement equipment*; *coordinate
   registration*
visual inspection, see *inspection*

water (cleaning)
   anti-foaming agents, 400
   aqueous solutions, 398–400
   dispersants, 400
   hardness, 398–9
   neutralizer, 399
   saponifiers, 399
   surfactant, 174–5, 378, 399–400
water separator, 391–2
water soldering, 347–63
   air knife, 356
   bridging, 354, 361
   dual wave, 206, 212, 352, 357–60, 361
   flux application, 349–51
   icicling, 354
   inclined conveyor, 355
   lambda wave, 355
   oil intermixing, 355, 363
   omega wave, 357, 361
   peel back, 355, 360
   preheating, 351–2, 361

safety, 363
shadowing, 357, 358
single wave, 352–7
temperature profile, 351–2, 361–2
theory, 347–8, 352–60
use of rosin fluxes, 349
use of water-soluble fluxes, 349
wetting, 124
wetting balance test, 133, 136–41
wetting index of solvents, 380
white residues, 375–7

wicking of solder paste, 131, 234, 315, 327, 335
Winchester drives, 299
wire bonding, 99–100
workpiece holder, 217–18, 277–8

X̄ chart, 412–13
X-ray inspection, see *inspection*

yield strength of solder, 154, 155